READER'S DIGEST
Condensed
BOOKS

Reader's Digest

Condensed Books

Volume 3 · 1957 · Summer Selections

THE READER'S DIGEST ASSOCIATION
Pleasantville, N.Y.

Contents

Illustrations by William A. Smith

The Lady

A condensation of the book by

CONRAD RICHTER

IN THE New Mexico territory of seventy years ago Doña Ellen Sessions held an enviable position: she had wealth, beauty, a devoted and distinguished husband. But Doña Ellen was Anglo-Spanish, and her tumultuous Latin emotions often overwhelmed her cool English control. A paradox of weakness and strength, she wielded her power effortlessly, conquering by charm all men but one — her brother-in-law and deadly enemy.

Through the appealing character of an orphan boy under her protection, Conrad Richter tells the gripping story of a courageous woman's struggle with a man bent on destroying her — the story of a great lady.

CHAPTER 1

I WOULD never believe that my father had run away with the money.

Oh, I knew well enough what the people of Moro were saying: that no one really knew anything about us but Judge Sessions and he had known only my mother; that my father was too fancy a dresser to be an honest "commission boy"; that he used to pay attention to a questionable woman who less than a month before had left the country, and that they were probably together somewhere in Colorado right now.

It was a barefaced lie, I told anyone who spoke it in my hearing. I said he had gone to the woman only to learn Spanish, which he needed at the commission house. I said many other things to his credit, and not a word of the thing I knew he had failed to do: bring my mother West from Missouri when they found she had lung fever. She had wanted to come. The malady ran in the family. Her cousin Albert Sessions had been expected to die with it, but he had gone to New Mexico territory, had married into a wealthy Spanish family, and was now a judge for three or four counties.

I can still hear my mother tell my father that if she got away from the steamy air of the Missouri she would be well again. But he had breathed the air of the Missouri all his life, he told her, and it hadn't hurt him. Only after her death did he give up the house and hunt up my mother's cousin in New Mexico. He said he did it for me, to save me from the weak lungs of my family, but I rather thought it remorse.

However, many men fail their wives without failing their employers. My father wasn't the sort to do both. I have his photograph now, yellow with age. It's hard to believe that he was only twenty-nine years old. He looks forty, a fine figure of a man with a soft brown mustache. He carried himself straight in his well-cut clothes, and his eyes looked out at you steadily. Never, I felt, would he have abandoned me in a place like Moro, a thousand miles from Missouri, and it wasn't in him to have gone off with so little fuss, saying he was just driving up to the vicinity of the Greenhorn Mountains, yet knowing all the time that he was deserting me for good. He didn't even raise the whip or look back as he drove off in one of the rigs from Caldwell's Livery Stable. I stood watching his dust till buckboard and white-footed bay horse were lost in the blurred horizon.

Only one thing troubled me. Why hadn't he let me go along? I was crazy to go with him and had begged him to take me. He had the room and packed nothing more than a sack or two of oats that I could see. But he said no, he couldn't, and wouldn't tell why.

Later on we knew that old Boreas Luna had sent two of his Mexicans down to the commission house for cash to buy another flock of sheep, that Mr. Kidd hadn't trusted the money to them, and so had sent it special with my father, in gold eagles and a few silver dollars, all done up in sacking, sewed compactly, and hidden at the bottom of the oats. There were different accounts of the amount going around. Some said six thousand dollars and some swore it was eleven.

About every day after that I went down to the commission house to see if my father had come back. On my way I passed Caldwell's Livery Stable. Most of the rigs were kept outside and the horses in a corral. A long way off I could see that the bay with white feet wasn't there. That didn't prove anything, I told myself stoutly.

My father and his horse might both be down at the commission house.

The sign on the commission house read: KIDD & Co., *Forwarding and Commission Merchants*. The largest building held the offices, among other things, and the first thing I looked for was my father's desk. As a rule, ledgers and daybooks lay open together with bills of lading, all held down by lumps-of-ore paperweights. But now the desk had a bare emptiness that gave me suddenly a sick feeling. I went on to where I used to find my father sometimes, in the dark warehouse aisles smelling of tea and green coffee, of dyes from the bales of ginghams and calicos, of rope and saddles, of bacon and lard, of the cold metallic smell of hardware, the good sharp scent of tobacco and the strong chemical odor of sheep-dip.

He wasn't there, nor on the great splintery platforms where freight cars and pack trains were loaded, so I went to the feed warehouse, which I liked best. Here were walls of flour piled in sacks and barrels, and bins of corn, barley and oats. Only the feed-house men were there, and I went on to the last of the warehouses, piled to the roof with hides and greasy fleeces. It was the custom then to send the fleeces out to the scouring mills, and when the wool came back it was light and fluffy. Often had I jumped into the huge bins and rolled around in the soft drifts, but today I only looked into the dark hot cavern and then went back to the office to try to find out when my father was coming.

The men had always been very friendly. Now they hardly let on that I was there. Only Mr. Kidd would actually look at me. He was a thick, bald-headed man with black mustache and eyebrows, and when he caught sight of me he'd bark low and short to Mr. Younger. After a while Mr. Younger would come over to me. "How are you today, Jud?" he'd say, and his hard-bitten face would give me a smile.

"Is he back?" I'd ask, quick hope from his cheerfulness rising in me.

"Not yet. At least not so far as I know," he'd say as if to make my father's absence less final and to hold out a hope of him still coming, although all of them knew then that old Boreas had sent word he had seen neither the money nor my father.

I'd stand for a little while, digesting the disappointment and getting hold of myself.

"Could you use a boy today?" I'd ask him.

"Not right today," he'd say thoughtfully and no hint that they wouldn't hire or trust the son of a man who ran off with eleven thousand dollars, just regret that there was no opening, and the door left open for tomorrow.

I don't know how long this might have gone on if one day I hadn't come in and found a new man at my father's desk. I knew then, despite what Mr. Younger implied, they never expected to see my father back, and for a long time I didn't go in again.

My FATHER and I had rooms in what had once been a fine house on the plaza. People still called it La Casa Nuñoz after the original owner although all the rooms facing the street had become shops. Like most native buildings, it had but one story. To the rear was a large patio with a gallery running part way around it.

We weren't burdened with furniture, just a hard Mexican bed, a chair and my father's brassbound trunk in one room; a cookstove, pine table, chair, small bench, a few dishes and water bucket in the other. Most times we dined here on eggs from local ranchers and on bacon, crackers, coffee, dried fruit and pickles my father got wholesale at the commission house.

At first when my father didn't return, I lay awake half the night wondering what would become of me. Hailing from Missouri, my father thought himself superior to the Mexicans and sometimes had embarrassed me by showing it in front of them. Lying there in bed, I could imagine them talking among themselves with satisfaction of the just fate that had befallen the Anglo boy whose father had run off with Señor Kidd's gold.

How little I knew of Mexicans then, of their natural sympathies and pity for someone whose father or brother had come afoul the law! I found that, instead of hating me, they gave me soft pitying glances from their dark eyes. Our neighbors, Señora Padilla and Señora José García, fed me tortillas. But it was another of Spanish blood who was my deliverer and ministering angel.

This was the lady called Doña Ellen, the wife of my mother's

cousin, Albert Sessions. A native-born New Mexican, she was the daughter of a Mexican mother and English father. Of course, I knew that New Mexico was a territory of the United States, yet to me it was as if Cousin Albert had married someone foreign as from Guatemala or Brazil. Cousin Albert always spoke to me on the street, but his wife had never recognized or spoken to me, perhaps because I so assiduously avoided her.

This very day I had seen her around town in her fancy buggy with space under the sides of the seat for the rubber-tired, brass-rimmed wheels to turn with a flourish. The buggy had yellow spokes, brass lamps on either side of the patent-leather dashboard, and a matching yellow cloth top to shield Doña Ellen from the New Mexican sun. I had just passed the lumber yard headed for home when I heard a rig overtake me and stop beside me in the deep floury dust. When I looked up, there was the stylish buggy with the yellow top and the lady herself holding the tan reins.

"Good afternoon, Jud. You are Jud, aren't you?" she asked brightly. "You're the very one I hoped to see. Won't you get in with me and I'll drive you back home."

To my surprise, her accent was English rather than Spanish. The stylish slant of her sailor straw and the genteel softness of her driving gloves were certainly non-Mexican, her hair a golden Anglo color against her blue eyes. But never would I get in beside her at that moment. There flashed through my mind the tale they told of her Spanish temper and her wild English love for horses. They said she was a girl away at school when a *mozo* had put a spade bit on her favorite riding horse and after long and cruel training taught him to bow low. When she came home, he had proudly showed her horse off to her, but one look at the maimed and bleeding mouth, and she had struck the *mozo* down with the heavy end of her crop. The story was that she had killed him.

When I asked my father he said he didn't know if it was true or not, but I must remember that she was a Johnson y Campo, that the Johnson y Campo sheep ranch, the Rancho Zelandia, took in a great Spanish grant beyond the Prietas. For generations her people had had the power of life and death over their peons, and a fine horse to them meant more than a peon.

When I held off, I expected her to drive away with English abruptness and dismissal, but she was all feminine Mexican wile now. "Don't you want to ride with me?" she asked, wrinkling her eyebrows in that playful Spanish gesture of hurt, a characteristic I was to see in her a thousand times afterward. At the same time that she spoke to me so lightly, there was something indefinably sad about her. I suspect now it was only the faint melancholy of her Latin blood. But at the time it seemed as if some secret sorrow of hers, like mine, was sucking the joy of life from her.

I think that is what quieted my fear and stitched a bond between us — that and something else I didn't recognize at first. This was her complex femininity. She could be very capable, determined, willful, also satiric and funny at times. All this on occasion could vanish and an appealing helplessness come into her blue eyes and even into the way she sat or stood, so that others, and especially men, could not forbear throwing themselves into her cause, bringing to pass what she wished.

Today she seemed to me innocent as beautiful, what she asked so reasonable, that before I knew it I was stumbling around the wheels, climbing up on the cushions of soft rose cloth, and we were off down the road with a feeling that no automobile can give me today, of flowing animal limbs and muscles, of a bright tan harness with silver trimmings and a silver whip socket engraved with a name in script that I couldn't read. Everyone, I noticed, looked up with lively interest to see us go by. I saw with pride that she drove her favorite horse I had heard so much about, the fastest in the territory and her great pet. I remembered my father saying that, when he asked her how many children she had, she had told him two, both boys, one nine and one seven years old. My father learned later that she had given birth to only one child, my cousin Willy, whom I had never met, and that by her seven-year-old boy she must have meant this horse called Critter, who had been named by her father half in jest before he died.

Presently, in front of the large shabby Casa Nuñoz, we stopped and alighted. "Will you hold Critter for me?" she asked. "He hates to be tied, but he's so curious. He likes to examine everything, and I don't want him wandering around town with a buggy."

Never had I held a horse, and I felt sure this one she called Critter knew it. He was a shade called *oscura,* a peculiar shade of brown with faint black inner markings. I had seen much more handsome and spirited horses and wondered why a lady like Mrs. Sessions with such a fancy buggy liked him well enough to consider him one of her boys.

Today I was to get an inkling of the reason. As I took his bridle I saw him examine me quietly. He saw my fear of him, I'm sure. I also like to think that he saw the confused loneliness of an insecure and half-starved boy. After a minute or two he turned his attention to his surroundings. I could have sworn that he surveyed intelligently and in turn the church, the bell towers, the Sisters' school next to it, the bandstand in the center of the little park and La Casa Nuñoz closer at hand.

Mrs. Sessions stayed in the house a long time. Then young Gus Padilla appeared and with importance took hold of Critter's bridle. "Doña Ellen wants to see you inside," he informed me.

I went, somewhat puzzled and reluctant. In our rooms I found a little group of people, including old Ezequiel Salazar, owner of Casa Nuñoz, Mrs. García, Mrs. Padilla, and a number of their children, all at a respectful distance from Mrs. Sessions.

"Jud, we've been holding a little junta about you," she said almost gaily. "The judge and I don't like you living here by yourself. We're afraid you don't get enough to eat. How would you like to come over to my house and stay till your father gets back?"

"I want to stay here," I stammered, retreating toward the door, but the stout form of Mrs. Padilla blocked my way.

"He is in reality very unhappy and lonely here, Doña Ellen."

"How can he expect to live here alone?" that old villain Ezequiel added. "He cannot pay for these rooms. To make ends meet I should rent them to Abundio Sais, who asked me about them."

"It isn't good for him to be so much alone, Doña," Mrs. García spoke up. "In your house there would be Epifania and Manuel, and later on when you came to town he would have your son."

Cousin Albert's wife took my arm as if it was all decided. "Manuel will come for your trunk and other things. Now let's go over to the house and I'll show you where you will sleep."

Before I knew it we were out on the plaza, where she left Critter looking curiously after her while we went on foot nearby to a street called La Placita, one of the spokes radiating from the square.

The white Sessions house, known as the Johnson y Campo house, looked large and imposing to me. Cousin Albert's wife pulled the fancy bell rope and the door was opened by a flurried Mexican woman whom she called Epifania.

When we entered I found myself in an immense dim hall, wide as a parlor and twice as long, with mysterious doors on either side, one of which was open, revealing ghostly shapes of sheets over indeterminate pieces of furniture. Mrs. Sessions took me to a nice room with a white iron bed, the figure of Christ on the Cross on a wall, and soft washed Navajo rugs on the floor. This was Willy's room, she told me, and the bed would be mine until they moved in, when another bed would be put in for me.

"You are all right now, Jud," she promised me. "Friends of your father will look after you till he gets back."

Her references to my father and his friends, and that he would be back, warmed me like wine, but after she had gone something went out of the house. It seemed foreign. Even its air smelled like incense. Unseen presences with a strong Spanish will and flavor seemed to come out of hiding to cast their influence in the air.

After going to bed I remembered what my father had said of the Johnson y Campo family, its power over life and death of its peons, and the story of Doña Ellen and the *mozo*. There came to me the peculiar memory of the lady's hands today as they had held the reins and as one of them had taken my arm. I felt a certain indefinable power and mastery in them. I was glad that she and Cousin Albert planned to stay out on the ranch until fall. By that time, I was sure, my father would be back.

CHAPTER 2

NEXT MORNING, with the New Mexican sun shining in my window and lying brightly across the kitchen floor during breakfast, the house seemed like a different place, and the world, too.

Not only then but after I sallied forth from the house, I found my status in town had changed.

Old Ezequiel, the picture of avarice and chicanery, stopped me on the plaza to talk to me with deference in front of everyone. Lawyer Beasley, whose house stood next door to my Cousin Albert's — he had married Doña Ellen's sister, Doña Ana — acknowledged my existence by inclining his head curtly but unmistakably to me when he passed. And the town boys talked to me of my absent father with new and evident respect.

"Your papa will be back soon now," Goyo Sánchez promised me. "His cousin the judge will see that he goes free."

"For a while he may go to jail, but it will not be so bad," Pas Ramírez assured. "My uncle Angel is in the penitentiary at Santa Fe for six years. They let him come home for weddings and funerals."

"Yes, and you'll have Señor Kidd's eleven thousand dollars besides" — this from Lino García.

I answered angrily that my father had never taken the money, but they looked at me with instant dismay and disappointment. I saw that I must not object to my rank as embezzler's son if I wanted to swim with them in the river, rope milk cows and ride barebacked on broken-down horses. At Epifania's orders, I went back to the house for midday dinner and found a great dish of frijoles, hot with chile that burned all the way down.

But it was the first day my stomach had been filled since my father left, and I felt that life was sweet again, and the one who had saved me was Cousin Albert's lady, who had put me under the protection of the powerful Johnson y Campo name. Cousin Albert's house seemed to me a citadel of peace and security.

In this I found that I was mistaken.

My first inkling came the second week the judge moved back to town. He had come alone at first, called by the September term of court. He slept in the town house during the week, returning to the ranch for the week-end. Any uneasiness I felt for his coming soon vanished. He had me call him Cousin Albert, and treated me kindly, almost as a son. He was a slender delicate man with a white skin and an unusual heavy black beard. This together with his deep voice and powerful phrases never ceased to surprise me in one so frail. Sheets still hung over the furniture in the parlor, and tonight as usual he sat in the wide hall by the hanging brass lamp which he had pulled down to read the Denver paper that had come on the evening train. In the shadows on a settee, I lay content just to be near this one remaining link to my mother. Presently the bell tinkled, and the judge rose and went to the door himself.

"Oh, good evening, Amado. Come in," he said heartily, and I saw a durably dressed Mexican with strong, brown, almost Oriental face and eyes. I knew him as Sheriff Martínez. There were two Martínez brothers in Moro. It was the custom for Amado to run for sheriff on the Republican ticket and Francisco on the Democratic. Whichever won appointed his brother as first deputy, and a Martínez had been sheriff for Moro County since most men could remember. Usually it was Amado. At his silence tonight and the grave way he entered, I saw Cousin Albert's heartiness dissipate.

"Is anything the matter?" he asked.

"You haven't heard from the ranch?"

"You mean our ranch?" Cousin Albert seemed surprised. "Sit down, Amado."

But both men remained standing.

"You remember last year, Judge, when Señor Beasley drove his herd through Ojo Canyon? I don't mean that the *patrón* was there himself. But Jeffcoat, his foreman, said Señor Beasley told him it was too far to drive around on the public road through Canyon del Norte. The cattle would lose weight. Señor Beasley said his wife was a Johnson y Campo herself, a sister of Doña Ellen, and that Jeffcoat could come through Ojo Canyon and the Rancho Zelandia. I didn't see for myself what the cattle did to your señora's garden, but I heard. Also what Doña Ellen thought of that garden. Your señora and Jeffcoat had very hard words. She warned him never to come over your private road with a herd again."

"Yes, yes, of course," the judge said impatiently as if to urge him on.

"Well, Jeffcoat's men came through again this morning. He had a herd of fat steers Señor Beasley wanted to ship before the early price dropped. So he took Ojo Canyon like the other time. There was Doña Ellen's new garden and rosebushes and a new fence around them. Jeffcoat did not stop."

"We mustn't blame Jeffcoat. This is Beasley's doing," Cousin Albert said angrily.

"Perhaps," the sheriff spoke under his breath, "perhaps it is a pity that Señor Beasley wasn't there instead of Jeffcoat."

The judge looked sober. "You mean someone was hurt."

"About as bad as a man can be hurt," the sheriff said gravely. "There was only one shot, a very good shot. The bullet found the forehead."

The judge stood almost like a statue. "Did his men say who did it?"

The sheriff avoided his eyes. "Who knows? A herd of cattle makes much dust. It is hard to see. But all could hear the rifle speak from the portal of your house."

"How long was the shot?"

"From all accounts," the sheriff repeated, looking away, "it was a long shot and a very good one."

Cousin Albert was silent for a while as if wrestling with something grave. "Well, I expect you to do whatever is right and necessary, Amado."

"*Gracias á Dios,* I don't have to do anything. Don Carlos came in tonight. He said it was him who fired the shot."

"Charley! Why didn't he come here to see me?"

"He told me he thought you wouldn't like to leave him out on bail on a murder charge."

"Thank you, Amado." I could see that Cousin Albert was much affected. He laid his paper on the table. Then he took his large cream-colored hat from the rack. "I'll walk along back with you and talk to him," he said.

Later, in my bed, I lay going over what was said and the pictures created in my mind. There had been something incomplete about the story, something that passed between the two men that puzzled me, something not so much spoken as left unsaid but which each understood. I wondered how Charley Johnson y Campo could have done such a violent thing. They said that he had once been a good enough shot with the rifle, trained by his English father, but of late the only things he was known to do were drink whiskey and drive fast horses. He was still more blond than his sister Doña Ellen. We boys called him the Englishman, from his light hair and florid cheeks.

Next morning when I got up Cousin Albert was already gone, but Pas and Goyo were waiting for me outside the back door. They informed me that the Englishman's horse was in our stable, and we spent the morning standing around him talking in suppressed excitement. It gave me a curious feeling to see him standing there so calmly, unaware that his master was locked up for murder only a few blocks away.

"It is not he, they say, that killed the Anglo," Pas said at length.

"Who was it, then?" I asked.

"It was not a he, but a she," Pas declared mysteriously.

For a moment I didn't know what he meant. Then I saw Manuel bearing down upon us. Doña Ellen always referred to him as a *mozo,* which meant "boy," but he was some fifty years old, a short powerful man, with a tremendous face now distorted with rage.

"What lie is this, you son-of-a-goat!" he roared and tried to get his huge hands on Pas. But Pas was too quick for him and dodged out in the alley.

All that morning I thought about the story of Doña Ellen as a girl and a whole procession of uneasy thoughts troubled me. Exactly what did Pas mean that it had not been a he but a she that had done it?

It was late noon when I found Doña Ellen's buggy outside the stable and her pet horse, Critter, in the next box stall to her brother's bay. An empty carriage that had evidently been filled with baggage and servants from the ranch stood in the driveway while its horses out in the alley chewed corn from nose bags before starting back to the Prietas.

Manuel scowled at me.

"You better make steps for the house. If you are wise you will say nothing from that young liar of a he-goat," he warned me.

The house seemed another place when I entered it. Moving slowly down the hall, I saw that the sheets had been taken from the familiar shapes in the long parlor, disclosing wholly unfamiliar furnishings. There were twin scarlet sofas, chairs in red-and-gold brocade, a tall object with filigree brass legs rising to marble shelves and crowned with a painted china lamp. Broad walnut frames inlaid with gold on the wall held only the tiniest of pictures. Another frame enclosed a wreath and one a bunch of withered flowers, mementos of some funeral.

The doors to the other rooms off the wide hall were open now, and I saw across the way a second parlor, not so long as the other, but with a couch, an organ, a blue-tile fireplace and a globe on a stand. As I went on I had glimpses into high-ceilinged bedrooms. Most every room had, in addition to the bed and other heavy furniture, a couch or lounge of some kind. I had never seen such a lot of them in a single house.

I stopped before reaching the dining room, but Doña Ellen must have heard the front door. She came out in the hall looking even more delicate and blue-eyed than I remembered.

"Hello, Jud! Where have you been?" she greeted, as if I and not she was the one who needed comforting. "We've had to start. Come in."

She drew me into the dining room, where dinner stood on the massive table affixed to the floor, flanked by long polished benches of enormous pine planking on either side.

"This is Willy," she said, leading me where a dark-haired, delicate-looking boy sat. "Your place, Jud, is right beside him. I hope you two will be friends. You're cousins, you know, and blood is thicker than water."

I saw Cousin Albert at the head of the table looking kindly and approvingly at me. His wife didn't take the seat I expected, but sat opposite Willy and me. I soon found that she needed no formal position at the doña's head of the table to hold court, but could take care of herself wherever she was.

She asked me questions about myself, confided to me one or two intimate things about the ranch, then wove the four of us into her conversation. Her flow of talk was fluent. She seemed to make light of their unspoken affliction. I found this a characteristic I was to see much of, her manner of disregarding trouble and danger by making fun of them both.

At first, sitting there at the table, I wondered if shooting and death had actually occurred. Then, with dinner done, it was as if the pleasant interlude, like an act in a play, was over. Faint sadness settled on her face. Gravity returned to Cousin Albert. When I glanced at Willy his dark eyes looked back at me wordlessly. What the look meant I had no idea, but I felt that I liked him and that we would get along.

There was no telephone in the house those days to inform your friends that you had come to town, but news traveled about as fast then as now, particularly upon an event like this when your friends were expected to rally around and offer support. It was a revelation to see the house bright and almost gay that evening, with wine in glasses taken from a rack of four marble shelves along the wall. The company consisted mainly of sheep people or those who did business with them.

Others arriving later included Tom Dold, a bachelor with a fund of good humor and the family lawyer since Cousin Albert had sat on the bench. Not a word was spoken of Ellen's brother languishing in jail, but Mr. Dold's stories and confident manner spoke continuously, saying, have no fear, everything in Moro County is under control.

When Willy and I were sent to bed, his mother came to tuck him in and kiss him good night. Then she came over to my bed, which had been placed in the room, and did the same to me.

No one had kissed me since my mother had done it several years before. I remembered Cousin Albert's wife's hands as brisk and masterful, but when she pressed the covers around my neck and shoulders I thought I had never felt a touch more gentle and soft. That such hands could have the stain of blood on them seemed to me unthinkable. I felt myself relax, grateful that for tonight at least sleep would solve all problems.

"*Buenas noches,* Jud," she said.

"Good night, Doña Ellen," I said.

"Call me Cousin Ellen," she corrected, and waited.

"Good night, Cousin Ellen," I replied dutifully.

She looked down at me in warm approval, but even as she smiled I imagined I saw deep inconsolable shadows in her eyes.

CHAPTER 3

USED to think the Moro County courthouse was imposing, a kind of family government house since Cousin Albert held the highest office in it and ruled over it like a king in his palace. Now, after what had happened on the ranch, the aspect of the whole building changed. I found myself avoiding it whenever possible. Something dark, unfriendly, almost frightening had come over it and the jail where Ellen's brother, Charley, awaited trial. I knew it couldn't be Charley or his fate. He meant little or nothing to me. Then I remembered what Pas had hinted at. That must be the secret of my shock, an implication so terrible that I didn't dare think of it openly.

From the beginning I looked to see if anyone else might know and feel as I did. Willy came under my scrutiny first. He was a quiet boy, and there were times when he looked at me with something inexpressible in his dark eyes. I watched Cousin Albert, too, but his grave face told me nothing.

I waited for Willy's grandmother to come in from the ranch for the trial. They called her Mama Grande instead of the usual Abuelita. A short, stout woman with a swarthy face, she had the blackest of eyes. She had a tongue that ran on rapidly in Spanish, but her face and black eyes to me remained unreadable.

When Ellen's sister, Doña Ana, came over from next door to see her mother, I thought I caught a glimpse of fear in her face, but I felt it might have been fear of her husband. Even before coming to my cousin's house to live I had heard how since their marriage Lawyer Beasley had dominated and restrained her, taking over her inheritance, keeping her on a strict allowance, naming the prices she must pay even for such small things as eggs and chile, trimming the wages of the native servants until she had to put up with some of the poorest.

Epifania had once told me how Cousin Ellen and Doña Ana had looked as girls. "Ah, you should see them together when they are little. About the same size. Only a year between them. But such a difference! Doña Ana dark. Dark skin, black hair, black eyes.

And Doña Ellen with white skin and hair of gold like her father. You wouldn't believe they come from the same mother."

Now Doña Ana was older-looking than Ellen, worn-faced and somber-eyed. It was strange to think that before her marriage she had been beautiful and gay. She seemed apprehensive, to have no will or decision of her own. "I'll see what Snell thinks," she said several times; and, when Ellen asked if she would sit with her and their mother at the trial, "I'm not sure what Snell wants."

I suspected she was here today without Beasley's permission. More than once her daughter, Felicitas, said they had better go. Doña Ana hung on as if she feared to stay but hated more to leave. From the start, Felicitas refused to sit down. I thought her the prettiest girl I had ever seen, with hazel eyes and golden hair. I felt that this was how Ellen must have looked when she was young, but Felicitas would have little to do with her Aunt Ellen now, regarding her with an attitude I was sure came from her father. Indeed she treated us all with veiled hostile coolness. Only on Willy when he wasn't looking did I see her glance soften.

Meanwhile the trial was approaching and Willy and I were told we would have to attend. I suspect it was the idea of Tom Dold, who defended Charley, that we boys sitting with Ellen and her mother would arouse the sympathy of the jury. But all the time that Willy and I had to sit there, with witness after witness being questioned, with Cousin Albert sitting watchfully on the bench, and people crowding the room to the doors and windows, I remembered what Pas Ramírez had hinted and waited for it to raise its ugly head in the courtroom.

The witness I disliked more than any other was Lawyer Beasley. "That's my Uncle Snell and he hates us," Willy had whispered the first day. "When Grandfather died, he wanted us to let him take over and manage the ranch. But only Tía Ana would sign."

I remembered the first time I had seen the name in an advertisement in the *Moro Sentinel*:

J. SNELL BEASLEY, Attorney at Law.
Legal Advice and Counsel. Collections Made.
Loans Arranged. Mortgages.

My father said he was the shrewdest and richest lawyer in the county and told me stories to prove it. One, I recall, was how Beasley was engaged by a cattleman named Lassen to defend him for the murder of a Mexican sheepherder. There was no doubt of his acquittal, but Beasley had fixed a juror to hold out for conviction, or so everyone openly said. This hung the jury, and a new trial was ordered, when Lassen was acquitted. The first time Beasley took Lassen's cattle as his fee, the second time his ranch, and this was the ranch whose foreman, Jeffcoat, had been shot.

And now here Lawyer Beasley was in court before me. A short thick man with a red mottled face, he was put on the stand as owner of the cattle, and let loose long blasts on his wife's right to send their cattle through Ojo Canyon and Rancho Zelandia. But no word did he breathe of the specter that lay on my heart.

My chief hope was from something Tom Dold had said. "Don't worry about Charley, Ellen. Every man we let on the jury is a sheepman, not a cattleman. Most of them have Spanish blood besides."

But I think that Snell Beasley must have expected a hung jury, for the last day he let Doña Ana make the show of attending her brother's trial. The jury was out scarcely an hour when they came in with a verdict of not guilty. Freed now, the prisoner pushed to his mother and Ellen in the crowd. Doña Ana was so carried away by the excitement that she, too, made her way to their side. It was a pretty scene, Charley hugged and kissed by his mother and sisters while the sheepmen stood around watching with enjoyment and approval. In her emotion, Doña Ana looked years younger.

Then suddenly the red face of Lawyer Beasley appeared. The excitement seemed to go out of Ana. Her face aged visibly as her husband took her arm and they moved away.

I went home in peace. My relief was great, not so much that Charley was freed but that court and jury had recognized no other who could have fired the shot. At supper Ellen said Willie and I had stood by loyally, that already we had missed so much school it wouldn't hurt us to miss a little more and so she was taking us out for a week's holiday to the ranch. It seemed then that God was back in His heaven and all was right with the world.

There was a celebration at the house that evening, with dozens of guests, including the family of Apolonio Sena, who had testified in Charley's behalf. Next morning Charley went back to the ranch, taking his mother with him. I think the idea was to get him away from town while the cattlemen were still around.

We made ready to leave early that afternoon. Manuel brought Critter and the yellow-top buggy around to the front of the house. The horse, which had hardly been out of his stall during the trial, was impatient to be off. It was exciting to ride with Ellen again, her light talk, her feminine presence very near to me, her superb mastery of the horse. Pleasure in my new life swam about me. Once we had forded the river and were up on the escarpment with the broad mesa stretching before us, I could hardly wait for the hunting that she promised us. Ahead, the Prietas were a long wall of dark rock sprinkled with cedars and pines where mule deer and mountain lion could be found.

Halfway across the mesa we overtook a group of horsemen, evidently cattlemen returning to Baca County from the trial. They looked around and saw us coming but did not get out of our way. Ellen's famous yellow-topped buggy must have symbolized for them their defeat in court at the hands of their ancient enemies, the sheep ranchers. Ellen had to turn Critter aside to pass them on the level mesa. "Hu-cha! Hucha!" one of them sent up the sheepman's cry derisively after us.

"Don't look back!" Ellen cautioned us, but presently the same voice yelled again. I couldn't understand what it said, but I think Ellen did because something in her face changed.

I heard hoofbeats coming after us, and that was when I learned the congenital truth about Critter, that he could never let another horse around him, and at such a time not even Ellen could hold him. Now as the hoofbeats came closer, he answered with a burst of speed that left the other quickly behind. Ellen tried to curb him. I still retain a vivid picture of her in my mind, her gloved hands sawing on the tan lines, her slight body half lifted to its feet.

"You fool!" she cried. "They'll think we're running away."

She could do nothing with him until sounds of pursuit behind us had ceased. Then she slowed him down, furiously turned him around, and drove slowly back until close to the horsemen. Here in the trail she waited for them to come. The transformation in her astonished me. It was a revelation to me to see with what hard relish she faced the oncoming riders. Her helpless way had vanished and been replaced with something else, still feminine but without pity and boding no good for anyone, herself included.

Critter stood perfectly quiet while the riders came, as if his honor was not involved so long as he faced them. They gave us a wide berth. None of them even spoke to us, but when they were by and Ellen passed them again they let out a series of shrill derisive Texas yells. This time she did not stop. We drove on toward the mountains, and nothing more was said about it.

If I thought Ellen a lady in town, she was still more so out here. Over the years I always thought her to be at her best among the natives. Hardly had we approached the scattered cluster of adobe buildings, dominated by the great ranch house, when Johnson y Campo Mexicans surrounded the buggy. The swarthy women smiled. The black eyes of the children shone at their *patrona*. Men who looked to me like rascals and thieves asked with gentle courtesy of the health and well-being of Ellen and Willy, whom they called Guillo. I was introduced as Willy's cousin and my well-being became instantly their concern. But never for a moment could I treat them as Ellen and Willy did. There was, I soon found, a great art in it, a precise stage between superiority and warm interest which I could never attain.

The second day Ellen took us on the promised hunting trip. She drove me in the buckboard along a pair of wheel tracks that wound for miles through the cedars and then out to a lonely expanse of plain. Willy rode his blue pony. Up near a round treeless mountain, Ellen pointed out distant motionless objects which gradually took shape for me as small brown living creatures.

They still seemed in entire safety from us when Ellen suddenly stopped the horse, passed the lines to me, drew a rifle from beneath the seat, stood up in the buckboard and fired. The lunge of the horse threw her back into the seat, but not too quickly to keep me from seeing one of the inquisitive brown wraiths drop to the range while the others fled. When we reached it, I found a beautiful

small deerlike creature lying on the grass with blood running from a well-directed hole in its graceful head.

It seemed incredible to me that the antelope had been shot so accurately and at such a great distance. I didn't understand at first why Ellen's splendid shooting should bother me. I helped her lift the game to the buckboard, and then we drove back to the ranch house. It was very strange. Our hunting had been successful. This was exactly what we had come out to the ranch for, and yet some inexplicable shadow for me had fallen over the sunlit plain.

CHAPTER 4

WE STAYED at the ranch for nearly two weeks, school or no school, and it was a bit long for me. I was glad to get away, especially from the game dinners and the dead antelope and deer hanging in a row in the cold dry air out of reach of the dogs and sun. Town had become somehow peaceful and civilized in my mind, and when we drove back through Ojo Canyon I felt escape from something, I didn't know quite what. It gave me a wonderful feeling to see Moro lying far below us, hardly distinguishable at this distance except for a wisp of smoke hanging above it.

Town seemed even better as we drove into the plaza. Then we came to the white house on La Placita and saw workmen laying brick between the two houses.

"What in the world are they doing?" Ellen asked Chepa and Epifania, who rushed out when they saw us.

"It is to be a wall, Señora," Chepa said.

"What in heaven for?"

"Señora! Doña Ana and Felicitas daren't come over any more! Not even Suplicante! They must stay over there and we must stay over here. As long as we live."

"It is to be a high wall, Señora," Epifania said. "Seven feet up and from street to alley, Suplicante told us."

Ellen did not ask who had ordered this. We all knew. She said nothing for the moment, but as we went into the house her face was frightening.

"I didn't tell you," Cousin Albert said when he came home from the courthouse, "because I didn't want to spoil your holiday. Snell is having his revenge now. He's working off his temper. It might even turn out to be a good thing."

I often thought later on how tragically wrong he was. Perhaps he knew it even then. He may have been trying to put the best possible face on a blight that would be evident to everyone in Moro and for miles around. No one had dared say anything outright about Ellen at the trial, but now, without saying a word, Beasley was giving notice that he didn't feel her a fit associate for his wife and child, who were her own sister and niece.

What Ellen thought I do not know. More than once while the men were at work on the wall, and especially when her brother-in-law came out to look it over, I saw her eyes like agates and that hard look on her face.

It was gone and in its place a kind of gay desperation when friends called. "Do you know you take your life in your hands to come? We're in quarantine and under siege, you know," she'd greet guests in her playful way. Her dinners were too late for Willy and me. We ate our supper much earlier, but in our room we could hear her poke fun at her brother-in-law and his wall.

Most every evening since we came back she either had guests at the house or was a guest in some other. But days were a trial to her. Many an afternoon we came home from school and found Critter hitched up in front of the house, with Ellen at the door, hatted and coated to take us for a ride.

Once the buggy wheels rolled clear of town, you could feel her other self return, her old self, the one I liked best. We drove lanes and the more populated roads, but mostly Ellen took the wheel tracks that crossed and crisscrossed, wheeled and looped on the mesa. It wasn't only to get away from town that she went, I think, but to be driving Critter. There was a certain relationship between Ellen and her horse. The brute was close to her, a silent companion who never failed her. When he obeyed and did her will, she drew from his strength as well as from her own.

But at dusk when we got back to the house, the wall was always there. Words you could reply to and criminal charges could be refuted in court, but how would you answer or disprove an evil brick wall? Every day when town and ranch folk went by, there it was to see and remember, reviving the dark whispers.

I think it was when she couldn't stand the wall any more that she would drive to the ranch, and that was why during the holidays we went to visit the Pereas at Rancho Antiguo. But she always gave other reasons for going.

"Wouldn't you like a white Christmas?" she asked as we walked home from midnight Mass. "The only snow this year is up in La Sierra. How would you like to run up and see the Pereas?"

She made it sound so easy, as if it were only an hour's drive, but I knew La Sierra was forty miles away and the ranch of the Pereas, up near the Colorado border, must be farther. The morning we left, Moro was still in shadow but far to the north the sun was already red on the snowy summits. Critter kept up his incredible trot all the way except now and then on the grades when he slipped back into a running walk.

"He's resting when he does that," Willy informed me. "It's the Indian shuffle."

I had never seen anyone received as Ellen was by the Pereas and their other guests at Rancho Antiguo. The men surrounded her and the women did the unheard-of Spanish act of listening. Long after Willy and I went to bed in a huge room with others younger than we were, we could hear her laugh next door in the old *sala,* a particular kind of laugh, a series of quick, tiny explosions, tumbling out all at once like mixed-up notes of music, very contagious, and delightful to hear.

But if Ellen was looked up to at the Pereas', Critter was not. The Perea family was noted for raising white sheep and black horses. They had no use for Critter's *oscuro* shade. "It's the color of the dirt," they said. Also, their horses were their chattels, not their friends. They reined them high and trained them to prance in style. Critter's lounging ways invited their contempt.

Moreover, Critter seemed concerned about us in this strange place. He declined to graze with the other horses, but hung around close to the ranch house. "Why are you such a baby?" Ellen scolded impatiently. "You won't stay with the other horses. You have to hang around me like a spoiled child around its mother."

When we went to the mountains, Ellen had him put in a corral so he couldn't follow us. We saw him looking after us as we drove away to scenery more beautiful than I knew existed. The crowning point of the trip was a grassy trail through a high valley called Canyon de Espíritu Santo, or Holy Ghost Canyon, where the blue firs and red-boled pines drooped with moss and a crystal-cold river rushed down from a snowy peak at the head of the canyon.

We came back elated from our trip, but the first thing we heard as we neared the ranch was Critter whinnying at us from where he stood with his head over the corral fence.

Early next morning I felt a hand shake me under the heavy blankets spun from native fleeces. It was Ellen saying that we must go. Sleepily Willy begged to stay another day.

"No, it's impossible," his mother said. "We could be snowed in for weeks up here."

When we got up we saw the ground already lay covered, and when we left we could see our tracks deep in the white road.

We didn't feel the force of the wind till we left the shelter of the mountains. Coming to the mouth of the canyon, we could see in front of us the white particles driven almost horizontally from the northwest. Critter saw them, too. His ears pricked and, tossing his mane, he answered with doubled speed.

Willy laughed. "He doesn't like it, Mama."

"I hope it stings him," his mother said. "He's been a very temperamental boy."

At first it was pleasant enough racing through the snow, but after an hour or two it had grown much colder and the snow was thicker and finer, a solid white curtain closing us in.

"How do we know where we are?" Willy wondered.

Ellen answered at once. "San Antonio knows."

"He might have forgotten us up here," Willy pointed out.

"No," she promised, "I told Father Goshard I'd get a new robe for San Antonio, the best China silk and a gold hem. If we get lost up here in the snow, San Antonio knows he'd never get it." Sometimes when the Spanish came out in Ellen, she surprised me.

The cold by now was intense. We huddled under blankets, the rubber shield of the buggy buttoned up tight with the reins passing through a slit. The isinglass peek holes were almost constantly blinded with snow except when a jolt from the wheels or our hands would clear them. But when we looked out, all we could see was the brown furry shape of Critter, a tiny moving island in the midst of a white wilderness. For the last hours Ellen had made no attempt to guide him, letting him choose his own way in the barren waste. At last I could not blot out a terrible conviction from my mind. I knew that he must be lost.

More than once Critter's trot dragged to a walk and sometimes he frightened us by stopping altogether. Peering out, we watched him rub one side of his head, then the other against the ends of the shafts. Ellen said she thought he was rubbing the icicles from his eyes. After this he went on, but sooner or later, I felt, the snow must stop him and bury us in its depths.

The day dragged, growing no lighter, and it seemed a week since we had left the Pereas and even since we ate the lunch they had packed for us. Suddenly Ellen startled us by her cry. Looking out of the peephole, I saw what appeared to be a wide gray streak in the snow. "You wonderful thing!" she screamed, and it was a moment before I realized it was to Critter she had called. "It's the Baca road!" she told us. "He never took the road to town. He's brought us down behind the Prietas straight for the ranch."

Down here there seemed to be less snow. We reached places where the wind had left our trail almost bare, and here Critter let himself go. He had been dragging a heavy buggy with three people through snow and often drifts for hours. By all accounts he should have been worn out, brought to one of those violent trembling spells that in a Western horse mean exhaustion and death. But now his legs fairly flew. The stable and alfalfa ahead seemed to tap new energies in his being.

There was great excitement at the ranch when we arrived. They hadn't known we had ever left town. Mama Grande, aroused by the commotion, called demandingly from the portal that we come in at once. But Ellen refused to go until she saw Critter cared for. He steamed in the frosty air like a railroad engine on a zero morning.

Fidel came running to take over the unhitching, and led him to his stall. The hay that we thought he had run for lay plentiful in his manger, but, now that he had reached it, there was no effort to touch it. He stood with hoofs somewhat far apart, head down, as if what he wanted most in the world was just to stand there and never move. This was how he stayed while Fidel and Teófilo rubbed him down. Only once Fidel spoke. His strong brown weathered face was grave. "Dios was with you, Doña Ellen," he said. "The snow drifts worse on the Moro road. Deep as a house sometimes. Had Critter gone that way, never maybe would you have got through."

It was late in the evening when he brought word to the house. "It is well now, patrona. Critter has started to eat."

THE BLIZZARD did something to Ellen. I never knew exactly what. Perhaps it had been the closeness of death. As she drove us back to town I felt her somehow changed from the person who had driven us to Rancho Antiguo. At home, confronted by the wall, she seemed to master her bitter emotions. In the days that followed I noticed that she avoided the wall, staying in parts of the house where it couldn't be seen, sewing the promised robe for San Antonio and taking it to church several times to measure and fit.

The second week she called Willy.

"I want you to go over to your Tía Ana for me. Say I hope they can come to dinner Saturday evening. It will be just family, theirs and ours. Of course, I expect Uncle Snell and Felicitas. After all, Ana is my sister and Felicitas your blood cousin. We love them and I'm sure they love us."

Willy stared at his mother. This was a new Ellen.

"But do you think he'll let her?"

"He should — if we think of him with charity and kindness. Charity and kindness can do wonders, Father Goshard says, even to Snell Beasley. You and Jud must treat him with love, Willy, when you see him."

"How do you mean?" Willy looked dismayed.

"Talk and act toward him as if he never sent his herd through our ranch. If we treat him with love, then perhaps everything will be all right."

We went outside, and reluctantly Willy took his way toward

the forbidden wall and then behind it. I could see that he was uneasy. When Felicitas sprang out at us in the patio, he fairly jumped. "Willy! You better get out of here!" she threatened.

Willy seemed relieved if anything by the encounter. "I don't need to get out," he stammered. "Mama says we love you and you love us and everything is going to be all right."

The girl moved up in front of him. "What did you say, Willy?"

"Felicitas!" Willy implored her. "Do me the favor. Go and tell your mother for Mama that we love you and you love us and she wants you over for dinner Saturday night. Uncle Snell, too."

"You better go, Willy, before Papa comes home."

Willy looked at me. His face was haggard. "Come in with me, Jud!" he begged. "Whatever you do, don't run off."

Slowly he pushed open the side door and went in with me close behind. There, looking at us, as frightened as we, stood his aunt. I think she had been watching from the window. "Tía Ana!" Willy cried, grateful to see her, and stammered out his mother's invitation.

Doña Ana startled us by bursting into tears. She hugged him and cried over him, then pushed him aside and looked quickly out of the window. "Now you better go, Willy," she said. "Tell your mother a thousand thanks. I'm afraid that we can't come next Saturday, but one of these Saturdays God will smile and it will be all right. I will let her know."

When Cousin Albert came home, Ellen told him. Cousin Albert nodded and looked at her gravely. But if he had judicial reservations, he kept them to himself. After all, she was the child of several races, with long lines of conflicting ancestors rising in her from the past for a moment or two before falling back into the rich and ancient blood stream.

What puzzled and almost awed me was the peace in the house that followed Ellen's offer of love. Even the icy heart of winter seemed mellowed; I had never seen a gentler January in Moro.

But the Beasleys never sent word about the dinner. Ellen kept Saturday evenings open for them, and when they did not come Willy and I would stay up to eat with her. Cousin Albert was at court in San Ysidro County. On this certain Saturday night, we were still at the mutton when we became aware of excitement in the kitchen. Then the kitchen door opened and Teófilo from the ranch burst into the dining room. "God help us, patrona!" he groaned, and fell down on his knees by Ellen's chair.

I had never seen anything like this, a man such as Teófilo acting like a grief-stricken child to a mother younger than he.

"What is it, Teo?" Ellen asked. "Is it Mama Grande?"

"No, *gracias á Dios.*"

"Is it Don Carlos?"

"He is the one, patrona."

"Is he living?"

"Thanks to God, when I left. But the holes in him are deep and he lost much blood."

"Blood!" Something hard and ugly had come into Ellen's voice. We all felt it, including Teófilo. Before saying more, he got to his feet, and the story came out swiftly and passionately. Charley had started for town that afternoon for his regular Saturday-night spree. At the mesa end of the canyon he had met two men on horseback. He didn't know their names but thought he had seen them before and that they hailed from Baca County. They had stopped him and asked if he was Charley Johnson y Campo, the one who had sworn in court he had shot and killed Frank Jeffcoat. Yes, Charley said, he was. Then they pulled their revolvers and fired on him and galloped off. Charley himself told all this an hour later to the sheepherder who discovered him and who had run to the ranch with the news. When Fidel and others got there, they found their *patrón* still alive.

When I looked at Ellen, the new gentleness of the last weeks had wholly vanished. "Run for Dr. Gammel," she ordered. "Send him to the ranch. Tell him to hurry."

"The doctor is already gone, patrona," Teófilo said. "I stopped at his house first."

"Then you can help Manuel harness Critter. I will drive out myself as soon as I change my clothes."

Before she could get away, Fidel arrived from the ranch on another smoking horse with the word that Charley was dead. He had met the doctor on the mesa and told him, but the good señor

doctor said he was the coroner and had to go anyhow. Besides,
Mama Grande would probably need him.

If Ellen mourned, it was in secret. Her cool English blood
seemed to take charge. She dispatched Manuel for the sheriff. The
door to the second parlor was shut while she talked to Amado
Martínez. All I heard was his promise to send a telegram to Cousin
Albert when he left.

Ellen drove Willy and me to the ranch. Once we had left town,
she seemed more Spanish than English. The cry of grief with
which she and Mama Grande greeted each other sounded almost
foreign to me, as did the *velorio del defunto* a night or two later
in the big house, with the natives coming in and sitting on benches
around the white walls, the songs of death and sorrow, murder
and revenge, and the supper served with the inevitable *café* and
vino. All the time the corpse lay in a coffin made by the ranch
carpenter and covered with black cloth, Charley's blond hair and
English features looking out of place here amid the foreign talk
and songs and dark faces.

Services for Uncle Charley were held in the ranch chapel, with
Father Goshard in charge. Only the family and important family
friends could get into the chapel. It was cold as a cave, but not
so cold as outside, where more than a hundred Mexicans stood in
the bitter wind listening to what sounds of the Mass came through
the open door.

Services were delayed, waiting for Doña Ana. Not till Father
Goshard was at the altar did she come with Beasley. I thought he
tried to keep her to the rear, but she slipped up to the front between
Ellen and Mama Grande, where she held a hand of each. That was
also the way they stood at the grave, while Beasley waited expressionless just behind her. I was next to him and had full opportunity to see the dark blood in his temples and the thick
immovable way he stood.

It was an unforgettable scene. A desert graveyard is to me one
of the loneliest sights in the world, an expression of man's tran-
sience and unimportance on earth, and the Rancho Zelandia
cemetery was no exception. The few stone markers had been
visibly mended after being twice knocked down by Beasley's herd.

Wooden crosses, split and broken by hoofs, had been bound by twine. This, with the empty tinsel that Mexicans like to heap on their graves, gave the place a shabby and pitiful air. To me our little group of humans standing there by the open grave looked helpless and insignificant against the vast spaces beyond.

A short distance from the open grave was the patch of unsanctified desert waste where Frank Jeffcoat's still partially fresh mound could be seen. His grave and Charley's were not a hundred yards apart. They stood out like unhealed scars from the rest of the landscape, and I wondered how many more lives would be dragged down into the dark and silent earth before it was over.

CHAPTER 5

NO ONE had seen two strangers in the vicinity on the day Charlie was killed.

But a week later Apolonio Sena, the sheep rancher who had testified for Charley's character at the trial, was shot and killed on his ranch, and this time the men who had done it were recognized and named. They were Grover Reid and Earl Paulson, both outspoken "Jeffcoats," a term we had begun to call cattlemen and their sympathizers. Most everyone, I think, felt at once that these were the same men who had done the earlier killing. First, there had been two of them, as Charley had said. Then, the shooting of Frank Jeffcoat was involved in both cases.

At first most of us were not too excited over the fate of the Apolonio Sena killers. Then we grew aware that there might be more to their trial than we thought. In fact, by the time it came around, the trial of Reid and Paulson became perhaps the most significant to take place in the county, not so much for the crime named in the case but because it stood for the more sensational murder never officially mentioned in the trial, that of Charley Johnson y Campo.

The first time I became conscious of possible ugly complications ahead was before the two men had been arrested.

"I hope those two Jeffcoats cleared out for Old Mexico," Tom Dold said to Cousin Albert.

It sounded strange to me coming from him. I expected Cousin Albert to reply that, no matter who they murdered, the two men should be caught and tried. To my surprise, he turned to Tom and confided in a low voice, "If I wasn't an official sworn to recognize the legal processes, I'd be tempted to suggest that they get out of the country before those processes catch up with them and us all."

Now what made him say that, I wondered, and especially the "us all"? Whatever his thoughts, I'm sure he said nothing of them to Ellen. She had been hard hit by Charley's murder. This was brought home to me when we were back in the house at Moro. Cousin Albert had returned to court in San Ysidro County. That evening Tom Dold and others were in the *sala*.

"Well, Paulson and Reid were brought in today," Tom mentioned. "The first thing they wanted was their lawyer."

I saw the quick lift of Ellen's head. "I should think no decent lawyer in Moro County would defend them."

"I'm afraid they didn't have to go very far."

We all knew whom he meant.

"I'm not surprised," Ellen said bitterly. "I shan't rest till both of them are convicted and hung." Her vehemence surprised me.

"The Jeffcoats are saying," Tom went on, "that, since Charley was freed by the court, Reid and Paulson should be freed also."

"But Charley didn't go free," Ellen declared swiftly. "He's dead, and that should be the fate of these men, too."

She said it with such passion and devotion to her murdered brother that I felt strong sympathy for her. Indeed, I thought her admirable as she sat there, faithful, with high principles.

When the motion was brought by Beasley that Cousin Albert disqualify himself from sitting in the case because of the linking of the two killings in the public mind, I heard Cousin Albert tell Willy: "To abandon the bench in this case would be deserting your mother. She'd think it public admission that I thought these two Jeffcoats had cause to do what they did."

Not till the Grand Jury had returned an indictment, the two men had been arraigned, and threatening Jeffcoats from several counties had begun rallying in their defense did I realize what lay ahead of us — another ugly and interminable trial, vindictiveness and more vindictiveness. I saw that the one on whom the brunt of it would fall was not Ellen so much as Cousin Albert, who had had little or nothing to do with it but must stand up for her interest, bringing in if possible a verdict she would regard as just, and then endure the storm that must break on him.

The trial was set for the fall term of court. For some time I had noticed that Willy was not himself; his face looked dead white. Ellen had Dr. Gammel examine him and leave twisted white papers containing an ugly-tasting powder. But all spring while the peaches and apricots were in delicate bloom against the raw brown land, Willy's complaint grew no better.

Now as I look back I think that Willy felt things ahead that I didn't. He wasn't trying to forget so much as to recapture while there was still time. For this he was given an exceptional summer. Everyone said they had never seen the range greener. When school was finished for another term and we had moved back to the ranch, he cleaved to his saddle like an axe bit to the handle.

There's a blessed amnesia about life in the saddle. To Willy the big ranch house was home, the Casa Grande, the house of many rooms. Whenever in the past there had been need of a new room, the Campos had simply laid out more dobe bricks to dry and added the walls they wanted. There were some twenty-six or -seven rooms, one entering the other or into some small hall, and all built around a central patio shaded by two narrow-leaved mountain cottonwoods. Willy knew every room intimately. He had been born in one.

But now, I think, Willy had begun to feel the emanation of things long past, dark ancient influences in the house, perhaps shadows cast by the future. We never spoke of them. All I knew was that when we went out of the house he seemed to feel better, as I did, and that once lifted to our ponies' backs we had freed ourselves for a time from the presence of evil or its power to harm us. Riding out, we were prisoners suddenly escaped to the un-fettered world of land and sky. Before, behind and beneath us swept the open range, fenceless, seemingly without border or end. This was the older, more joyous world where the Creator and the mark of His hand were still to be felt. We breathed air never before

tasted by a human being. We watered our horses in ponds un-named and unknown except by wild waterfowl. To come on these or on some bright wild garden of range flowers, blossoms that probably had never before been seen by the human eye, gave us a feeling of the largesse of God and of receiving favors directly from His hand.

The hour we liked best was just before sundown, when the glare of the desert day is gone. Then the soft red sunlight lies on the western slopes of the grassy swells and buttes and the violet light from distant mountains begins to reach out to you and beyond. Often we loitered in some distant spot so we could ride home through it without talking, our minds closed to such things as courts, open only to the delicious awareness of a more primitive existence.

Willy hated, I know, to see the summer days go by and especially in the cedars. They grew in a belt two to five miles wide and un-numbered miles long at the foot of the Prietas, a rolling, some-times almost level country of riders' delight. The open range is nearly always the same, but in the cedars the rider is swallowed up in an endless succession of glades and parks where for the distance of a few yards or rods the cedars and piñons for some unknown reason refuse to grow.

I remember two or three spots Willy showed me that the Mexi-cans said were evil. They looked to me like any other, patches of grama grass surrounded by clumps of the dwarf trees. "Once in the past a very bad thing happened here," Willy told me in a low voice. "Even our ponies know it."

It was true that they didn't like to stop and graze here as they did other places. Willy and I would stay as long as we dared, tasting the sensation of chill. Suddenly, as if some unknown thing was about to burst out of the deformed cedars, we would look at each other, dig our heels into our ponies' sides, and gallop off, heading for the open range where as far as we could see lay the calm peace of the wide spaces.

There was one thing, we were to learn, that we couldn't gallop away from so easily. This was the trial to come. It lay directly ahead, coming nearer and still nearer each time the sun rose.

WHEN we left the ranch in September, the coming trial had already taken over the town. Fall's Wagon Yard near the river looked full, we noticed as we drove by, and we found the plaza choked with horses and unhitched teams. It was all the more significant since this was roundup time on the cattle ranches. Of course, some of the visitors were sheepmen intent on seeing judgment overtake the enemy who had shot down two of their fellow ranchers in cold blood. But most of them were cowmen who hated sheep. Most of the cowmen knew Judge Sessions' wife as a Johnson y Campo, and they knew her yellow-top buggy. I noticed that those in the street gazed belligerently at us as we drove by.

"Pay no attention, *muchachos,*" Ellen said. "Looks don't kill. We won't perish."

Even in the sanctuary of the big white house on La Placita I could feel the tension in the town, an oppression that hung black over the mesa for days. Ellen felt it too and reveled in it. This was the Spanish in her, responding to crowds, emotion and suspense. Anyone could see now that the trial concerned more than justice to Apolonio Sena. The house had never been so filled since I knew it. First Mama Grande came in for the duration. Then ranching friends of the family visited while attending the trial, the Pereas from La Sierra, and others I had never seen before.

This time Willy and I were not required to go to the trial, but hardly a detail was spared our young ears. News from the court-room reached our kitchen and stable as quickly and sometimes quicker than it did the two parlors. At dinner and supper, at the head of the table, on her rawhide-seated chair overlaid with a scarlet cushion to raise her a little, Ellen reigned over her court, never letting it get out of hand, injecting lightness and wit when it became too serious. "There are two places," she would say, "where, no matter how dull, we must listen and never interrupt or ask questions or argue. One is in church." Everyone would laugh at Father Goshard if he was there. "The other is in court," and then the laughter would be at Cousin Albert.

To my surprise, the name of the lawyer who defended the murderers was never mentioned. But a great deal was said about *el culebrón,* "the large snake," and it took me some time to realize that this was their name for Snell Beasley, and then I understood the contempt with which the word was spoken.

Cousin Albert would say little or nothing about the case. "Ask me a month from now," he'd say when appealed to for some opinion bearing on the trial. "Today I'm just a piece of furniture pulled up to Ellen's table. I don't hear and I don't speak."

The only time Willy and I had to attend the trial was when Cousin Albert sentenced the killers. A verdict of first-degree murder had been brought in by the sheepman jury, a great victory for the prosecution. Only Willy and his father didn't seem to share in the triumph, which seemed unfortunate because, of all the participants, Cousin Albert had had the hardest time, hearing the endless testimony, ruling on allegations and motions for dismissal, silencing the angry demonstrations of the Jeffcoats from time to time, and keeping the case generally in hand. Now at the sentencing his eyes were stern as he gazed at the two prisoners standing in the box.

"Grover Reid and Earl Paulson, you cruelly and forever deprived a fellow citizen of life and pursuit of happiness, one Apolonio Sena. You are now remanded to the custody of Sheriff Martínez to be returned to your cells, and on Friday, February twentieth, you will be taken to the jail yard and duly hanged by the neck until dead."

The words and the way he spoke them sent a chill along my spine. He turned and glanced down into the packed court. His eyes met Ellen's. For a moment something passed between them. His look seemed to say he had vindicated her trust in him and delivered the murderers to their proper end. Then I thought he looked suddenly tired as he turned away.

"Well, thank the Lord they'll get theirs," I said to Willy as we went out.

He didn't answer and when we reached the bright winter sunlight I saw that he kept his face away.

Ellen had wanted to give a supper party that evening in celebration, but Cousin Albert overruled it. He said it would look unseemly and if she held it he wouldn't attend. It was the first time I heard him take such a firm stand in opposition to her and I thought the ordeal of the trial had steeled him. To my surprise, she did not mock or disregard him. "Whatever you think, Albert," she said.

From this time on I thought I detected a change in their relationship. Up to now Cousin Albert had been the one to come to her. He used to stand waiting a long time just to see her come out of her room or into the *sala*. Now it was she who came to him. Was he all right? Could she or Epifania do anything for him? And when there was nothing else, she would set herself to entertain and amuse him. Cousin Albert didn't try to resist her charming ways, but when she turned away, I noticed that the grave melancholy returned to his face.

I thought at first that her increased affection for him was gratitude, payment in her kind for his justice in avenging Charley, but later I was not so sure. I knew that some cattlemen were still in the town and heard that they had made threats against us.

After the sentence, one morning in the early hours, men on horseback shot out the plate-glass windows of both front parlors, and rode away again, yelling and shooting into the air. Ellen gave Willy and me strict orders to stay off the street except on our way to and from school. Mama Grande grew alarmed and would let Ellen go nowhere on foot. Only Cousin Albert went his usual way, marching twice daily to his court chambers.

All the time the hanging grew closer, and then came the night Manuel told us that the two godless savages had been finally hung, after refusing to kneel with the executioner and preacher when the latter prayed for them.

Now I expected the full fury of the cattlemen to be directed against us, but nothing happened. The hangman's victims were duly buried in the Protestant cemetery. The last cattlemen drifted back to their ranches.

"It's all over now, *gracias á Dios,*" Mama Grande said and went home to the ranch.

But I wasn't so sure. Once Tom Dold was closeted with Ellen behind closed doors when Cousin Albert wasn't at home. At noon and in the evening she grew restless until Cousin Albert would return from the courthouse. Long before his usual hour she began looking for him.

The court term at Moro was over now. Next on the calendar was the spring term in Baca County, which was cattle country. To get there from Moro Cousin Albert had to make a three days' journey with the matched pair of blood bays, Dan and Choppo, in his black pole buggy.

"Will you do me a favor, Albert?" Ellen asked him at the dining table one day. "Ask Judge Otero to take over Baca this spring."

He looked startled. "Judge Otero? But how could I do that?"

"You could say you were indisposed. You've had a long and difficult ordeal."

"I am a little tired, yes," he admitted, "but not indisposed."

"It's the same thing. Wouldn't you do it for me?" she begged.

Cousin Albert looked profoundly disturbed. "I would do anything within reason for you, Ellen. But this is impossible. Judge Otero and many others would think me afraid."

It was the word "afraid" that suddenly revealed the specter that haunted the back of Ellen's mind. For a moment I could see the wild uninhabited region Cousin Albert must traverse on his way to Baca County, the lonely canyons he must pass through, the remote mesas to be crossed, where a trail might lie for days abandoned except to wild things and stray cattle.

For about a week I didn't hear Ellen bring up the matter again.

"Will you take Willy with you, Albert?" she suddenly begged him the day before he left.

"Willy?" He drew back. "Ellen, you ask the most impractical things."

"Why is it impractical?" She saw him hesitate and pushed her advantage. A very torrent of Spanish words and a woman's reasoning ensued. Now when I glance back I think I can read her thought, her realization that it was she who had got him into the position from which there was no retreat, and this was her last resort to protect him. Her intuition told her that not even the most hardened of men would fire on a buggy if it contained a young boy. It may be she believed that, if like Abraham she would offer her son as a sacrifice, Dios would not take the life of one so innocent and unsinful.

"I cannot do it, Ellen," Cousin Albert declared. "If I did — "

Ellen interrupted, "If not Willy, you must take me!"

I knew then, and Cousin Albert knew too, that she meant it. I knew also that if there was one thing a man hated it was to hide behind a woman's petticoats. He considered a long time and his face was pale, but in the end he agreed reluctantly to her demand.

Willy's eyes lighted when his mother told him. He was wild with excitement over the chance to be with his father out in the range country, and he pleaded that I be permitted to go along. No, that would put too big a burden on his father, Ellen told him, and, besides, surely he wanted me to stay and look after her? He did not protest too much then.

Court in Baca County was to open Monday morning. Willy and his father left the previous Wednesday in the black buggy. A scattering of local people came to see the judge off. Among them was George Atkins, the druggist, with his camera and tripod.

I have an enlarged print of the scene he snapped that day. In the photograph Dan has one front foot raised, pawing to go. Holding the reins, Cousin Albert sits in the buggy, his back straight, his black beard covering his tie, wearing his Western hat with a narrow brim and a high crown. Beside him sits Willy looking happier than any photographer before had been able to snap him.

There is only a trace of Ellen's skirt in the photograph. But I have a vivid memory of her standing just inside the gate, her face colorless, her eyes straining after the buggy until it turned and vanished into the plaza.

CHAPTER 6

HERE ARE a few small things we know now about Cousin Albert's and Willy's journey. It is one of the most famous cases in New Mexican history. People still talk about it. But we knew almost nothing then.

With the others gone, Ellen left for the ranch in the morning. She did not ask me along. She seemed to have forgotten me. A week later when she came back from the ranch, she seemed calm, like her old self. The period of suspense was over. Cousin Albert's trip to Baca County took only three days at most. He must have arrived long since and everything was all right.

I suppose I looked a little forlorn.

"Pobrecito!" she said. "I shouldn't have left you alone in the house. You suffer like me with Willy away."

That evening at dinner she tried to make up for her neglect. "You missed the trip with Willy. Now I must tell you some things you missed. The country is nothing much. But the people make up for it. The first night you would have stayed with the Romeros. There is Cosme. He doesn't count. The all-important are his four sisters. They are the priceless ones. What one says, the others must say, too. Everything is said four times. It is like an echo. It runs all around the room. *Oye, oye, oye, oye.* Listen, listen, listen, listen. If one of them forgets to say it, the others look at her in horror. She's committed treason."

Her description of the Romeros made me laugh.

"And then San Mateo," she went on. "Have you ever spent the night in an Indian pueblo? Well, you would be an honored guest. You would be the cousin of Albert, el Juez Sessions. Carasco, the governor, is our friend. Your Indian bed is just a rug on the floor, and you think you hear strange primitive things during the night, but maybe to hear them you must have Indian blood in you as I do."

She was at her best regaling me with Cousin Albert's third stopping place, almost at the end of his journey.

"The Banburys are the English ones. They raise sheep and wolf-hounds. When you sit at dinner, there's a tremendous dog like a lean and hungry lobo sitting on each side of you, watching you eat. You think you better be quick getting the food to your mouth or it will be snatched away. You are in a dobe house five thousand miles from London, and yet everything, even their dress, is English. One time my father and I came just at dinner. A Lady Somebody or other was at the table in a low-cut evening dress. When she stood up I found she had tucked it into a man's riding britches."

I fancied at dinner that, all the while Ellen chattered and I laughed, Chepa served us with a cruel face. Ellen noticed it at last.

"Chepa. What is it?" she asked.

"Nothing, patrona," the servant said.

Ellen's eyes grew thoughtful. "There is something."

"Nothing, nothing, patrona," Chepa blurted and hurried out in the kitchen.

I saw now that Ellen had sobered. "Will you go down to the courthouse for me, Jud? Tell Amado I would like to see him. Right away."

It was necessary to go to several restaurants before finding the sheriff. I thought that he exchanged an uneasy look with the deputy, who sat across the table. When finally he arrived at the house, his brother was with him. It was not a good sign.

Ellen received them in the wide hall.

"Have you heard from the judge, Amado?" she asked at once.

"No, señora, not yet," the sheriff said.

"Well, have you heard anything about him?"

"No, señora, nothing definite. There is not time." He said it very elaborately.

"Everyone is so strange," Ellen declared. "First Chepa and now you. I am sure you know something, a rumor perhaps. What have you heard?"

The two brothers exchanged masked glances.

"We have a visitor from Baca County, señora, Señor Haddon, the deputy sheriff."

"Well, tell me! What did he come for? What did he say?"

"He just brought news that the judge was late, señora."

"Well, how late? Did he finally get there?"

"We don't know, señora. He told us there is no emergency. Court is being postponed till the judge comes."

"But why didn't the judge get there? Why don't you go out with your men and see where he is?"

"Señor Haddon just got here this afternoon, señora. There has not been time. We will go over the trail in the morning. But I am sure the judge is there by this time. You must not worry. If anything had happened, Señor Haddon would have found out about it on the way."

The sheriff and his party left in the morning, but learned nothing, except that Cousin Albert had never reached Baca. The story of the judge's delay, his unknown whereabouts, and finally his complete disappearance became the chief topic in the whole territory. Mama Grande heard of it at the ranch and sent Fidel for particulars. A succession of friends called at the house to ask for news. Now that the initial bad news was broken, the Martínez brothers called regularly to report.

It seemed incredible to me that posses of experienced men could search the trail and find nothing. They learned that the judge and Willy had spent the first night with the Romeros and the second at the San Mateo pueblo. Next morning an Indian boy shepherd had seen the judge and Willy drive by some eight or ten miles west of the pueblo. The judge had waved to him. Apparently this boy was the last to have laid eyes on either one. It was as if they had been swallowed up by the earth itself.

Of all the mysteries that ever gripped the territory, this, I think, has puzzled many of us the most. There had been tragic disappearances in New Mexico before, and have been since, but most of these have concerned obscure people. This had happened to a United States judge on official rounds of duty and to his eleven-year-old son.

It was hard on me, but Ellen was the one on whom the suspense centered. Afternoons and evenings she had to receive callers and hear their questions together with the recitation of all the wild stories and rumors going the rounds. One account was that the judge, Willy and the two horses had been shot and buried in the sand, along with the burned and dismantled buggy, and that, unless the winds someday might unearth them, their remains would never be found. Another was that Willy had been spared and taken to the lonely highlands of Old Mexico, where he was given to a remote Mexican family to raise so that in time he would no longer remember his mother and father or his New Mexican home. A third story was that Cousin Albert had fled with another woman and taken Willy forcibly along, and that he had died of homesickness and sorrow, to be buried in California.

What turned out worse than the ugly rumors as time went on were the clues that aroused hope only to be proved false. Some claimed they had seen Willy among the Navajos north of Gallup. Some swore the judge had been recognized in Denver or El Paso or some other place, that he had seemed bereft of his memory. Cousin Albert's horses were said to have been seen and identified in the hands of strangers, and his pole buggy as well.

Through it all Ellen bore up splendidly, her cheeks a little feverish, her eyes too brilliant perhaps. Sometimes I thought that she bore up too well, that she almost enjoyed the excitement, the attention, the stream of visitors, especially the constant consolation of Tom Dold and Dr. Gammel. She must feel some responsibility. And yet, here she was, affected certainly but still the lady, in the last extremity untouchable, the possessor of some quality difficult to name. In sorrow, as in pleasure, she was just a little beyond reach, not wholly duty-bound, answerable only to herself.

Then I learned that I was mistaken. The word came that the county authorities had given up the search. Amado Martínez himself broke the bad news one sunny afternoon. "I can't ask the men to keep on looking forever, señora," the sheriff said. "The country is too big and we have found nothing. Now we must stop."

This time Ellen didn't go to the door when he left. She sat in her chair, very pale. Her face had a transparent quality sometimes seen in the cheeks of the dead. "God forgive me," I heard her say in Spanish, "that I've never been able to cry."

I don't think she knew I was there, or cared. But now she turned and saw me. Something in her eyes seized on me. I thought afterward that what caught her was my kinship to Cousin Albert and Willy, that I was blood of their blood, the closest living thing to either of them she had left.

"Never let anyone stop you, Jud, from doing what you think you should do," she told me passionately. "Had I followed my senses, I would have gone with Albert, no matter how much he hated to hide behind my skirts. Then if anything would have happened, I'd have been with him. If the Jeffcoats jumped him, I'd have been there to talk them out of it. If in the end they killed him, they would have had to kill me, too."

At her words the old admiration, affection and loyalty for her flooded up in me, and more than once during the night, when I remembered what she said, warm tears rose to my eyes.

WHEN the authorities gave up, that was when Ellen said she herself would start looking for Cousin Albert and Willy. Tom Dold and Dr. Gammel protested. "No one will hurt a woman," she said. "Besides, I am taking Fidel and Teófilo along. And Jud," she added with a glance at me. "If he is not afraid."

"Few of us were afraid, Ellen, that they would dare touch the judge and Willy!" Tom Dold reminded.

"Albert never carried a gun," she answered. "I am going armed." Something in her eyes and the way she said it brought up the old uncertainties about her in my mind.

We left for the ranch next morning. Mama Grande heard the plan with her expressionless black eyes. "If it will help you to go, you must go," she said to Ellen. "But why take another boy into that bad country? What can he do?"

"Jud is Willy's cousin," she reminded. "Now he can see where Willy went."

I felt Ellen had another and deeper reason for taking me, one rather of fate and of meetness. Whatever happened to Cousin Albert she was willing to have happen to her, and what happened to Willy I was not above having happen to me.

We left the ranch in a brilliant sunrise. Ellen and I drove in her familiar yellow-top buggy, an object that would betray her identity wherever we went. Critter was in the shafts. Fidel and Teófilo followed in the light wagon, which was packed with provisions and bedding and several saddles. Spare horses were on behind.

It was good to look around and see Fidel and Teo following us. Both men had inherited the best qualities of both the Spaniard and Indian. I never knew them to be tired. Their eyes, black, sharp, shrewd, fearless, missed nothing. They were, I felt, the ablest of companions in this rough and dangerous country they knew so well. Neither wore guns, but Ellen had had them put firearms in the wagon. Her own light rifle was on the floor between us.

Ellen said she meant to follow Cousin Albert's route as faithfully as she knew how. Late that afternoon we arrived at the Romeros'. The four sisters greeted Ellen like a rich and respected cousin toward whom they felt fervid sympathy. Ah, true enough, the judge had stopped with them, and Guillermo. Who then would have supposed that this unknown and terrible evil was waiting for them beyond? The air was filled with *ah dolor, ah dolor, ah dolor, ah dolor* till my head swam.

I was glad to get away next day and I think Ellen was, too. "I hoped they'd remember something important Albert had said," she told me. "Some word that he had changed his plans. But they could tell us nothing but *por Dios, por Dios, por Dios, por Dios.*"

She mimicked them perfectly, but there was no fun in it today.

This beautiful Indian country, I knew, must have been one of the last things Willy and Cousin Albert had seen. But there was little pleasure for us in the cinnamon boles of the giant pines, the clear spring-fed mountain streams. Then we went down into a deep red rock canyon where we found the irrigated fields and adobe houses of San Mateo pueblo. Here Willy and Cousin Albert had spent their last known night. Just west of here the shepherd boy had been the last person to report seeing them alive.

The short stout pueblo governor, Carasco, a striking figure with iron-gray hair against a rich copper face and a bright-red headband, welcomed us with dignity. That evening in his own house he talked to Ellen about Cousin Albert. He spoke Spanish with a curious Indian accent, hard for me to understand.

"Who knows what happened to my friends, the white alcalde

and his son? There are devils that float through the air and hover
over their prey. Sometimes they even ride horses and lie in wait,"
he added, watching her closely to see if she caught what he was
saying.

"Yes, I understand, Carasco," Ellen said.

His short thick figure mounted on a black horse, he rode out
beside the buggy next morning. West of the pueblo, he pointed out
where the shepherd had seen Cousin Albert's black buggy pass.
We were in a broad semiarid country. The wind was blowing, and
the dust-shrouded sky gave everything a look of desolation.

"This is the place, Fidel," Ellen said. "From here on."

I knew what Ellen meant. I could feel it myself, a forsaken
quality that reminded me of the wind-swept cemetery at Rancho
Zelandia. But here something else could be felt, a wildness far
back in time and the human heart.

Presently Ellen motioned Fidel to drive abreast. They conferred,
and from here on either Fidel or Teo went on foot ahead of the
buggy, eyes keenly examining the trail and ground adjoining.
Sometimes one would leap on a saddled horse and ride him to the
right or left to investigate some peculiar landmark or shape of
sand. Once grazing cattle testified that we were now in the country
of the Jeffcoats. The hair at the back of my neck stirred.

I saw that our slow careful pace would leave us far short of any
habitation that night. Toward late afternoon we came to the malpais, a black ridge of broken blocks of lava reaching across the
face of the land. On one side the winds had created a region of
sand dunes several miles deep and running as far as the eye could
see. With the malpais still before us, we camped in a draw where
a slender rivulet of water ran clear as crystal from the ugly black
rock. That night, so far as I could tell, Ellen slept calmly in her
sugan. Whenever I roused, which was often, I saw that one of the
Mexicans remained awake, standing off in the shadows listening.

We stayed there for several days. Where the long arm of malpais
finally ended and the trail ran around it Fidel and Teo went over
the ground minutely, digging into hundreds of dunes and spreading the sand out on the ground. In the end they found nothing.

More than once I rode off into the rugged country, hoping to find a clue to the missing travelers, yet fearing to catch a glimpse of a Jeffcoat rider watching like an Indian from one of the ridges. But I saw no one and nothing, only the immense dry broken earth, the endless sand and the black landmark of malpais which made it impossible for me to get lost.

Each day I thought Ellen's face grew more weary and baffled. Not even the two nights we stayed at the Banburys' were able to soften it, the friendliness of the wolfhounds, the English hospitality. This was the first time, I think, that she ever admitted to herself the possibility that Cousin Albert and Willy might never be found, their fate swallowed up like the riddle of the Sphinx in the well-kept secrets of this aloof and silent land.

CHAPTER 7

I T WAS strange to come back to Moro without Cousin Albert and Willy, knowing no more about them than before. The town seemed an empty shell today. What gave me the strangest feeling was passing the courthouse. It seemed impossible that the county could get along without Cousin Albert. Now already a new man, Judge Saxton, had been appointed from Washington and was at this moment sitting at Baca County court where Cousin Albert was to have been.

The worst was to think of Cousin Albert and Willy gone, and then to see Snell Beasley going about his business unaffected, more alive and prosperous than ever. His political power, they said, had risen with Cousin Albert out of the way. Judge Saxton, we knew, was Beasley's friend and had been appointed through his influence.

Even Tom Dold, I thought, seemed impressed by Beasley's growing importance. He told Ellen that her brother-in-law had taken a younger man, George Steffy, into his office. Apparently it gave Beasley more time for outside activities.

One evening at dinner Tom said, "Ellen, Beasley wants me to argue a case with you in his behalf."

"Argue what case?"

"Your willingness to sell Critter."

Ellen went white.

"I wouldn't dream of parting with Critter, Tom. And if I did, hardly would I put him at the mercy of that brute."

Through the rest of dinner I saw that Ellen looked at him with intense questioning eyes. I suspect she kept learning, as I had, the bitter truth that Cousin Albert was indeed gone, that another power reigned and even Tom was ready to bow before it. The king was dead, long live the king.

But if Beasley was king now, at least he couldn't have Critter. It was a small thing, but it gave me satisfaction. We still had the fastest horse in the territory, or so I thought. I wasn't so sure of it when we heard that Beasley had bought a racing horse in Texas and was bringing him home to use in the shafts of his runabout.

When the horse was led down the alley to the stable next door, followed by a small crowd, Manuel told me, "Pretty fine-looking nag. Hardly six years old. Looks fast. Arabian blood. Day after tomorrow they exercise him on the track."

The Moro track was an open piece of dry sandy land on the other side of the railroad. I went there on Saturday afternoon and was surprised to see that a few other persons had gathered. My heart sank as I saw Beasley's new horse on the track. He was a thoroughbred, a little longer and rangier than Critter, a chestnut and more handsome. Moreover, he was younger than Critter, just coming into his power. His speed was impressive, and there was a professional look about him.

There was a great deal of talk in Moro about the new horse that month. Beasley challenged any horse in the territory, and this was freely quoted in talk and print. But if Ellen saw or heard of it, she ignored it. The only time she referred to it was when, nettled by her silence to the challenge, I blurted out that people thought she was afraid of running Critter.

I knew then by the instant brilliance of her eyes that I had struck fire. "I won't race Critter, Jud. Critter isn't a race horse. He's my buggy horse. He's devoted to me and I'm devoted to him. Long before Albert and Willy left us, people urged me to put him on the track. But I never have and I never will. I think this should be made more emphatic. The next time Tom comes to the house, I'll ask him to inform Snell and whoever else is necessary."

From the way Lawyer Beasley went by the next time I saw him, I suspected that Tom had told him. He had a look on his face that might be described as curdled amusement. But I didn't know then the extremes of cunning to which Snell Beasley's ambition went, nor that his amusement came from something else he was working out in his mind.

Ellen refused to put on mourning, not knowing what had happened to Cousin Albert and Willy. On the other hand, she had certainly given no parties since Cousin Albert had left. Mostly she busied herself with the ranch, was out with Mama Grande half the time. Once Dr. Gammel told me it was a good thing she had the sheep business to throw herself into. It took her mind off her tragedy.

Inevitably, when she was in town, she drove out for a ride in the afternoon. Often she took me along, and I could feel the good it did her when we got away from town, the wheels turning and Critter bearing her on.

This afternoon she was not at the house when I came home. I went out to the stable. Critter's box stall was empty. Manuel told me she had left two hours before, that she said something about driving north to the Saturnino Montoyas'. As we talked we saw Goyo, Beasley's stableboy, take the race horse down the alley from the stable next door.

"Now where is he going this time of day?" Manuel rumbled. "It's late for his *patrón* to drive anyplace."

Something in what he said aroused my curiosity, and I followed. As I went down the alley I fancied an air of expectancy in the town. More people than usual were out in the plaza. I found the race horse and runabout had stopped in front of Beasley's office. As I approached, Beasley himself came out. I couldn't hear his orders to Goyo, who started driving the race horse away. Beasley looked around, pleased, at the crowd. Tom Dold was across the street in front of the courthouse.

"If she won't race that fast horse of hers on the track, we'll have to do it on her own ground," Beasley called.

People were running toward New Town Road, and I followed along. A few spectators already waited there when we reached it, and the number increased as the news got abroad. A spirited air pervaded most of the spectators, but uneasiness, I thought, could be felt among the sheep people, and this was my own feeling.

Far up the road I could see Goyo driving slowly north. Not a sign of another horse or rig as far as my eyes could reach. Maybe she won't come, I said to myself hopefully, and walked north on the road to see what I could see. Finally, far up the road, I thought I saw a puff of dust rising.

Pas Ramírez was the first to identify it. "It's her — *la doña*," he said, adding the latter out of respect to me.

I couldn't be sure, but, as we went on and the speck came toward us, my eyes finally made out the yellow-top buggy. I knew the horse must be Critter, probably trotting a little faster on the way home. Alone in the seat would be Ellen, unsuspecting what lay ahead. As she approached we saw Goyo, still traveling toward her, look over his shoulder as if measuring the distance back to town. He drew the racer to a walk as the yellow-top buggy came close.

Hardly had the two rigs passed when Goyo swung the chestnut around. He waited until Ellen's buggy must have been a hundred yards in front. Then we thought we saw him shake the reins and the race horse started to come from behind. We were not close enough to see, but I could imagine Critter's ears pricking at the sound of hoofs overtaking him. All we definitely saw was Goyo pulling out to the left to go around, and then the two horses side by side and neither one passing, by which we knew they had started to run.

"*Mira!* Here they come!" Pas Ramírez yelled.

Those were the days of no fences. The road lay across the prairie and was wide as you chose to make it. Looking at the horses from in front, we had no idea how fast they were coming. Only in the nick of time did we recognize our danger. We got off the road just as they went by. I had a glimpse of Critter, the bit between his teeth, that stubborn forward look to his head and neck, and of Ellen looking helpless and exasperated in the buggy, sawing vainly on the lines to hold him, while half a length behind him the race horse tore on, his mane and tail streaming, Goyo half raised from the seat, the whip in his hand.

Once they were by, all we could see was a cloud of dust. By the time we reached town, they were far beyond. I had a glimpse of Beasley turning away darkly toward his office while the Mexicans chattered in great animation and the sheepmen looked solidly pleased.

We learned afterward that never for a moment had Goyo been able to get around the yellow-top buggy, that at the outskirts of town Ellen was almost a length ahead, with Critter still going like such a torrent that he was halfway to the railroad tracks before Ellen could stop him. When I reached the buggy, Ellen, white and shaken, was driving slowly back.

"You devil!" she was saying angrily to Critter as she stopped to let me in.

"He was wonderful," I told her.

"He's a stubborn, vain, unprincipled brute!" she answered. "I could kill him with good grace."

We saw a knot of people up around the courthouse waiting for her to drive back, but to my disappointment she turned up a side street to avoid them. I protested.

"They saw Critter come in ahead and that's enough," she insisted. "They shouldn't have seen that much. There was no occasion for a race at this time and no decency in it. They should know it."

Despite Ellen's anger over the race, it did her good, I think. Her victory over Beasley softened, if faintly, some of her bitterness against him. She felt more resigned. By fall, it seemed that the agitation over Cousin Albert's and Willy's disappearance had begun to blow over. Then word arrived that a sheepherder in a remote corner of Baca County had seen a cowboy riding Dan, one of Cousin Albert's horses. Salomón Baca, owner of the sheep, had taken his herder to town to swear out an affidavit. A few nights later the herder was killed. A warrant had been issued for the cowboy and Beasley had been engaged to defend him.

Now things were all stirred up again. The incident was on everyone's lips, reviving the earlier tragedy. Hardly had all this happened when word came that a body had been discovered. That evening Amado Martínez called at the house and was closeted with Ellen. When the sheriff left, he patted my shoulder. Ellen had then come out.

"I have news for you, Jud," she said. "They've found your father."

My face must have gone white, for she led me to one of the couches and put her arm around me. She told me quietly all the sheriff had said to her. The body had been found in a high canyon in the Greenhorn Mountains, where it had lain covered by snow most of the year. Apparently he had been taken there alive, murdered, and the money stolen. They were bringing the body back to Moro now.

"Don't worry. Your father will have Christian burial. I'll see Reverend Crandall myself in the morning."

All the while the minister read the burial service over the simple pine coffin, her mind, I think, was on the bodies of Cousin Albert and Willy, still unfound.

There were those who said that Ellen Sessions had refused to wear mourning for her husband and son but had put it on for the father of her cousin by marriage. This was unadulterated nonsense. My father's death and burial had only brought home to her the shocking realities of Willy's and Cousin Albert's disappearance. Now she felt she had no other way than to accept them as dead and all it implied. She wore no mourning at my father's funeral. The day afterward she took the train to Denver to buy materials, and, when she came back, called the dressmakers in.

She looked thinner and if anything more beautiful in black the morning she asked me to stay home from school. "I want to call on Mr. Beasley," she told me. "I haven't discussed the matter with Tom or anyone, but I feel I would like to have a witness. You're the only son I have now, Jud, and I wish you would go along."

Ellen seemed calm enough, but there was with it a certain sad and bitter dedication which she had never before affected. Much would I have given to get out of going with her to the lawyer's office, but the way she looked at me, I felt a dependence that made me more of a man. To my surprise, Manuel was waiting outside with Critter and the buggy. We could have easily walked the short distance. At the dusty brick building across from the courthouse I leapt out and helped her down. Then, without knocking, Ellen went into the office and I followed.

My first impression was the strong stale scent of tobacco. I saw George Steffy, Beasley's young assistant, look up in surprise. Behind him, through the sliding doors, I had a glimpse of a deeper and more dangerous region. This Ellen at once entered.

There was nothing for me to do except push after. I found we were in a large room with shelves. One whole wall was lined with yellow leather books, and on the other hung framed pictures. In the corner was a great flat-top desk piled with documents and books, and behind the desk the thick form and powerful face of Willy's Uncle Snell. He didn't lift his face, but his eyes peered up, almost squinted, as if to say, who is this? — the fierce large eye and the smaller drooping one, which I had heard referred to as his "little bitty eye." I didn't know which one frightened me more.

Ellen seated herself on the edge of a chair and regarded him for a few moments. "I've come in peace, Snell, to ask a favor."

She said it humbly, almost abased, but I saw it didn't appease her brother-in-law. Ellen seemed aware of this. She went on.

"I want to ask if you will speak to your clients for me. I mean the cattlemen in Baca County. I don't want to know who was involved in this terrible thing or any detail of what happened. All I ask of them is to let me know where the bodies of Willy and Albert may be found so I can bring them to Moro, have them decently buried and the Christian service read over them."

It seemed a small and deserving request to me, but I noticed no answering pity in his eyes. "And you feel my cattlemen clients should be able to tell you that?" he asked.

"I do," Ellen answered.

"Perhaps you feel that I myself might be able to tell you?"

"God forbid," Ellen said so low I could scarcely hear her.

"What do you mean by that?"

"Just God forbid," she repeated.

To my dismay, an expression of righteous indignation gripped him at her reply. The lower part of his face twitched.

"You say you come in peace and then insult me by your aspersions." He spoke in a surprisingly calm and controlled voice. "First, let me point out that there is not the slightest proof that your boy and husband are dead as you assume, let alone murdered and hidden in the wilderness as you insinuate. Secondly, you assume that the perpetrators of such a gross and hideous crime are my own clients who could tell you where the bodies are, if they wished, and that this makes me either a dupe ignorant of the true nature of my clients or a confederate equally guilty with them of murder. Thirdly, you set up this imaginary set of circumstances and accusations and forget that if these grossly improbable things were true it would still be you and your husband who by persecution of other human beings brought the final culmination to pass."

If he had stopped there, I thought he might have had something, but he carried on, his little eye twinkling like a dark star.

"Finally, you seem to have overlooked the report, which from association with you I must respect, that Albert has long been weary of your efforts to dominate and influence his judicial acts, so that finally he had no other course than to abandon you."

Ellen rose to her feet.

"That's a lie, Snell, and you know it."

He looked at her with satisfaction that was positively evil.

" 'The truth is great and shall prevail,' " he quoted. " 'Though the mills of the gods grind slowly, yet they grind exceeding small.' For a long time you have been riding high. You have done what you liked and been above the law. You have manipulated the law in the cases of others, causing in the end the ruin of your brother, your husband and son. Now you will have to face justice and reformed conditions. No longer can you dictate to the bench."

Ellen's cheeks were flat white.

"Are you going to get me the information, Snell, so Albert's and Willy's bodies can be brought home and decently buried?"

He gazed at her with baneful delight.

"I have told you that I know nothing, that my clients know nothing. Now I will add that, on the contrary, did my clients know something and had they given me the information in the priestly confidence that exists between an honorable lawyer and his client, I would tell you nothing, and the courts would sustain me."

He was a devil, the very devil himself, I thought. For a little while Ellen stood shocked and trembling. Then she took my arm and we left. Critter and the yellow-top buggy were waiting. I helped her in. We drove off. She said no word to me on the way home, not until she reached the door of the house.

"I hoped it could be done without further bloodshed, Jud, but now I see he must be dealt with as the dog he is."

"Cousin Ellen, don't!" I begged, following her into the house.

"What, Jud?" she asked quietly.

"I don't know," I stammered.

Her eyes probed mine.

"I'm glad you came along, Jud. When you are young, you feel

the world is good and troubles can always be avoided. But it's better to know that life may be inescapable, that you may finally get to a point where you can no longer live honorably, when the dead cry out for justice but nobody will administer it and you've got to attend to it yourself."

I didn't know fully what she meant, but I knew enough. As she disappeared behind the door, I had a moment's glimpse of her room, the carved bureau and wardrobe, the Brussels carpet on the floor, the polished French brass bed, a painted fragile china lamp on a stand. All was very feminine except for one jarring note. In the far corner beside the bed I had the glimpse of an object from the ranch. Only the barrel was visible above the elaborate bedcover, but it was enough. I knew that ever since Charley had been shot she had kept a pearl-handled revolver lying on the marble-top table at the head of her bed. Now I was aware that she must have brought her light rifle to town.

Ellen didn't appear for lunch or dinner that day. This was most unusual. Even on the day the news had come about Cousin Albert and Willy, she had not taken to her room. I hoped that Dr. Gammel or Tom Dold or some of her other friends might come this evening, but no one called.

"How is she?" I asked Chepa when she brought out the tray that evening.

"She just walks the room. She is like a *leona*," Chepa said.

That evening there was something about my room that gave me an unpleasant feeling. I looked out of the window. Then I knew what it was. Light shone in the Beasley home next door, especially in the room opposite Ellen's bedroom. I could see just the top of the window. Before the wall had been put up Willy and I had often watched his Uncle Snell sitting in this room. Invariably he was at his desk under the light of a green-shaded oil lamp. The same colored light came from the window tonight. Standing on the bed, I could peer over the wall and see him sitting at the desk now, going over a pile of papers.

Ellen's room was next to mine. From the absence of light falling on our side of the wall, I could tell that it was in darkness. And yet from time to time I thought I heard her moving about. I couldn't lie still, but had to stand up on my hard Mexican bed and stare at the black target of Beasley sitting at his desk. I would stand a long time, rigid, waiting, listening, until from sheer weariness I would lie down again.

Once when I pushed back the covers and stood up, the light from Beasley's window was gone. The brick house was dark, the windows dim and silent. I lay down, gratefully closed my eyes and let sleep overtake me.

CHAPTER 8

I SELDOM saw Ellen now until noon. She stayed in the seclusion of her room. When she came out at last, I was always shocked at what I saw. This was not the Ellen I knew. She looked as if she hadn't slept, as if she had had a battle most of the night.

Nights were bad for me, too. I thought what a relief it would be to leave the tragic white house and go to the ranch. Out there I felt I could sleep untroubled by every stir and creaking. I spoke of it to her, but she would shake her head and something would come into her face. "No, Jud, I can't. Not yet."

Several times when I heard Chepa or Epifania going in or out of her room, I tried to post myself where I would get a glimpse inside. I wanted to see if the rifle was still there, but never was I quick enough.

Tom Dold and the doctor called most every day. I know Tom asked her to marry him, and I felt that the doctor had always wanted her. But she was impatient with them both.

"Why do some men talk too much?" she asked me once. "It's a woman's art and right. A man should sit quietly and let a woman do the talking. He should be warmed and refreshed by it. And if the woman is in no mood to talk, he should be sympathetic and silent. But I must listen to Tom Dold and the doctor reciting all the petty doings of the court, especially of Snell Beasley, and all the stories going the rounds. Half of them they've told me before."

The third of the faithful trio who came to see her was Father Goshard, the big gaunt Belgian. He liked young people and usually asked me to stay in the *sala* when he called. Ellen seldom treated him with the pious reverence showed him by most of her people. The first time I heard them together I feared he would be offended, but soon I saw that he took delight in her attitude toward him as an equal and in her quick readiness to give her opinion on the most sacred of matters.

Once after they had disputed back and forth for an hour, Ellen turned to me. "It's not in me to let any man get the upper hand of me, Jud, not even my saintly and dogmatic spiritual father."

The priest seemed heartily to enjoy her unpredictable contradictions. But he did not laugh at her bitterness over the impunity of Snell Beasley. "Why should he still be alive after what happened to Albert and Willy?" she asked once.

" 'Vengeance is mine, saith the Lord.' "

"Then why are there public trials and executions?" she asked quickly. "Why not leave it all to God?"

"There is the duty of serving the established courts of law and order," the priest said. "And there is taking the law into our own hands, serving the baser passions in our own breasts."

"I fight," Ellen said in a low voice. "But it goes hard and takes very long."

" 'My yoke is easy, and my burden is light,' " the priest quoted. "You are young. There is still peace and happiness for you."

"If you refer to another marriage sometime, Father, it could never be even if I wished it," she said. "I'll never really know if Albert is dead."

The old priest watched her. "Why don't you submit to the will of God, child?" he asked. "Where and by what means Judge Sessions and Willy came to leave this life, we don't know. But the fact of their departure is evident to all. It's better to accept it. You put your faith not in God, but in rumors," he chided. "I hear these rumors, too. Somebody has seen the judge or Willy in California or Wyoming or Old Mexico — mostly in Old Mexico. They are living or kept there now against their will. It takes money to investigate these rumors. I hear someone is always traveling far for you at your expense."

"What is money beside the lives of those you love?" she asked.

"There are many rumors in the world and little truth in any of them, child. Their only vitality is in the hope they arouse. When they prove false, there is bitter disappointment and renewal of hatred."

"That's true, Father," Ellen admitted. "But if someone tells me he has seen Albert or Willy alive, I can't sit idly by and do nothing. They may need me. And I can't sit idly by when my own brother-in-law defends the man seen with one of Albert's horses and who murdered the sheepherder who testified to it."

"Have no fear, child," the priest said, "God will not defend the wicked. The courts will never acquit him."

That's what we all had thought. It was a shock when word came that the Baca County jury, putty in Beasley's hands, had freed the cowboy seen riding Cousin Albert's horse.

I was standing in the alley looking gloomily at the house next door and wondering how it would all end when I saw a hand beckon me from the Beasley stable. Walking closer, I saw it again.

The doors were open. Beasley's runabout and sulky were both there, the shafts up against the wall, the racer in his stall, but Goyo, the stableboy, was out somewhere. I wondered what I had seen. Then Felicitas stepped out from behind the steps as I went in.

"Here," she said, swiftly coming to me and taking a small bunch of flowers from under her apron. She held them out to me.

"For Willy," she said in a low voice.

"Willy's dead," I said harshly.

"I know," she told me.

For a moment I considered taking the flowers from her hand and throwing them on the manure pile, but in the end I took them to Ellen, saying they were for Willy from Felicitas. For the first time in days I saw Ellen's face soften. She poured water from her bedroom pitcher and set the flowers in a vase on the marble-top table in her room.

Gracias á Dios, Chepa used to say, that we mortals never know what is ahead for us. Now I have heard Mexicans speak otherwise, especially old sheepherders who had spent their lives reading the sky and range. They insist that the future is written down for us, every whit, that there are always signs. Fidel, the wisest man on the ranch, used to answer, yes, of course, it is all written down, but who can read the handwriting of *el Dios?* As for signs, who knows for sure what they mean until he can look back and see what they portended by the things that came to pass?

What was destined to happen is all to be found today in dusty files. First came the heavy winter snowfall that turned the range the following summer into a garden for those sheep that hadn't been smothered by the snow. Then, like the lean years in Egypt after the fat years, came the great drought. For some twenty months no snow or rain worthy of the name fell.

But the worst was not yet, not until after the national elections. I remember going to the depot for Ellen to get the latest returns. Cleveland, if elected, had promised to exempt foreign wool from tariff duties. What happened is history, but the interpretation is something else. I have heard it argued endlessly; some claimed it was the free wool that brought the panic of '93, others that it was the drought. All I know is that wool dropped to seven cents a pound, in some cases to five cents, that sheep sold for a dollar apiece, and that such a time of ruin and wretchedness ensued over the territory as I never saw before or since.

The only good I knew it to do was to bring an end to Ellen's mourning over Willy and Cousin Albert. "Thank God they are not living now!" more than once she told me.

Energies that had lain dormant or been dammed up in her so long began to be released again in their natural channels. I remember her especially the following spring on the ranch, which by now had become a ghastly place. The great Johnson y Campo lamb crop, once a rich source of income, had turned into a cruel liability. As they were born, lambs had to be killed to save their mothers. Here Ellen was the *patrona* again, and I can still hear her voice heartening the discouraged lambers, the range around them desolate with dust and dead sheep under a pitiless sky.

The lambing was scarcely over when Mama Grande died. "She knew better days. These were hard for her to take," Ellen told me. "She is better off out of this kind of world!"

But if Mama Grande was better off, Ellen wasn't. Just the sight of Beasley, when he arrived for the funeral, brought up all I had heard of him lately — that there was no holding him, that these were times ripe for him and his kind. He was making himself a great fortune, perhaps the largest in the territory, calling notes, foreclosing, buying ranches for little or nothing.

He came to the ranch alone driving his race horse, which he ordered Teófilo to put up, almost as if he himself were the *patrón*. He met Ellen coolly.

"Your sister hasn't been too well," he said. "I thought it best if she were spared the ordeal of the funeral."

"I'm sorry for Ana's sake that she didn't come. All of us have only one mother," Ellen said.

He gave that cool look of his, hinting without words or details of things still to come. I watched him at the funeral and afterward, not mingling with the mourners but striding about, asking sharp questions of the peons, inspecting the ranch buildings, finally ordering his horse and buggy and driving off with no good-bys.

In the days that followed I was worried. I knew that Ellen was hard hit. She had spent thousands trying to solve the mystery of Cousin Albert and Willy. Most of it she had borrowed. Now for some time banks and private lenders had been calling in their notes. Money was hard to get. Ellen was forced to sell thousands of sheep to the packing houses, and the pitifully small price per head was quickly swallowed up in interest and running expenses. I had hoped that Mama Grande's death might leave enough to pay Ellen's debts, but all she left was her share in the ranch, evenly divided between her two surviving daughters, and this brought not a dollar to Ellen.

The singular thing was that Ellen seemed unworried. The worse her situation, the more her debtors hounded her, the more it seemed to mend the deep wounds of her unsolved tragedy, to help her believe that perhaps Willy's and Albert's deaths were for the best after all.

She and Critter were inseparable again. She drove him and her yellow-top buggy everywhere, to the ranch to manage what she had left, to her creditors to appease and stave them off, to her old Mexican family friends to borrow a little so she might hold on until better times returned. It all agreed with her. Activity was her nature. I never saw her looking better.

When Mr. Kidd offered me a job at the commission house, I jumped at the chance. It meant I could contribute a little toward our expenses of living, although I knew I never dare mention this to Ellen. When I told her I wanted to take the job, she gave her consent reluctantly. "But you must never leave me, Jud," she said. "Remember, this house is yours as long as you live."

It was like a breath of fresh air and a new life to leave the gloomy old white *casa* for the commission house, if only in the daytime. I found the commission-house clan a big jolly family, patronizing the same restaurant and dance hall, taking the same train to Trinidad on holidays, playing tricks on one another and especially on me, the newest member.

And yet through all my daily life in this hive of commerce, I couldn't shut out the ugly day-by-day reports from the panic-ridden range, the sad things that were happening to others and which inevitably must engulf Ellen and the old Johnson y Campo name. The tragic part was that men still had to fight for their existence when times at last had begun to improve. The cycle had turned. Rain was already falling on the range, new grass appearing. Wool and lamb prices had steadied. The worst was over and most ranchers had begun to breathe hopefully again.

That was when Beasley played his hand. All through the months of drought and panic when expenses were heartbreaking and income nonexistent or trifling, he let Ellen struggle with Rancho

Zelandia. But once the hardest times were over and recovery and profit began to appear, then in the name of his half-owner wife he entered suit, filing a bill in equity, citing mismanagement, neglect, and nonpayment of interest and principal on Ellen's notes which he had bought up in his wife's name, demanding an accounting, a receivership, and public sale of the ranch's real and personal property.

He entered the suit swiftly and without warning while court was still in session, and Judge Saxton put it through at the end of the term. Tom Dold struggled manfully, but he was no match for the weight of debt. Ellen had neither cash nor collateral left to fight Beasley; moreover, she refused to testify on any allegation that would make out her sister a liar. "That's Snell, not Ana, speaking," was all she would say.

Even if Judge Saxton had not owed his appointment to Beasley's influence, he would have had little choice in the matter. The famous old Johnson y Campo ranch and stock, including the Spanish grant, were put on the block and bought by Beasley for less than fifty thousand, none of which would be divided with Ellen. Her share was to be paid to her sister on Ellen's unpaid debts.

I heard of the final blow at the commission house one afternoon. The same day Pas Ramírez, now a loader, cornered me against a car of outgoing wool.

"It is too bad, but she will fix him now?" he said.

"If you mean what I think you do, Pas," I told him, "you are dead wrong."

"No, you are the one who is wrong, *amigo*," he said. "Years ago the wolf howled for his due. But the Anglo in her waited, thinking the foolish Anglo thought that if you pet him the wolf will turn into a dog. Now he has everything and she has nothing. She will not let him take the ranch, the only thing she has left. She will fix him now like she fixed Frank Jeffcoat long ago."

I went home hating to face Ellen that evening, but friends had taken her home to dinner after the sheriff's sale. "She left a message for you," Chepa told me. "She must go out to the ranch tomorrow. It is the last time. You must go with her."

That day when I asked Mr. Kidd for leave, he gave me a look from under his black eyebrows and ordered me into his office.

"You know that this is the end of her and the ranch?" he asked.

"I'm afraid it is, sir."

"I suppose you think I should have given her a hand?"

"I didn't think about it, sir."

"Well, we carried her for some nineteen thousand dollars. I could have sold the debt to Beasley long ago at twenty cents on the dollar. I didn't then, although it looked at the time like we'd never get a penny. Did you know that?"

"No, sir."

"Jud, do you know what a lady is?" he went on.

"Yes, sir. I think I do."

"I don't think you do. A lady is a woman of great charm or position or both who because of it has never had to do anything for herself but has always had somebody to do it for her. Did you ever think of that before?"

"No, sir."

"Well, it's time you understood some of these things. Ellen was a Johnson y Campo. If there was a Campo who had more than she had, I never heard of it. She was born to the purple, to the ranch, to the family name, and money. There was always something or somebody to take care of her. When she was young, it was her father. When Frank Jeffcoat ruined her garden and one of them shot him, she had her brother Charley to fall back on. When Charley was tried, she had Albert to free him and to convict his murderers when they came to trial for another crime. Now Albert and Charley are gone. Her father and mother are gone. The ranch and her money are gone. She needs someone more than ever, somebody to take up her cause, solve her problems, and take care of her. There she is, attractive, beautiful, worldly. Tom Dold is a gentleman, but he's not your Cousin Albert by a long shot. There's nobody left to come to her rescue any more."

I kept thinking about it on the way to the ranch next morning with Ellen. The mesa had never looked more beautiful, the air like wine, the Prietas crystal clear, and the ranch headquarters, when we came to it, like the capital of some small empire. It had rained during the night and the Johnson y Campo range looked fresh and green.

It was an ordeal. As we came up on the portal, one of the doors opened and Snell Beasley, thick, active, all business, appeared.

"You can come in," he said curtly, and I looked to see how Ellen liked being invited into her own house. She gave no sign, entering the familiar *sala* almost as a visitor, seating herself presently in the chair Beasley indicated, as if this house was not part of her, as if she hadn't been born in one room and spent much of her life in the others.

"I had hoped Ana would be here," she said quietly.

"No," Beasley answered. Then as if something in her remark had nettled him, he went on sharply: "Before we get to the few things you may claim, I want to tell you that I might have claimed a good deal more. We could have taken everything you have, the house in town and your horse and buggy."

All she said was a low "Thank you."

"No," he said heavily, "we don't want your house now or your horse. He's getting up in years. I have a better one. Now shall we get down to business?"

All through the scenes that followed I marveled at Ellen. How could she give up all this so calmly? What was going on in her head? Was she really the gentlewoman taking her humiliation with good grace? Or could she be waiting, as Pas implied, seeing how far he would go, which would give her final violent act all the more reason and sympathy? Without some planned solution in her mind, I felt she couldn't control herself like this.

In the end she had me carry some small things to the buggy. She asked her brother-in-law to deliver the rest with Teófilo.

"Now we must go, Jud," she said.

First she drove around the ranch headquarters, the lambing pens, the chapel, then to the edge of the cedars where Willy and I used to ride. She was taking a last look at everything.

"Look," she said once, "I don't need to touch a line. Critter knows where to go."

It was true. Critter seemed to know. He went to the cemetery and beyond it to a spot where the whole grant could be seen spread out before us with the Greenhorn Mountains a white crown to the north.

When we returned to the ranch house, the Mexicans were waiting for us. I saw again how charming Ellen could be with servants, peons, children, those who looked up to her. She stepped down from the buggy to shake every hand, had a word in Spanish for each, an act that caused many of them, especially older men and women, to break down and fall on their knees, kissing her hand or skirt.

What Beasley must have thought if he watched from the window I have no idea. But as we drove up through the canyon I bled for her. I began to see more clearly what Mr. Kidd had said, that always she had had this great ranch behind her, someone to espouse her cause and solve her problems. All she had now were a house in town, an old horse, and a young stripling like me.

As for Critter, he seemed weary as I. I noticed that he dragged. It was true he had already traveled from town to ranch that day, but there had been a time when twenty miles would scarcely have laid a hair on him. I mentioned this to Ellen.

"He's older," she said. "But not really old. He's younger than Willy. They were born almost on the same day two years apart."

Just the way she said it made me glance at her. She sat there on the faded cushions of her yellow-top buggy, erect, well dressed as always, her little green hat with the feather jaunty, her driving gloves open at the wrist and flaring.

"We're all older," I said.

"He says you're older, boy," she said.

At the sound, Critter broke at once into a faster pace, but presently slowed again to his old trot. We were well on the mesa when I glanced back and saw another rig behind us, just emerging from the canyon. Farther out I looked again. It was almost the same distance behind us as before. Whoever it was showed no disposition to close the gap between. But later when I looked back I thought the rig was definitely nearer and that the horse looked like Beasley's.

Ellen didn't look back at all. We were on the almost level part of the mesa when I thought I heard a steel shoe strike a stone.

Glancing again, I saw the rig closer behind us now and coming fast. It was definitely the runabout and the racer with Beasley himself driving. I'm sure Critter heard the sound, too. His ears had pricked and his pace increased. Ellen heard it now and looked over her shoulder.

Afterward she told Tom and me that her first impulse had been to turn Critter directly off the road to the north. She guessed at once, as did I, that Beasley had chosen the spot to race, that he was unsatisfied with taking the ranch and sheep, that now with the town just ahead of us in plain view across the river he intended to beat her horse and take the only laurels she had left. For a moment, she told us, she hesitated to humiliate Critter, make him show the white feather, and by the time she had made up her mind it was too late. Critter had definitely accepted the challenge.

I had been in races behind Critter before and have been in others since, but there was something about this one that troubled me from the start. It was Critter who moved me the most, no longer the pet but the old servitor unwilling to admit his years.

Some men mellow as they age, leave the fires of manhood behind them and handle better than in their youth. Critter was none of these. Ellen knew it, I'm sure. I had seen her half stand at the lines before, but never her body weight and strength so thrown against the bit. But there was no stopping him today more than any other time. He had the will to go, and there was nothing to do but let him have his way.

I did feel that Critter had the advantage of the road. The racer would have to take the rougher ground beside it. Critter's mane and tail were streaming and yet as we went on something in him fell short. I remembered his old effortlessness, when he seemed to fly like a road runner, half on the ground, half in the air. Today he seemed to run as fast as he ever did, but the magic of easy power was lacking. I could feel the undercurrents of exertion, striving and strain.

Slowly but steadily the racer pulled up beside him. When he was younger, the near approach of the other horse would have been the signal for Critter to let loose a burst of speed that would have left his rival far behind. Now it was apparent that Critter had

already given his best. I had a glimpse of Beasley squatting forward on his light runabout seat, his arms outstretched. As he came abreast he flicked his whip and the chestnut started pulling ahead.

"Help me, Jud!" Ellen suddenly panted.

She was having trouble with the right-hand line, I noticed, and the moment I took hold of it with her, I knew why she had called me. Critter was pulling hard toward his rival. I used both hands but without effect. We might as well be pulling on a locomotive. Never had he let a horse around him, and he wouldn't now. With a furious swerve that carried us with him like matchsticks he threw himself against the chestnut and all was lost in a crashing of buggies and bodies and horses upturned with their legs in the air.

They said afterward that a dozen people in Moro watched the race. In almost no time riders and rigs were hurrying to the scene. What had happened they couldn't tell from town, but they knew it was bad. What they found was a boy with a broken arm, a

woman with a scarred and bleeding face, one horse still on the ground, the other standing quietly by in broken shafts, his only sign of disaster the brown dirt smeared on his sweated hide. That was the racer, but his driver lay under the overturned runabout, and when strong hands righted it he still lay unmoving.

Ellen waited till Dr. Gammel finished with him.

"Look at Critter!" then she begged him, which he did.

"He's done for. The broken shaft hooked him. The kindest thing you can do for him is let me shoot him and put him out of his misery."

Such a look of blinding anger came into Ellen's eyes that I thought the doctor quailed.

"I would shoot you first, George!" she told him, and sent to town for Manuel.

We stayed until Manuel came and got Critter up on his unsteady feet. Then we drove down with Tom Dold in his buggy.

People on the plaza watched silently as we drove by. When we reached La Placita, a little group stood in front of the Beasley house.

"I must go to Ana first," Ellen said.

I followed with my arm in a rough splint. Tom Dold and the doctor helped her up the steps. She did not knock. One of them opened the door for her and she went in. I had a glimpse of Ana surrounded by Beasley's friends and their wives. What would happen now I had no notion. But when Ana looked up and saw Ellen, it was as if no one but they were in the room. A strange nameless cry rose from each of them, and the two sisters ran into each other's arms. Tears flowed from them both. It was the first time I had seen Ellen cry.

It was strange that at a time like this I should remember what Mr. Kidd had said, that Ellen's deliverers were all gone, that there was no one left to come to her rescue any more, and yet here she was, delivered in the arms of her only sister, the widow of probably the richest man in the territory.

I wish it were possible to add that Willy and Cousin Albert came back. For years I kept saying to myself, it can't end like this — they will surely turn up someday. But they never did. Their bodies were never found. Only the whispering wind knows where they lie, for those unknown men involved in it must be dead today. Now, looking back over sixty years, I feel this may be the reason why the unsolved mystery remains to many of us the most haunting of earlier happenings in the annals of New Mexico.

Conrad Richter

CONRAD RICHTER was born in Pennsylvania in 1890, the son, grandson, nephew and great-nephew of clergymen. It was intended that he too study for the ministry, but on his graduation from high school he went to work, taking such varied jobs as drover, farmer, timberman and reporter.

In 1928 he and his small family moved to New Mexico, where his heart and mind were soon captured by the Southwest. Many men and women who had lived through the eventful frontier days were still alive, and these he sought out, to draw from them authentic material for a shelf of notebooks. From this time on he devoted himself, with growing success, to fiction. He is the author of such well-known works as *The Town*, winner of the Pulitzer Prize in 1951, *The Sea of Grass, The Trees* and *The Fields*.

A Houseful

A condensation of the book by

MARJORIE HOUSEPIAN

of Love

strations by Henry C. Pitz

*I*T WAS a modest little brownstone just off Lexington Avenue in New York City — the house with the doctor's sign in the window — but to the narrator of this delightful memoir it was a houseful of love. A houseful of laughter, too, especially when it contained such picturesque relatives as blustery Uncle Pousant, the proud and fierce proprietor of the Armenian restaurant around the corner. Or Hadji, his tattoed wife, who could read the future. Or ancient Marta-mama, whose dream was to see the orphan boy she had raised happily married.

These and other colorful characters warm and brighten the pages of *A Houseful of Love,* the beguiling account of a closely knit family and their fortunes in a new country.

I<small>F</small>, <small>IN</small> the early spring of 1929, you walked east on Twenty-fourth Street, New York City — past the pretzel man on the corner of Fourth Avenue, past Yomuro's Japanese Imports, past the Syrian Coffee Shop — you would see Father's M.D. sign in the first-floor window of our brownstone house — more red than brown, actually, and narrower than those which in a trim row faced Gramercy Park just six blocks away.

Uncle Pousant's restaurant was just around the corner on Lexington Avenue. In summer you couldn't miss it if you followed your nose, for the odor of cooking spices and *shish-kebab* greeted you a block away and enticed you to the sign that read: P<small>OUSANT'S</small> A<small>RMENIAN</small> S<small>PECIALTIES</small>; and beneath, in smaller letters, *Pousant Tekmekian, Prop.* If it was midafternoon, Uncle Pousant would be in the kitchen, peeling artichokes or muttering to himself about the price of eggplant as he basted the evening's lamb. Setrag, the dishwasher, would be hovering nearby trying to look busy. He had long ago learned to make the chopping of an onion seem an insurmountable task. Uncle Pousant rarely tolerated inconsequential sounds, but he seemed to take comfort in the grunts and groans Setrag emitted while waiting for some dishes to wash.

Uncle Pousant's wife, Hadji, would be setting the tables at this hour, squeezing her huge hulk between tables and chairs. If her sleeves were rolled, as in summer, the magnificent religious tattoos which made it apparent that she was a *hadji* — one who has made the pilgrimage to Jerusalem — would catch your eye at once. If Hadji liked the looks of you she would wave you in, after a furtive glance toward the kitchen, since Uncle Pousant considered it an insult to his profession to be asked to serve meals at odd hours. But Uncle Pousant had sharp ears when he suspected that his principles were being challenged. "Who's there? A derelict?" he would bellow, not caring whether or not you understood Armenian.

"Respectable-looking man, Pousant. Looks hungry. A puny fellow."

From the kitchen would come a tremendous crash. When he was irritated, Uncle Pousant reached for the iron frying pans on the shelf above the stove and dropped them, one by one in rapid succession, to the cement floor. If you had not by this time bolted for the door, Hadji would seat you at a table, hand you a menu and squeeze her way between tables to the kitchen. By the time she disappeared you would realize that the menu was a mere gesture, for it was printed entirely in Armenian. Even at that moment Uncle Pousant would be murmuring oaths into his handle-bar mustache and carving generous slices off the lamb, while Hadji scooped cold beans, beets, *sarma* — rice rolled in grape leaves, spiced meat and black olives onto a smaller plate as hors d'oeuvres.

Uncle Pousant would carry the main course to you himself, to be satisfied that you were in truth undernourished. He liked to say that all Americans starved themselves . . . "But who can blame them? Look at what they eat!" The fat ones? "Cake," said Uncle Pousant. "Their cooking is so inedible that the poor creatures must devour flour to quench the appetite." As the meal was placed before you Uncle Pousant would study your expression carefully. If you were sufficiently foolhardy to insist a sandwich was all you wanted, you would find yourself departing swiftly and unceremoniously from Pousant's Armenian Specialties, and for the rest of the day no one could talk to Uncle Pousant.

Were you to sniff appreciatively, however, when Uncle Pousant laid the platter before you, he would return to the kitchen looking as content as he ever could behind those fierce black mustaches. He might even toss a word or two in Setrag's direction, jerking his thumb toward your table: *"Zavalluh"* — pitiful creature — "first decent meal the man's ever had." And he would resume his tasks, humming the "Marseillaise."

IT WAS on just such an afternoon in March that I flew into the restaurant after school. It made an ideal stopover for assuaging midafternoon hunger pangs; for at the age of ten a perpetual hankering for food was the greatest cross I had to bear. This particular afternoon I had in tow a gangling, nearsighted classmate, Caroline Crews, who had come new to my school only that morning. Over our lunchboxes I had discovered that Caroline also loved to eat; she was very willing to come with me to Uncle Pousant's after school.

When we came into the restaurant the strains of the "Marseillaise" were coming from the kitchen. Something has put Uncle Pousant in a good humor, I thought gratefully. I led the way through the pantry, where the salty odor of drying fish and cabbage pickle made one thirsty, into the large bright kitchen. Hadji had her back to us and was packing food into an enormous wicker basket. Uncle Pousant saw us at once. He stopped singing and shouted: "See who's here! That starving orphan who has not eaten in two days has come again. Ah!" he added as he saw Caroline behind me. "She has brought another. *Asvazim!* I shall go bankrupt!"

Hadji threw up her hands to show how glad she was to see us. *"Parev, parev,* you came at the right time. I was packing some things for Marta-mama and now you can take them to her before you go home. Hallo, nice girl," she added to Caroline in English. Caroline nodded nervously and bobbed a curtsy.

"Vagh, yavrum," said Hadji kindly, "poor child. She is all arms and legs, like a spider."

"Feed her. Feed herrrrrrr!" bellowed Uncle Pousant. "I cannot tolerate skeletons in my restaurant!"

I exchanged greetings with Setrag, who had been sitting in a corner, chopping onions. Now, as Uncle Pousant continued to shout for us to be fed, he jumped up and began running around to cupboards and icebox, lifting out plates of pastry, rolls, dishes

of leftover *kebab,* cheese, olives, cold artichoke, yogurt and beets. Caroline's eyes bulged behind her thick glasses.

"Just a little snack," I said offhandedly. "Help yourself."

As we went around tossing a heap of this and a little of that on our plates, Hadji stood behind us giving advice. "Tell her to take more olives. They add bile to the liver. She needs a clove of raw garlic each night before retiring. It would strengthen her blood. These thin children usually die of consumption before they reach twenty. Just look at her eat! The family must be destitute."

"She's not poor," I said. "Her family has two maids."

"These rich children just starve to death," Hadji declared. "The servants take all the food home to their husbands. Tell her to eat some more of the beans. Yah, yah, nice girl, eat."

I turned to find Caroline staring, bug-eyed, at Hadji's bare arms.

"She went to Jerusalem a long time ago," I said, "and got tattooed to prove she'd been there. It makes you a kind of saint." This was slightly inaccurate, but how else to explain what a *hadji* was?

"Gee!" said Caroline. "You have the most *interesting* relatives. None of mine are tattooed."

"That's too bad," I said.

Hadji had now filled the wicker basket with pistachio nuts, dates, apricots, cheese and *lochum* candy which Marta-mama would munch on all week as she sat by her window. "I don't think anyone has been over there today," Hadji said. "She will be glad to see you."

"That donkey of a Levon Dai, out there in the wilderness!" Uncle Pousant's voice boomed from the depths of the oven he was scouring. "It has been three weeks since he wrote to Marta-mama. Small comfort your offerings will be!"

"Hush!" said Hadji. "She knows he is busy. He thinks of us constantly. She knows that too."

"Pah!" said Uncle Pousant. "His heart is lead. He thinks only of money money money!"

"Are they fighting?" Caroline was beginning to look nervous.

"Naw," I said, "they always argue over Levon Dai. He's a rich relative out West. He owns a dry-cleaning factory."

"Your relatives own such *interesting* things," Caroline said forlornly. "Mine just own stocks and stuff like that."

"Gee, that's too bad," I said. I felt very sorry for Caroline. "Say," I added, trying to cheer her up, "why don't you come with me to Marta-mama's? She's the oldest relative I have. She's older than anybody you ever saw, I bet." Caroline said she'd love to.

MARTA-MAMA lived in a brownstone tenement on Second Avenue where her nephew Levon Dai had installed her when he had her brought over from the old country, shortly after his own arrival. It was the best he could afford at the time, they told me when I asked why Marta-mama lived among cracking walls and chipping plaster, in a room where even the sunlight looked dusty. Later, they said, when Levon Dai had the means to rent her a fine apartment, she had refused to move. "Shame on you," she had told them when they urged her, "that you want to disturb the remaining few months of an old woman's life!" That was five years before, when Marta-mama was only ninety-two. But Marta-mama lived on and on. One by one she outlived her brothers and sisters, then most of their children and then several of their grandchildren. Longevity was her only luxury, and she constantly reminded everyone that she had not asked to live so long.

"Let me see Levon Dai once more," she had said many years ago, "and I shall die in peace." But after Levon Dai had come East and returned to Iowa, Cousin Meline was expecting a baby; and then she had to see Uncle Kelesh, who was to arrive in America. She would have nothing more to live for, Marta-mama said, as soon as she had Kelesh safely here. So Kelesh came, but then there was Cousin Meline's baby's christening, and Azniv was to come to America, and Uncle Boghos was to get his citizenship papers.

Several times a week my father went up to Marta-mama's apartment carrying his small black doctor's bag. Marta-mama chided him for squandering his time and his medicines, and my father scolded her for refusing to live with relatives who could take care of her if she were to get sick.

"You are a stubborn old woman!" my father would tell her.

"Yah yah, Doctor, but who is to say I am not right?"

MARTA-MAMA lived on the third floor of the tenement. We entered without knocking because she would not have heard anyway. I knew without looking that she would be sitting by the window crocheting another square for the large multicolored spread she had been working on for years; I could recognize several of my old sweaters woven into the squares. The room was small, and pleasantly cluttered. Post cards and pictures were heaped in a corner cabinet. On the table were a water pipe and fez that had once belonged to Marta-mama's husband. In a corner was a victrola of 1917 vintage, and on this a carton filled with every size and color of rag imaginable.

I looked at Marta-mama's face before speaking to her and saw that her eyes were staring and that her mouth hung open.

"Oh lord!" shrieked Caroline. "She's dead!"

I wanted to scream, too, but it would be admitting that Marta-mama was dead. And she couldn't be. "She's *not* dead. Here, hold this," I said, handing Caroline the basket. I began rubbing Marta-mama's hands. They felt chilly and stiff and damp. "You're not dead," I kept thinking, not daring to look into her face again. "You can't die today! You told me last week you were waiting for Levon Dai to get married, remember? Just wait a little longer. . . ."

"Look!" Caroline cried suddenly. Marta-mama's eyes had moved, and I could feel some slight pressure in her fingers.

"Marta-mama!" I shouted. "It's me. Look, we brought you some things Hadji sent. Are you all right, Marta-mama?"

Her mouth moved a little. "Hadji . . . Call Hadji . . . Doctor."

"Sure," I said in relief. "Sure, Marta-mama, you just wait and I'll go call them. They'll be right here."

Caroline and I raced to the restaurant. "Hadji!" I screamed as we ran through the dining room. "Hadji, *please* hurry! Marta-mama — she's awfully sick!" By the time we reached the kitchen Hadji was putting on her shawl. She didn't stop to ask what had happened but only said, "Go call your father," before she lumbered out through the restaurant.

"That donkey of a Levon Dai!" said Uncle Pousant when I caught my breath and told him what had happened. "Why can't he live nearer, like a civilized man, and let the old woman die in peace!"

But even Uncle Pousant's wishes would not bring Levon Dai East before he was ready. And Marta-mama lived on.

2 THROUGHOUT the twenties both our house and Uncle Pousant's restaurant were terminal points for Armenian émigrés who happened to come from the vicinity of Smyrna, where my mother was born, or from Antioch, which my father had fled, smuggled out in a cargo boat during the political persecutions at the turn of the century. Often these new arrivals were related to us in some vague way.

They flocked in, singly or in families, of assorted ages and professions. For most, this was the last in a long series of journeys since they had left their native towns: one last step before settling down to the rug business or photoengraving or a drugstore somewhere in the United States.

There was Cousin Dikran of the handsome profile. Mothers of daughters came often to our house, until he got a job in a photoengraving plant in Astoria, Long Island, and moved to a furnished room near his work. And there was Azniv, who weighed three hundred pounds; she finally opened a butcher shop in Newark.

And there were others. They all sat around the large oval table in our living room and ate mussels stuffed with spicy rice and toasted one another and America with raki and heard how the vineyards flourished in Fresno. Some, like Papgen, went to California, bought land and did very well for themselves, just as Hadji, in reading their coffee cups, had said they would. Others, like Kelesh, whose name meant "bald" but who had a shaggy head of jet-black hair, stayed with us for six years. Kelesh wanted more than anything else to own a yogurt factory. Meantime, he was studying the classics at Columbia University.

Uncle Boghos lived with us, too. He was an artist. He painted from postal cards: nostalgic scenes of the Bosporus and the Red

Sea; Saint Sophia at sundown. Uncle Boghos was not a patient man and when we criticized his canvases he often collected his paints and retreated to the bedroom. But it was lonely in the bedroom and Boghos could not paint long in solitude. Soon he would be back, punctuating the conversation with bits of cynical philosophy. Only my mother encouraged Boghos in his art, and he did not take her seriously. My mother, after all, encouraged everybody.

Long after the meal was over they would sit around the oval table, cracking salted melon seeds, speaking longingly of the sweet odor of the ripening melons in the old country. Even the eggplant there yielded a fragrance, they said. None but the demented would want to return and yet, if you were speaking of fruit, where could you find such fruit as in the old country?

"The devil take the old country," the men said, telling one another how fortunate they were to be out of it.

"The devil take the old country," the women echoed. And still, who could dispense with it without a tear shed for this one, or that. *"Vagh* for Father Nishan," they said, wiping the corners of their eyes. "Where will we hear the Mass sung like that again?"

They spoke of Agpar the Pastry Man whose bell-festooned cart had tinkled on spring afternoons as he pulled it through the narrow cobbled streets of the village. Where again, they asked, would *paklava* taste the same?

"In America," the men said, "he would have become rich. In this country one's luck is open. See, after all, what has happened to Levon Dai!"

Could ever an evening pass without mention of Levon Dai, who had had the temerity to go West, alone, and to prosper? The pretended disdain with which the men spoke of him gave away their admiration and envy. The making of money, they insisted, was for clods. Anyone could do it in America, provided he were boorish enough to subject himself to certain indignities.

"Hush," cried the women, who adored Levon Dai and always rushed to his defense. They excused all his shortcomings. When he wrote letters home only at monthly intervals enclosing a check for Marta-mama, they forgave him this, too. He had to live alone among strangers. For this was he not to be pitied?

"Who told him to go to Iowa?" the men scoffed. "There are, after all, Armenians in other places. Who asked him to go to *Iowa?* Pah. He must like it."

"Hush," the women said, "how can he like it? It is merely the price he has to pay."

IF YOU begin with Levon Dai's arrival in America in 1919 (it is Hadji's story) you see him, dark-complexioned, of medium height, long nose slightly hooked (sign of intelligence), shaggy eyebrows and piercing black eyes peering from under a mass of black hair. His clothes, Hadji says, look as though he had been buried in them for several months before being exhumed, and he is carrying a cracked leather suitcase, older than Noah.

"And what does Levon Dai *carry* in the suitcase?" she cries. (Everyone knows what Levon Dai carries in the suitcase but they look expectantly at Hadji.) "Clothes?" she asks sarcastically. "Nice clean white laundered change of union suit? Spats? Shoe trees? Bundles of letters tied up with fancy ribbon, and a sweetheart's photograph?" Marta-mama chortles.

"No!" continues Hadji. "Levon Dai carries *fifty one-pound cans of sesame-seed oil!*" Everyone breaks into talk at once. Those who, like Uncle Pousant, pretend to disparage Levon Dai's accomplishments laugh coldly among themselves.

"That is supposed to be a sign of genius, friend Kelesh," says Uncle Pousant. "Remember that. Put fifty pounds of sesame-seed oil into an old leather suitcase and carry this, at the risk of breaking your back, from Jerusalem, to Egypt, to France and then to America. If you do this, soft-headed women will canonize you." As Uncle Pousant intended, Hadji has heard and her eyes narrow.

"Yes," she says, speaking to Kelesh, "if you have the imagination and the strength and the courage, because it is next to the last money you have, *buy* fifty pounds of sesame-seed oil! Pack it in your suitcase, lift it to your shoulders, and carry it to New York and then to Minas the grocer, whose customers cry for it, at five hundred percent profit! Then," Hadji goes on, "write abroad to get more oil, on credit this time. And, if you are not yet tired, travel on foot to the four corners of New York City disposing of the oil that is yet to arrive; at a nice profit, mind you, so that before you are ready to leave New York you can afford to dress like a gentleman and carry a *new* suitcase. Yes, do it," says Hadji, still speaking to Kelesh, "but if you cannot, then by all means laugh!"

Kelesh, for want of a reply, lowers his head and begins to sulk. Eventually he will think of one, but this often takes so long that the effect will be lost in a welter of irrelevance.

Of course Levon Dai's story does not really begin here. Marta-mama recalls to us how Levon Dai's mother died at his birth, how Marta-mama raised him; with pride and love and even a little awe, since he was the son of her gifted brother, Torcom Dai. During the long months when Torcom Dai, a lawyer, was traveling on business among the capitals of Europe, Marta-mama nursed his son through measles and diphtheria, watched fearfully and silently when he selected the tallest trees to climb, and spoke to him firmly yet lovingly when he was caught fishing from the cliffs over the Bosporus when he should have been at school. When Levon Dai was nine years old, his father had set out on one of his frequent trips, and a few weeks later his body was found in a desert between Rakka and Der-Zor. Everyone knew his death was the result of speaking too freely on politics. Torcom Dai was transformed into a martyr, and Marta-mama saw that his son never forgot him.

There was more to the story: how, when he was grown, Levon Dai had managed to get them both across the border and later maneuvered Marta-mama's visa so that she arrived in America not six months after himself. At this point, if there are newcomers in the crowd, and no one asks how Levon Dai happened to end up in Iowa, Uncle Pousant will turn to one and say: "Did I ever tell you how it was that Levon Dai went to Iowa?"

Because the rest of us have heard this many times, he will vary the story a little here and there, elaborating one point or another. But he always begins by telling how, after Levon Dai sold enough sesame oil on consignment to buy a train ticket, a new suit of clothes and a new suitcase, he decided to go to Chicago, having heard that there was a rapidly growing sesame-oil market there.

"It was fate," says Hadji. "I read his cup the day he left and told him he would never come back East to live."

"All right, *you* tell it!" shouts Uncle Pousant. He cannot bear to be interrupted, though he interrupts others frequently himself. "I start to tell a story, you kill it. I am finished!" He shoves his cigar between his teeth.

"Continue, Pousant Effendi," we say. "Our ears are yours."

"My patience is limitless but there are times when even a saint will rebel," says Uncle Pousant. He shrugs. "As I was saying, Levon Dai started to go to Chicago. With my own hands I rolled fresh *sarma,* which Hadji packed for his journey. A man can starve to death on these American trains. What is there? Two slabs of dry bread and between them a thin piece of rubber they call 'cheese.'" Uncle Pousant pretends to spit, then the story goes on.

It seems that, after he had been on the train a short time, Levon Dai sensed that the woman beside him was studying him out of the corner of her eyes. He began to feel uncomfortable. He thought: Is my suit the wrong color? Is her taste outraged, perhaps, by my choice of necktie?

As she continued to study him, he said to himself, "Aha, if in this country it is thus permissible to be rude, then I too can quench my curiosity," and he turned to look at her. What should he see but a small wart of a woman, costumed from head to foot in that disgusting shade of mauve of which gray-haired American ladies are so fond. On her head sat a hat of the same color, festooned with artificial violets and all manner of feathers. Even her hair, Levon Dai swore, was tinted a shade of light orchid. And to think that it was *she* who was pretending to contemplate *him* became a matter of great amusement to Levon Dai.

After a while Levon Dai's stomach told him it was lunchtime and he opened the package beside him; it contained, besides *sarma,* white cheese and bread, sour olives and generous slices of garlic-seasoned pressed beef, *pasterma.* It must have been the fragrance of the latter, Levon Dai guessed, that forced the lady's eyes to stray toward the box which now lay open in his lap. Quite naturally Levon Dai invited her to try some of the contents and he perceived that despite her outlandish costume there was in her manner a good-natured simplicity. The fragrance of his lunch, she told him, was positively tantalizing. Levon Dai urged her again to join him, and before long they were happily sharing the food, the orchid lady exclaiming joyfully over every morsel.

As they ate, the lady asked Levon Dai all sorts of questions, although she scarcely waited for his answers. She had never before met an Armenian, she told him, although she had spent many months collecting money for the "starving Armenians," and she appeared to be surprised and possibly a little disappointed that Levon Dai was not in an emaciated condition. Her home community in Iowa, she said, had become very much interested in Armenians, and she was anxious to hear all she could about him so that she could report at first hand to the Ladies Auxiliary of the First Presbyterian Church.

By the time they reached Cleveland, Levon Dai, through no fault of his own, had learned a great deal more about the lady than she had about him. He had learned, for example, that her husband, Mr. Pryam Slater, had died some five or six years before, and that he had been a banker, that Mrs. Slater had been visiting grandchildren in New York, and that her own home was in Council Bluffs, Iowa. (Uncle Pousant pronounces it Coon Seal Bloof.) Her interests, beyond the welfare of her grandchildren, were the Ladies Auxiliary, choral music and peonies.

Gradually, Levon Dai's brain began to grow numb to the tune of Mrs. Slater's incessant droning. For a time he resisted sleep. Then he discovered that, by resting his elbow on the arm of the seat with his head in his hand, he could shade his eyes and give the effect of deep and concentrated attention. Thus posed, he surrendered and slept. A series of rude jerks woke him with a start at the demented hour of five o'clock in the morning. He was unpleasantly surprised to see Mrs. Slater, crisp and refreshed, smiling at him and chatting amiably about the merits of riding day coach over Pullman. Levon Dai had the impression that she had not ceased talking since he had gone to sleep four or five hours earlier.

"I have been thinking," she said, "how interesting it would be if you could come to Council Bluffs and speak to the Ladies Auxiliary about your fascinating life." Up to this time Levon Dai could not recall telling her very much at all about his life. He began to think perhaps he had been talking in his sleep.

"There are no Armenians at all around Council Bluffs," she went on. "You can't imagine what a boost it would give the ladies to meet you and hear about some of your interesting customs. I've been thinking, perhaps you could show us how to tie turbans and things. We always have a dreadful time with the shepherds in the Sunday-school pageant at Christmas."

"Turbans?" Levon Dai was startled. "Armenians don't wear turbans, Madame. Perhaps you are confusing us with the Hindus."

"Oh, dear," said Mrs. Slater. "It's all more or less the same area, isn't it? You would be far more picturesque in a turban. And it would be fascinating to see some of your prayer customs — when a man gets up on a tower and turns . . . east, isn't it?"

Levon Dai started. Now she was confusing him with the Moslems. "You may not be aware, Madame," he said rather severely, "that the Armenians were Christians long before the Presbyterians; they adopted Christianity in the fourth century."

"My goodness," said Mrs. Slater absently, "I had no idea. I *do* hope you'll come to Council Bluffs sometime. Would you mind giving me your address?"

"I must tell you, Madame, I see not very much hope of coming," Levon Dai confessed cheerfully. "Soon I must return to New York. Who knows how long it will be before I can again afford to travel?"

"Oh, dear me," said the lady, "I'm sure we realize that! We would pay your expenses, naturally, besides a small lecture fee."

Levon Dai gave the lady his address, but until he received the letter (addressed with purple ink on orchid letter paper) he was by no means planning to accept. However, examination proved that the invitation included railroad tickets.

The more he thought about it — at this point Hadji takes over the story — the more apparent it became to Levon Dai that it was in fact his *duty* to speak to these natives of Council Bluffs. Perhaps, he thought, in this way I can do my small part toward the enrichment of the American mind.

"You can see what a challenge this was to Levon Dai," Hadji declares, glancing triumphantly at Uncle Pousant. "This, then, is how it was that Levon Dai went to Iowa."

How HE remained there is another story. It is very late by this time. Uncle Pousant is snoring. Kelesh is hunched over a crossword puzzle; he has almost finished it. Though he cannot express himself well in English, he is proficient at obscure vocabulary such as a three-letter word for Tibetan Beast of Burden. He has pretended disinterest in Levon Dai's story all evening.

Uncle Boghos, too, is bored. Poor Uncle Boghos! It is very rarely that he hears his favorite subject — Uncle Boghos — discussed. "Levon Dai Levon Dai Levon Dai! There is no longer any other subject for discussion. Kingdoms rise and fall; great works of art are created; who is there to care? Oafs! Know-nothings! Wasters of life!"

He rises importantly to leave. It would be a majestic exit except for the fact that during the evening he has kicked off his shoes, which now lie under the table. In a few moments he must return and grope under the flowing tablecloth on all fours until he finds them.

"Eshalah. Levon Dai'n paghtu Kezi ulah," the ladies tell each other as they leave. "May God will it that you have Levon Dai's luck." Only Uncle Boghos mutters the Armenian equivalent of "phooey" as he walks out of the room, his shoes in his hand.

3 It was customary on Saturday evenings for Hadji to read the cards. Her skill in telling fortunes by them was well known. Light, short-term problems she took care of by reading the dregs in Turkish-coffee cups after meals. But, as everyone knew, the cards were far more reliable.

Two weeks before that Easter in 1929, Hadji read the cards for Marta-mama. It was a few days after I had found her ill with a stroke, and my father said it was doubtful that she could recover at her age. But on Saturday night, when it was my mother's turn at Marta-mama's bedside, and after Father had left the house on a sick call, Hadji opened the cards. She fanned them out on the table, slapped around aces and queens for a while, and finally pronounced that Marta-mama would be fine. After that no one except Father was surprised when Marta-mama began to sit up, ask for her crocheting, and proclaim loudly that she wanted to die. "As soon as Levon Dai is safely betrothed, oh, Lord!"

A week later the family was assembled in the living room after dinner. Hadji said, "Ardavast Sulyan came into the restaurant today. His niece, Satenig Sulyan, arrives tomorrow from Rumania. She has only a visitor's visa, so if she does not marry a citizen within a year — pft! — she goes back."

"*Vagh,*" said Boghos. "Is she pretty?"

"Too pretty for you, my hairy friend," shouted Uncle Pousant. "If she is under fifty and her eyes are uncrossed, she is too pretty for you. Ha-ha!"

"She might be just the one for Levon Dai," said Hadji.

"And you would send a nice girl like that to Iowa?" cried Uncle Pousant. "Have you no heart?"

"Iowa can be no worse than Rumania," said Hadji.

"Who knows what they *eat* in Iowa!" said Uncle Pousant.

"Mayonnaise on pears, probably," said Boghos.

"Please!" said Uncle Pousant. "You are upsetting my stomach."

While the dishes were being washed, Kelesh began explaining to a visitor, a newcomer to America, the object of a magazine soap contest. Kelesh was tall and lean and sorrowful, with a propensity for misfortune that made him at once ridiculous and endearing. With a doggedness that denied fact, he spent every available hour in the pursuit of chance: bingo games, the Irish Sweepstakes, puzzle contests. Mornings, he attended classes at Columbia; afternoons, he traveled from church to church, to bingo games. He brought home umbrellas, cake mixers, cheap perfume, bedside lamps, satin pillows, and (once) a fairly nice bathrobe, as he described it, which he forgot and left in the subway. He had been to schools in Athens, Constantinople and Paris, and he spoke fluent Armenian, Turkish, Greek, German and French, but he was somehow never able to master English beyond the minimum necessary to follow a course. At this moment he was trying to write, in twenty-five words or less, why it was that he liked Purelan Soap.

"This is an American puzzle," he explained. "Whoever wins receives twenty-five thousand dollars. That is, let me see, approximately seventy-five thousand liras in Turkish currency."

"Seventy-five thousand liras! Kelesh Effendi, this must be a very difficult puzzle! You need much education for this."

"On the contrary," said Kelesh, "it takes only a small amount of imagination. You need only put yourself in the place of this young girl, and say why it is you like this soap she is using."

"You are joking, Effendi. For this foolishness they are giving seventy-five thousand liras? I cannot understand their mentality. But let us say you win the seventy-five thousand liras; what will you do with so much money?"

It was like this, Kelesh said. There were one hundred and twenty million people in America. There was plenty of milk. Americans were insane about milk. Even adults drank it. The doctors said there was no healthier food. *But,* do Americans know about yogurt? It is, after all, nothing but milk also, but more nourishing, promoting longer life, curing the ills of the stomach. Have not the people of the East known this for centuries? Now, with a little capital, say, a few thousand dollars, you open a yogurt factory. Then *you let all the people of America know that yogurt is healthier than milk!* You put signs on all the roads. You make puzzles: "I keep my beauty with yogurt because . . ." You find famous physicians who swear on Bibles that yogurt is healthier than milk. Americans are absurd, you can teach them even to wash their faces in yogurt. "But for this you need money," said Kelesh softly. "Perhaps I shall win this contest."

There was silence for a moment. Then Hadji started to pour the coffee. "May you see many days, Kelesh," she said. "May halos of light play over your head. May you be blessed for your patience. A toast to Kelesh Agha, and may his yogurt factory flourish."

"May his yogurt factory flourish," everyone echoed as they sipped their coffee.

Cousin Dikran, our ambitious young photoengraver, was visiting from Astoria, and Hadji had promised to read his cup. She saw a house in it, a house with a piazza, which meant that Dikran was destined to live in the manner of a gentleman. He would get married, too, for who could live in such a house alone?

"Aha," laughed Dikran, sounding pleased. "A house with a piazza, equipped with a wife, that is worth waiting for."

"Boghos Agha," said Hadji, "hand me your cup and let us see where your fortune has been hiding these many months."

"My fortune means nothing to me," said Boghos sourly. "The muses recognize no fortune. Money is for the soulless. I cannot abase myself to search for it."

"Truly spoken!" shouted Uncle Pousant. "To make money one need only have the soul of a donkey. How long has it been since we wrote Levon Dai that Marta-mama was ill, by the way?"

"Only a week now," said Hadji. "We will have a letter tomorrow, you will see. He will surely tell us he is coming for Easter."

"Pah!" said Uncle Pousant. "Levon Dai is a barbarian. Now that he is rich he neglects his relatives."

The front door opened and slammed shut, and I knew it would be my mother, returning from Marta-mama's. She came into the living room, and said that Marta-mama was feeling so well she was becoming somewhat of a problem. "She resents someone staying with her all the time. This is aggravating her so much that we may have to leave her alone some, so she won't get sick again.

"By the way," she added, "I hear that Satenig Sulyan is arriving tomorrow, and that she is a beauty. We must arrange for Levon Dai to meet her when he comes home for Easter."

"My feelings tell me it would be well to hurry and arrange something," Hadji said. "Who knows, he may even get himself entangled with a foreigner out there. One cannot imagine there are many attractive women in Iowa; yet he is lonely, and at such times anyone can lose his head. I think I shall open the cards for Levon Dai. I have not read them for him lately."

She slapped the cards onto the table and after a moment she sighed. "Ahhh, I was afraid of this. There is a romance. He must be thinking of getting married."

"You are joking," said my mother. "Who could he marry in Iowa? Has he someone in mind?"

Hadji was silent as she maneuvered the cards. "He has found someone — " she said at last " — a blonde. But he is still making up his mind."

"He could have come to New York and looked around before making up his mind," said my mother.

"It may still not be too late," said Hadji. "Once he comes to New York and meets a few civilized people again. Be sure and invite that Satenig Sulyan for Easter."

"Don't you worry, I'm going to call Sulyan right now!" said my mother as she went to pick up the telephone.

A FEW DAYS later I became sick. Father said it was from overeating and put me to bed. Uncle Boghos moved his easel into my bedroom so that I could keep him company while he painted. Mother was spring-cleaning, Father was busy with his patients in the front of the house, and Kelesh had gone to his classes. It was so quiet that it distracted him, said Uncle Boghos, who often pretended to long for the peace and solitude of the scenes he painted from his vast collection of post cards.

"Ah well," he said, "here now, we shall begin a new master-piece." He first removed his shirt and hung it on the bedpost, exposing an expanse of chest so hairy that it resembled a black fur rug. Next he placed a small postal card on the easel next to the bare canvas and proceeded to mix his paints.

"What are you going to paint, Boghos?"

"The Lake of Sevan," said Boghos. "The most beautiful lake in all the world. In the distance hovers Mount Ararat. See the ancient church on the shore. It is built of stone and it remains just as it was almost sixteen hundred years ago. Here — look at the postal card." I looked, and there it all was. "Ah, the *hairenik!*" said Boghos, and I knew he meant not the country whence he had come but the true homeland he had never seen, the old Armenia that once lay under Mount Ararat. "How beautiful our country was," he said, "and yet always it was a battlefield. From the earliest days we lay in the doorway of the conquerors: the Romans, the Persians, the Tatars. Later, the Crusaders came, with whom we were one. But when they withdrew, we were left to the mercy of the enemy, even to this day. The wonder is that we have survived at all; as races go, there were never very many of us." He wiped his brushes.

As he sketched the shore line Boghos continued to lecture to me about Armenian history. Although I could not follow more than half of what he said, an occasional nod seemed to keep him well satisfied. After a while it occurred to me that Boghos' oratory was being wasted on me, and I asked him why he did not go out and give lectures as I had heard Levon Dai had done when he first went to Iowa. Boghos put down his brushes and stared at me with a very pleased expression on his face.

"You think that this has not occurred to me, too?" he said. "Listen . . ." And because I had managed to tap a spring deep in Boghos' well of ambitions, he began to tell me about it, slowly at first and then more and more excitedly as he abandoned himself to an image of himself lecturing before an audience, vast and hushed, which hung upon his every word.

"If Levon Dai in his ignorance could give lectures," Boghos said, "what brilliance could I not re-create for an audience?"

Long ago, Uncle Boghos reminded me, when Levon Dai went to Council Bluffs to give a lecture to the Ladies Auxiliary of the First Presbyterian Church, the family had received an urgent letter from him pleading for some details about Armenian history. "These people seem to be under some misconception about us," Levon Dai had written. "Be good enough to send me a brief summary of our history so that I may enlighten them with facts."

Uncle Boghos was indignant at the idea of Levon Dai, who had spent his childhood avoiding school whenever possible, enlightening anybody. "What luck that fellow has," he said. "Why could someone not ask *me* to go out and give a lecture?"

It was true enough that Levon Dai had been fortunate. "No sooner had he arrived in Council Bluffs, for example," Boghos said, "than he found a delegation of ladies waiting to greet him at the railroad station." And no sooner had the lavender-haired lady from the train, Mrs. Slater, introduced Levon Dai to the others than he discovered himself to be the center of a controversy that must have been raging for some time before his arrival.

It seemed that several of the ladies, led by one Mrs. Portlemaine, had decided that Mrs. Slater was running the Ladies Auxiliary too singlehandedly. Levon Dai could see that instead of thanking her for her willingness to manage their tedious affairs they were in effect sabotaging her efforts for the sake of something which they called "the democratic process." Mrs. Slater could not open her mouth to make a suggestion without Mrs. Portlemaine's demanding that the matter be brought to a vote.

Now Levon Dai was tired when his train arrived in Council Bluffs. He had been looking forward to supper, a warm bath and a refreshing sleep in a soft bed such as Mrs. Slater had intimated in her letter would be provided for him. He was not in the least prepared to have Mrs. Portlemaine say, after the introductions were complete, "Well now, Mr. Levonian, I believe the ladies have decided to give you a tour of the city before it gets too dark. This is my car, right here. Mrs. Slater will follow us in hers."

"Now, Sarah," Mrs. Slater said peevishly, "I thought it was all settled that Mr. Levonian come home with me now in my car and rest up. We can have the tour in the morning."

"It seemed to me, Eloise," said Mrs. Portlemaine, "that we discussed all this at the meeting this afternoon, and decided to take Mr. Levonian on a tour in *my* car this *evening*. However, if you are unconvinced, the democratic process dictates that we put it to a vote. I move that we take Mr. Levonian in my car for a tour of the city before it gets dark. Second?"

"Second," said a small voice in the background.

"Allinfavorsayaye," said Mrs. Portlemaine, very fast. "Nays? Motioniscarried. All right, Eloise, Mr. Levonian will ride with me and you just follow along with Mrs. Price and the others."

"Just hold your horses a minute there, Sarah," said Mrs. Slater, arching her voice for a fight, if one was necessary. "The democratic process might dictate that we bring this to a vote, but parliamentary procedure dictates that the chairman conduct the voting. *I* am chairman. Will someone make a motion that we take Mr. Levonian directly home so that he can rest for his long day tomorrow?" Mrs. Slater looked squarely at her group of followers.

"I so move," said a tall, gray lady.

"Second," said another voice.

"I would like to discuss the motion," said Mrs. Portlemaine loudly, gathering her forces for a filibuster.

As parliamentary procedure took its slow, circuitous course,

Levon Dai shifted from one foot to the other and wondered whether it would be unseemly to sit down on his new suitcase. His new shoes were hurting him and he was worried, as it began to dawn on him that he had made no preparation for his speech, and had no idea what was expected of him. Presently, however, he perceived that through the good offices of a box-shaped lady the discussion began to reach a compromise.

"In view of the stalemate," the square lady said, "I move that we take Mr. Levonian to *my* house for some supper. I'm sure we must all be starved." Levon Dai felt everlastingly grateful to the square lady, especially as her suggestion seemed to strike everyone except Mrs. Slater and Mrs. Portlemaine as a splendid one. The motion was carried without further discussion and with only two "nays."

In the days that followed, Levon Dai spent a good deal of time waiting around for the ladies to decide what to do with him. He was staying with Mrs. Slater, but Mrs. Portlemaine frequently challenged Mrs. Slater's monopoly of her guest. However, he was relieved to observe that whenever Mrs. Portlemaine insisted that an issue be voted upon, and the discussion became deadlocked, the square lady could be counted upon to inject a note of compromise. Levon Dai decided that the democratic process would be a gruesome thing indeed without someone like the square lady to pull it together now and again.

When the evening came for his talk, Levon Dai was in a state of agitation. The information he had asked for had not yet arrived from New York, and he had been feted so much that he had not had time to write a proper speech.

"I do hope you'll wear your turban, Mr. Levonian," said Mrs. Slater when it was nearly time to go to the church, "and your sari — is that what you call the long white garment your people wrap around themselves?"

"My dear lady," he said, somewhat exasperated, "I believe you are referring to the Turkish charshaf, which is quite different from a Hindu sari. Armenians, Mrs. Slater, wear *suits,* just as the Americans. I have no turban, nor have I a charshaf!" Mrs. Slater was already rummaging around in her linen cupboard and apparently had heard not a word of what Levon Dai said.

"You didn't bring it with you? What a shame," said Mrs. Slater. "But never mind. Here — how would this runner do for a turban, do you think it's long enough?" She produced a long narrow piece of linen cloth and insisted that Levon Dai wrap it around his head. "I know it's not exactly right, but the girls will be terribly disappointed if you don't *look* authentic. Now, here's a sheet we could use as a — whatever you said the word was. I'm sure you'll look as authentic as can be once you get it wrapped around you. But please do hurry, Mr. Levonian, it's almost six thirty."

So, at seven o'clock, there was Levon Dai, wrapped most appropriately for a Turkish bath, wishing he had been endowed with better luck in picking train seats, and in a very poor frame of mind for speech giving. Half a dozen safety pins were holding the turban more or less in place, but he was afraid to move his head for fear of jogging the whole thing loose. The sheet was a constant threat to his modesty; however, as he said later, "I put myself in God's hands and stopped worrying. What more could I do?"

There was little more Levon Dai *had* to do, as it turned out. From the moment that Mrs. Slater ushered him proudly into the Church Hall a small cry went up among the ladies, indicating that his wrappings, at any rate, met with their approval. "How thrilling that you have worn your native costume, Mr. Levonian!" Mrs. Portlemaine had come up to shake his hand, and when Levon Dai on an impulse raised it to his lips, he could see that in just such small gestures lay the success of his visit. Levon Dai had never been addicted to hand kissing, but he swears that on this occasion he kissed more than forty-seven hands, not counting those he was certain sneaked in for a second round.

After the potluck supper the time came for him to speak, and Mrs. Slater delivered a long and elaborate introduction. Everyone applauded and Levon Dai gathered his sheet close about him and made for the rostrum. The necessity for keeping his head still lent a certain dignity to his bearing, which he tried to capitalize on, although when standing up he had to keep one hand clutched to his stomach in a somewhat modified Napoleonic gesture, to keep the sheet from slipping around too much.

When Levon Dai found himself looking at fifty-odd upturned,

expectant faces, he was momentarily tempted to fling sheet and turban aside and flee the Hall in disgrace; but such was not basically his character, so he took a deep breath and spoke.

"My dear ladies and gentlemen," he said, "I wish to tell you a story, and I shall tell it to you in Armenian, for that is the language in which it was intended to be told. But first, I shall explain to you what the story says. The story is of a man who had no homeland, and he therefore wandered for many years over the face of the earth in search of one — through the hot deserts of Arabia, across the green hills of Cyprus, into the land of the Nile and thence over mountains into the heart of Europe. And in each place he found something of perfection: the deserts offered infinite space; the hills rendered him peace; the Nile possessed an ancient culture; while in the mountains his eyes were filled with scenes of overwhelming beauty. And still he was not satisfied, and still he searched.

"At last, after crossing a vast ocean and wandering through many strange cities, he came upon a very ordinary city, one in which a stranger would come to rest only by accident. And yet it was here that he at last found the very thing for which his soul had hungered: the kindness, the generosity and the friendship of the people."

Here Levon Dai paused to wipe his forehead with the back of his hand. A trumpet-like noise broke the hush, and he saw that Mrs. Portlemaine was blowing her nose and dabbing at her eyes. Thus far, it was his own words which had directed him, almost unconsciously, to the point he discovered himself to be

making. Now that he could see his audience so deeply moved, he sensed within himself an unfamiliar emotion: partly relief, but partly a realization that his words were not totally untruthful. He suddenly felt for them all a feeling of warmth as he thought of how he must be affecting them at that moment. A tear or two stole into his own eyes, which he wiped away with a gesture so elaborately touching that his audience was moved all the more. "And now," he said, hurrying to capitalize on the moment, "I shall tell you this story in my own language."

When spoken slowly, the Armenian language is hauntingly musical. Levon Dai spoke very slowly. An operatic tenor could not have surpassed the sob in his voice, nor could a violinist have used more deftly the crescendo and the sudden pianissimo as he brought his words to an end. There was a long moist silence. And then suddenly he was virtually mobbed by well-wishers who shook his hand until it threatened to disintegrate, and told him that Council Bluffs was his very own.

Now it should be mentioned that there were some husbands in the audience, as this fact is important to the story of why Levon Dai stayed in Iowa. Ladies may praise, flatter and even lionize, but in the end it is from a man that one most often receives the practical opportunity for success. Very fortunately for Levon Dai, among those who squeezed his hand that evening was one Abner Kingsley, a ruddy-faced, bald-headed gentleman who owned a chain of dry-cleaning shops throughout Pottawattamie County. His greeting, Levon Dai later said, habitually consisted of clearing his throat with a sound resembling that of a rather belligerent dog barking.

"Arf, arf," said Mr. Kingsley, "m'boy, you laid it right on the line. More power to you, m'boy, arf arf. Like your gumption. Like your running all over t'hell 'n gone 'n wanting to settle right here. Best place in the world. Great opportunities. Could use a boy like you 't my place. Come around t'morrow. Keep up the fight. Arf."

Levon Dai had had no intention of remaining in Council Bluffs, but what harm would there be in going to see Mr. Kingsley?

"Learn the business inside out," said Mr. Kingsley the next day. "Start 't the bottom. I did. Work y' way up. I did. What's wrong with that, heh? Arf!"

Nothing wrong with that, thought Levon Dai. Already he had been booked for two more talks. So for several months Levon Dai spent two or three evenings a week giving talks at churches and clubs all over the county, while by day he learned the dry-cleaning business inside and out. With his salary, and honorariums here and there, he accumulated a tidy cash box — especially since he had not yet any living expenses. For as long as he was a town celebrity, Mrs. Slater was loath to let him go as a guest for fear Mrs. Portlemaine would grab him up herself. At Christmastime Levon Dai further ingratiated himself with the citizens by going from church to church expertly tying the turbans on the heads of little-boy shepherds in the Christmas pageants — free of charge.

Within a very few years Levon Dai acquired a chain of dry-cleaning shops, as well as a plant which served all the cleaning establishments within a radius of fifty miles. He became a Mason, and a leader in the Rotary Club; and now, although as a civic responsibility he still tied turbans on the shepherd boys at Christmas, there was no thought of his wearing a costume himself, or giving lectures.

"The lectures were merely a steppingstone to amassing wealth," Boghos said to me bitterly. "*Vagh,* that such an opportunity to impart knowledge be wasted, while I, who could teach them so much . . ." He struck his brow with a closed fist.

"I think it's awful that *you* can't give lectures, Uncle Boghos."

"But I can!" said Boghos, brightening. "To tell you the truth that is precisely why I am secretly very anxious that Levon Dai come at this time. With his connections, it should be a simple matter to arrange for me a circuit of talks throughout his region."

"Oh, he'll come," I said. "I bet we get a letter tomorrow."

Boghos was far away. "Ah, the glory of it!" he said. "I could illustrate with my own paintings!" Boghos was already on the stage, furiously imparting his vast and accurate knowledge.

5 IN A few days I was well enough to go back to school, with orders from Father to try to stop eating before reaching the gorging point, which was difficult to do with the res-

taurant so strategically situated. In order to avoid it after school, I suggested to Caroline that we go over to the Sad Park — our name for Madison Square Park. It lay a few blocks west, and consisted of scattered patches of scrubby grass, littered with pigeons and yesterday's newspapers. Pairs of legs protruded from under many of the papers as their owners took all-day siestas, and its benches were dotted with occupants all looking exactly alike in their unshaven lassitude. I found it repellent, yet fascinating.

The bench we sat on already had one occupant but his head was buried in his hands. I stared abstractedly at him for a few seconds, and then suddenly, although his face was hidden, I realized it was Kelesh. A pain enveloped me with the thought that something of home, and therefore of me, should be a part of this atmosphere. I bolted back to the street behind the bench.

"Hey, where are you going?" Caroline joined me on Madison Avenue. "We just got here!"

"Oh, I'm tired of that old place," I said. "Let's go home, huh? It's probably getting late."

Caroline didn't argue and only reminded me that it was my turn to walk home with her. After I'd left her at her door I walked west toward the park again.

Kelesh was still on the bench when I got there. "Hello," I said, tapping his shoulder gently and kissing his cheek so that nobody in the whole park could doubt that Kelesh had a home.

"Oh!" he looked up, startled. "Oh. What are you doing here, little one? Is it so late that you are out of school?"

"It's after four. Didn't you win anything today? Did the game end early? Is your Easter vacation starting soon? Mine starts day after tomorrow," I babbled, pretending nothing was wrong.

"No, little one," Kelesh said, staring at his shoes. "I won nothing. As usual I bring home nothing."

"Oh, but you bring home lots of things!" I said. "All those ash trays and pillows and lamps and things . . ."

"Worthless," said Kelesh.

"*I* think they're beautiful," I said, meaning it. "Why, I bet some people play for years and years and never win anything at all. I just bet you're going to win the Sweepstakes next time. Then you can start your yogurt factory. I just know you're going to win!"

Kelesh smiled sadly. "It would take such a small amount of capital," he mused. "A mere two or three thousand dollars. We would have to find a decent site, naturally."

"*I* know!" I shouted. "Let's go look for a place to put your yogurt factory — we haven't done that for a long time."

"If it amuses you," Kelesh said, looking pleased. "Why not?"

Automatically, we turned toward Fifth Avenue: its air of undisputed prosperity always cheered us, in contrast to the aura of struggling mediocrity in the side streets we had to take to get there. Jewelry shops were abundant on Fifth Avenue in 1929, and their displays attracted us like moths. In one, a diamond brooch laced with flaming rubies had been in the window for months. Kelesh was to buy it for me when his yogurt factory prospered, and we were relieved each time we passed to see that it had not yet been sold.

"Here's one!" I had spotted a FOR RENT sign in an empty show-case. We peered through the door. "Is it big enough?"

"Hmmm," said Kelesh, "it would make an excellent office, and the showcase is big enough to accommodate a mechanical cow."

"A what?"

"Such a device would attract attention. What do you think of a life-sized mechanical cow, and beside it a beautiful, live milkmaid — someone borrowed from the Follies, perhaps — milking it of yogurt?"

"What a marvelous idea!"

"I have many ideas," Kelesh said sadly.

"Oh dear," I said, "we really must hurry and get you a Sweep-stakes ticket before this store gets rented."

"Today," Kelesh said, "a brave thought came to me. Why could I not ask Levon Dai to lend the money to us? As a shrewd and foresighted businessman, why should he not welcome this golden opportunity for increasing his fortune?" Kelesh's eyes brightened.

"Why, I'll bet he'd be insulted if you didn't ask him!" I said.

Kelesh squared his shoulders and took a last look at the empty showcase. "Why not!" he said, as we started home. "But this sort of proposition is one which can only be discussed face to face. I hope we find a letter to say he is coming!"

As IT happened, the letter arrived the following day. I stopped by at the restaurant with Caroline after school, calculating that Father could scarcely begrudge a token celebration of the begin-ning of our Easter holiday. Uncle Pousant was in a frenzy cleaning mussels, but Hadji was in the happiest of moods as she waved the letter at us and asked us to help ourselves to the icebox.

"Levon Dai is a busy one!" she said. "Clothes, clothes, clothes. You can imagine the cleaning just before Easter."

"Pah!" said Uncle Pousant. "What do you think a *restaurant* suffers at Easter! Mussels, mussels, mussels. *Open,* you idiot!"

"He's talking to the mussels," I told Caroline, who jumped whenever Uncle Pousant shouted.

"He was worried out of his wits about Marta-mama," Hadji continued. "Here — he says, 'I have been very worried about Marta-mama's indisposition. I trust that the good Lord will once again spare her, as He has done so often in the past twenty-five years.' "

Uncle Pousant pretended to choke. "He sounds as though he is demented with worry!" he said in a mimicking voice. "He is swimming in a sea of tears. He has neither eaten nor slept in two weeks. *Open,* you idiot!"

"But is he *coming?*" I asked impatiently.

"Tee tass," said Uncle Pousant, "peef paff. Hee haw."

"All right, listen to this" — Hadji began reading again from the letter — " 'I am very anxious to be with you all this Eastertide. As you know, this is a very busy season for dry cleaning. In addition there are a great many obligations which in my position it is difficult to forego. However, be assured that I will make every effort to come.' Did you hear that, Pousant? *'Be assured that I will make every effort to come.'* "

"I am bursting with anticipation. If you wish that I commit suicide, I shall hold my breath until he arrives."

"These 'obligations' worry me a little," said Hadji, ignoring him. "It is well that he comes and meets this Satenig Sulyan. Today again I heard she is a pearl. Come," she added, "if you two have finished eating let us all go to Marta-mama's. I have a basket already prepared for her and I must read her the letter."

Caroline was a little nervous about visiting Marta-mama after her initial experience, so she left us at the restaurant door and Hadji and I proceeded together. Hadji was dressed as usual in a hand-made brown monk's-cloth garment that fell loosely about her two-hundred-pound frame and hung almost to her ankles. She had three others, in black, navy and gray, and when one wore out she replaced it with another exactly like it.

We started out, walking east across Lexington Avenue, and Hadji stopped, as she always did, to greet the sculptor who sold religious art in a store on the corner of Third Avenue. His name was Khutumian, which means Christmas Eve, and I thought how appropriate it was at the proper time, but how out of season he must feel during the rest of the year. "What's new?" he asked, and Hadji told him in detail of her worries.

"It is likely that if he stays there long enough he may get involved with a foreigner," she said. "He speaks in this letter of 'obligations.' One wonders if this obligation does not wear a blond fez. I read the cards," Hadji said, shaking her head. "It does not look promising. Have you seen Satenig Sulyan, incidentally?"

"Mmmmmm-ph!" said Khutumian, blowing a kiss. "A rosebud — a lily among buttercups. A Cellini masterpiece."

"We have spoken to Mr. Sulyan," Hadji said. "He is much interested in Levon Dai, and why shouldn't he be! Where would she find a better catch?"

Khutumian saw us to the door. "Christ is risen," he said. It was the traditional Armenian Easter greeting.

"May His spirit be with you," said Hadji.

Marta-mama was crocheting the border on the multicolored spread when we arrived. While Hadji unpacked the basket Marta-mama said she hoped that she could just complete the border on the spread. Levon Dai would no doubt be coming for Easter, and she wanted him to have it to take back with him — or at least for his wedding.

"I had a nice talk with the janitor today," Marta-mama said. Marta-mama knew six words of English: *uptown, downtown, no good, okay* and *bum*. Around them she built entire conversations by interspersing these words with Armenian, Turkish and a pseudo-English all her own. "I told him my shirt fell off the fire escape and he went and got it for me."

"How did you say it in English?"

"Uptown, downtown, shabeek fertown," said Marta-mama as she illustrated the shirt's descent with her hands. Hadji and I were laughing with her when Marta-mama stopped suddenly, looking at Hadji. "Have you a letter? You are not saying anything."

Hadji drew the letter out of her pocket.

"And you did not say anything! *Vayreni!*" said Marta-mama. "What does he say? Is he coming for Easter? Hurry, torturer."

Hadji pulled the letter out of the envelope and read it aloud.

"So be it," said Marta-mama. "He may come, or he may not come. The good Lord knows what He is doing, I suppose."

"We are arranging that he meet this Satenig Sulyan," said Hadji. "They say when she was but ten years old she was keeping house for her father and six brothers. With a wife like that, he might even manage to survive the rigors of Iowa."

Marta-mama did not appear to have heard. She was slowly and deliberately unraveling the border of the spread, winding the wool around her fingers. "What are you doing?" I cried, but Hadji waved to me to be silent.

"It will take me until Easter to put on the border again," Marta-mama said at last, and she seemed to be talking to herself. "I made a pact with myself to work the spread until he comes. Old age, Hadji, is no more than a prolonged period of waiting. It is better when one does not wait idly. After Easter I cannot have much longer to wait, I suppose, one way or another."

6 ON HOLIDAYS, it had long been a tradition at our house to invite some lonely ones to dinner, along with the family. *Zavalluh,* we called them, prefixing the surname with the word: Zavalluh Kosrob Pesa of the once-glorious tenor voice; a little worn now, and cracking somewhat on the higher registers; like Tommy Tucker, poor Kosrob Pesa often sang for his supper now, at charity dinners and testimonials.

There were, too, heroic *zavalluhs,* like General Garabed, who had once led a famous charge against the Turks. His small army had been slaughtered, but he had escaped to Russia and thence to America, where he lived now in fourth-rate comfort; a jar of yogurt on a sooty window sill, faded ribbons decorating a warped mirror, spending most of his days reading someone's discarded *Times* in the lobby of the luxurious Fifth Avenue Hotel, where he had once stayed.

"I've asked the General," my mother said to Hadji on the way home from church on Good Friday.

"Ha!" said Hadji. "How many does that make now?"

"Sixteen," said my mother, "counting Marta-mama; the doctor said we could carry her over for the day. That's absolutely all the table will hold. The plates are so close together now my elbows will be in your soup."

The doorbell rang incessantly all Friday. Fat Azniv had left the hired boy in charge at her butcher shop in Newark; she was at the door by noon, her big happy face shiny with perspiration, in her arms two huge shopping bags full of meat — four legs of lamb and the odoriferous *pasterma*. One could safely wager she had had no trouble getting a seat on the bus from Newark.

"Ouf, Azniv, you have brought the whole butcher shop again! Here, let me take them, you sit down and rest." Azniv parked herself with a series of groans and began wiping her face with a large polka-dotted handkerchief.

"Only for a minute, I want to cut the *shish-kebab* before Pousant comes. He always cuts the chunks too big. Come here, my pigeon, and let me kiss you," she said to me, and when I did she enfolded me in the vast garlic-scented expanse of her dress. Much as one loved Azniv it was something of an ordeal to be kissed by her. She was Hadji's first cousin, but twice as large and correspondingly gentler in her ways, as though humbly aware of her unsightliness and almost embarrassingly grateful for signs of affection, especially from the young. Babies, who knew no better, cried in terror when she came near them.

"How is Marta-mama?" she asked my mother.

"Not so well these last few days; it would be well for Levon Dai to be married soon."

Azniv leaned forward. "They are saying in Newark that miser Karpajian has his eyes on Satenig Sulyan for his son."

"The one with the adenoids? Ha! Rumors. How can anyone imagine Sulyan would give that lovely girl to a Karpajian?"

"Aha, but the rug business is flourishing now."

"Never mind the rug business," said my mother. "Don't worry, Sulyan is bringing her here on Sunday."

The doorbell again — it was Dikran this time. The photo-engraving plant he worked in was "union shop," Dikran explained proudly. So, since he had the day off, he had come to help. He was promptly set to work washing windows.

Kelesh arrived next with Cousin Meline. He had gone to meet her train from Binghamton, since her husband, Melkon, couldn't come until Saturday night. Meline had not been with us since Thanksgiving. There were more kisses and a few tears shed for

Meline's mother, dead now for over twelve years. Hadji was the last arrival and the kissing began all over again.

"Work time now," said my mother, and all the women suddenly became very businesslike. Boghos, Kelesh and Dikran, feeling the time had come to make themselves scarce, took off for the Syrian Coffee Shop next door. From the kitchen came the clatter of pots and pans, and in a few minutes the aroma of simmering onions gradually unfurled and dominated the house. Hadji had brought her baskets, filled with artichokes and plump eggplant, bursting ripe. They had to be washed, soaked, cut, soaked again.

"Come grind the chick-peas," Mother said to me. No one stayed idle long two days before Easter. Over the grinding, simmering and chopping, the women exchanged gossip and reminiscence.

"Asped Toros' grandchild had another girl."

"*Vagh,* five daughters!"

"In this country it makes no difference."

"Ah, Meline, your mother used to cook this like an angel. Pure gold and honey . . ."

"These artichokes have no aroma. They grow them big but tasteless here; can you remember the artichokes in Ismid?"

The doorbell began ringing again, impatiently. My mother sighed. "The patients are starting to come and the doctor is late from his calls." I ran down the hall to open the door. It was Mr. Wong, one of Father's Chinese patients, with his index finger wrapped in a blood-soaked handkerchief. Mr. Wong bobbed his head and smiled graciously while blood dripped on the doorsill.

"Velly bad chop chop, Missy, docta home please?"

Mother was right behind me. "He should be here any moment, Mr. Wong." She led him to the examining room to prepare a tourniquet.

After Father arrived, we alternated between the doorbell and the kitchen most of the afternoon. Hadji was making filling for the *topig,* the traditional Easter patties of onions, sesame oil, currants, pine nuts and spices, encased and steamed in the chick-peas I had ground. Meline was the *cheureg* expert — the semisweet, fragrant dough for Easter bread was rising in tin tubs. Azniv had finished cutting the *shish-kebab,* which lay marinating in the icebox, and started in on the *sarma*. The next day there would be soup stock to make; beans to be cooked — tomato-and-garlic-flavored; mussels to be cleaned and stuffed with rice. Mother remarked that amid all this plenty there wasn't a thing in the house to eat for supper — we would all have to go to the restaurant.

We gathered that evening at the long banquet table at the far end of the restaurant. Uncle Pousant had obviously had a bad day. He sat at the head of the table hardly eating, pulling at his mustaches and saying not a word. Mother mentioned that we had to remember to get more tomatoes tomorrow.

"Tomatoes!" Uncle Pousant grew red in the face and gave the table a loud *smack*. There was a momentary, stinging silence. Hadji explained in a low voice that a customer that noon had asked for ketchup on the *shish-kebab*.

"Ketchup!" said Uncle Pousant. "After I spent the morning imbuing that exquisite meat with all the subtle flavors of heaven. My *soul* went into that lamb! 'Ketchup,' she says."

Everyone nodded sympathetically and waited for Uncle Pousant to regain control.

When he did, after a few moments, Hadji exclaimed: "Ahh, just think, Sunday we'll have Levon Dai with us! How long it is since we last saw him!"

"Eight years and three months!" said Azniv, who kept close track of dates. *"Asvazim!* He is a wandering one."

"Of a wild, untamed nature," said Hadji, "may God bless and prosper him. How many times I told him, *write,* write and tell us when you are arriving so we can have a proper home-coming for you."

"He'd better come *this* time," said my mother. "Satenig Sulyan is not just coming to eat *topig,* I'll tell you that now."

"He'd better come is right after all this fuss," said Boghos. "Who would you think was coming. The Prince of Wales maybe? John D. Rockefeller?"

"Oh, they're after her all right," said Azniv. "I was telling Maryam today about miser Karpajian's son."

"You've got to watch those rug dealers, I tell you," Hadji said.

"I might have won an icebox today," said Kelesh to no one in particular, "but I heard about it too late — the Sunrise Appliance Store had a raffle. Do you really think he will come?"

"He said he would make every effort to come," said Hadji. "What can prevent him from coming if he makes *every effort?*"

WHAT A perfect Easter Sunday it was! The sun danced all over the front room pronouncing it an ideal day for welcoming visitors, precipitating romances, dressing in my new red silk and shouting aloud, "Happy Easter!"

There was much speculation on the way to church as to what time Levon Dai might arrive. The train should have come in at nine thirty in the morning, but it was likely that Levon Dai had decided to drive across country in his new Graham-Paige touring car. "Ah, he always was a sport, that one!"

Everybody was in church. The *zavalluhs* were out in force. The Archbishop sang the Mass in the ancient Armenian, a beautifully mystical tongue older than Latin. *"Christos Haryav y Merelotz!"* I could not understand all the words but the music spoke for itself. No wonder the women wept.

But the world beamed again outside the church where everyone milled and gossiped. At last, after extricating my father from a circle of admiring patients, we were on our way home with the General, the tenor Kosrob Pesa and the Archbishop himself.

The General was an imposing man: over six feet tall, with piercing gray eyes, he walked as though he held a swagger stick in his hand. He and my father and the Archbishop walked ahead of the rest of us. The very appearance of the Archbishop exuded ecclesiastical authority — his beard was profuse and savagely black, his belly portly as a churchman's should be. He was renowned for his great learning and wit. He spoke six modern languages fluently, and was versed in ancient Greek and Aramaic as well as Armenian. He did not know Chinese, however, and this was unfortunate, for there on the stoop of our house, grinning broadly, sat Wr. Wong, Father in his customary absent-mindedness having forgotten to let Mother know he'd invited him to Easter dinner.

"Come early. Happy day!" said Mr. Wong. Father introduced

him to everyone while Mr. Wong bowed and said, "Happy day, happy day," a dozen or so times.

Inside, everyone divided into groups. The women and Uncle Pousant were all business in the kitchen. Melkon and Dikran were elected to fetch Marta-mama while the rest of the men read the Sunday papers or discussed politics and Levon Dai's arrival.

At two o'clock Marta-mama was brought in and with great fanfare was settled on the couch. She was all dressed up in a navyblue silk dress she had bought years before to wear to a wedding. "Agh, I'm getting too old for this kind of nonsense," she said, but she seemed nevertheless faintly pleased with herself.

When the sounds from the kitchen indicated that dinner was almost ready, the doorbell rang. Everyone stiffened perceptibly. "Quick, quick, don't keep him waiting . . ." I raced to the door. It was Mr. Sulyan, with his niece.

They made their way into the living room, where everyone was now gathered. "Miss Sulyan, you know His Grace Surpasan Hayr, Mr. Sohokian, General Garabed, Mr. Melkonian . . ." While Miss Sulyan was being introduced I had a chance to study her. She was decidedly plump, the sort of satisfying Levantine roundness on which Uncle Pousant might comment approvingly — "Look there now, you *know* that's a woman!" Her hair was chestnut-colored, and she was light-skinned and pink-cheeked — a highly prized complexion among Near Easterners. She had vivid black eyes and arching eyebrows, the kind of eyes Hadji would say could talk through a veil. The eyes sparkled even though she kept a modestly restrained decorum throughout the introductions, and did all the correct things, such as kissing the Archbishop's ring, and lowering her eyes on being introduced to the younger men. She ultimately placed herself on the couch next to Marta-mama and began talking to her softly. Like her figure, her husky voice was rich with promise. It was obvious that everyone was captivated.

"Nice girl, Sulyan," said the General with a nod of approval. Mr. Wong followed suit with a big smile. Boghos and Kelesh both looked pleased and interested at the same time, for once; but it was Dikran who appeared to be transfixed. He sat gazing at Satenig Sulyan with a look of limitless admiration.

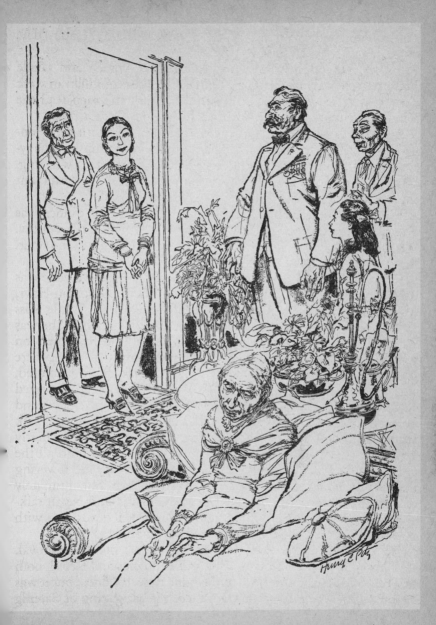

After a brief discussion it was agreed that the soup should wait no longer. Mother explained to the company that Levon Dai was probably driving, and it was hard to judge just when he would arrive, adding that we were not certain, of course, that he was actually coming. It was the first hint that hopes might be waning.

It was a lively enough dinner, marred only by the unspoken suspense that is always present when there is still a faint hope but greater doubt that the guest of honor will arrive. The Archbishop said a poetic grace, and toasts were drunk to everyone's health. Hadji and Azniv sat on either side of Harutune Sohokian, a poet who came from a village where it was considered impolite for a guest to partake of food until he was urged to the point of nausea. They were therefore occupied throughout the meal with the thankless job of pleading with him to eat.

"I will sit down merely to keep you company, dear friends," he said in a weak, martyred tone as they pleaded with him. "I have just eaten." Now this was obviously a lie, because it was now after three o'clock and we had been with Harutune Sohokian since eleven, when we met him in church.

"Just a little of this soup, Mr. Sohokian, please. We made it especially for you, just a little taste as a favor to me."

"Eh, a very small portion. I really should not but it is difficult to refuse you. Oh, oh, that is far too much!"

"A little bread, Mr. Sohokian, I beg of you."

"No, no, Madame Azniv, I am full up to here."

"Come, Mr. Sohokian, just one piece?"

"Eh, a *small* piece then." And so it went, getting progressively harder with each successive course to keep Sohokian from starving.

Mr. Sulyan was obviously thinking of Levon Dai's defection. After clearing his throat he brought up the subject of the rug dealer Karpajian in Newark. "I understand he is becoming extremely prosperous. We were there for dinner the other night. Fine family." Azniv looked sideways at my mother.

"Agh, I wonder what is delaying Levon Dai!" Hadji said.

"It doesn't seem likely he'll come after this," said my father. He was innocent of the hopes that hung on Levon Dai's visit, so he didn't sound particularly disturbed.

After the Turkish coffee Father started up a game of back-gammon with the General while Mr. Wong and the Archbishop looked on. Dikran was still watching Satenig Sulyan so intently that after a few moments she proceeded to the kitchen to help with the dishes, her eyes lowered in confusion. Marta-mama had been helped to the couch again, and she lay staring into some far-off, ghost-cluttered world. She had scarcely spoken all day. How tired she looked! And old, so old as to seem ageless now, dust-gray.

"Come, child," she said. She had seen me watching her.

I went and sat beside her. "He will come," I said. "If not today, in the summer. He said so in his letter."

"I was not thinking of that, child," she said. "I know he will come someday; whether I'm here to see him or not does not matter very much. It matters only that he is happy. He must be, or he would come now. I was thinking rather that when he was a very small boy he liked pistachio nuts. He liked them so well he thought I must like them, too, and he walked two miles to the *fustughji* to get me a box for Easter. Two miles there, two miles back. I never cared for them very much before that day. Hand me one there, let me bless your eyes."

"That girl in there would make a fine wife for him," Marta-mama went on. "She appears bashful, and that is good, but she is not dead inside. There is fire in her, one can tell."

"Dikran Effendi, what do *you* think of that girl, eh?" Melkon fancied himself a rake. "A little too thin, you think?"

"Are you out of your mind talking like that?" Dikran spoke with the resentment one would properly show if his wife or sweet-heart were being glibly discussed.

Just then the telephone rang. Father left his game to answer it, and returned to the room: "Council Bluffs calling. . . ."

"Levon Dai! Hurry!" Mother and Hadji ran out of the kitchen, hands wet and soapy. Marta-mama was taken to the telephone. Mother, Hadji and Azniv stood by, waiting their turn.

"Kelesh," I whispered, "go talk to him. Tell him your idea about the yogurt factory, Kelesh, do!"

Kelesh shook his head. "It's not the sort of thing one can discuss on the telephone. If he comes, it's another story."

"Agh!" Hadji returned, wiping her eyes on her apron. "Poor boy, he thought until yesterday morning he was coming and then some important hullabaloo came up last night and he had to go." Uncle Pousant let out a snort so derisive that even the backgammon players looked up for a moment.

"You can't blame people if they have different ideas about social obligations," said Mr. Sulyan with sarcasm.

"It's for his business; he *has* to do these things. But now he is coming for sure, right after the Fourth of July!" Hadji directed these last words to Satenig Sulyan. "He won't be very busy then, he says."

"I'm sure Madame Marta will be happy to know that," said Satenig softly. "I am happy for her sake."

"Did I ever tell you how it was that Levon Dai got rich?" Hadji asked suddenly, addressing herself to my mother.

"No, no. Tell it, Hadji!" Mother knew the story better than any of us, but her eager smile bespoke admiration of Hadji's strategy. So Hadji, looking straight at Mr. Sulyan, told of Levon Dai's conquest of the Iowa ladies, and of his job with Mr. Kingsley in the dry-cleaning shops.

Now THIS Mr. Kingsley, it seemed, was far from the traditional old rascal whose leathery hide and barbed tongue conceal a heart of gold. Mr. Kingsley, as Hadji described him, was pure cold flint, from one side through to the other. For six months Levon Dai worked faithfully at pressing and spotting. During these six months he saw Mr. Kingsley only once: at a church supper (he was still pursuing his part-time career of lecturer) when Mr. Kingsley greeted him with a grunt over a dish of cole slaw and took no further notice of him.

For several weeks he had been intending to ask Mr. Kingsley just how long his apprenticeship would continue. Now, after this snub, he determined to go to the manager and resign immediately. If Mr. Kingsley was not going to be civil to him, why should Levon Dai do him the courtesy of resigning to him personally?

The manager was a stooped little man with watering eyes and perpetual sinus trouble. "What is id?" said the manager.

"I am leaving," said Levon Dai.

"That's fide. Bister Kiksley jus dold be do led you go."

"Were my services unsatisfactory?" asked Levon Dai, bristling.

"Do, you did jus fide. He jus don deed you eddy bore."

Never, said Hadji, had Levon Dai's temper come so close to combustion. Still, where others would have rushed home in an uncontrollable rage, Levon Dai decided to take a long walk and think over his situation. He had realized for several weeks now that demands on his evenings were becoming less and less frequent. He had even overheard Mrs. Portlemaine, at whose home he was temporarily sheltered, actually offering him to Mrs. Slater for the following week. He glanced at the savings bank book he carried in his vest pocket: he now had almost $500. He could either go back to New York and resume the sesame-oil trade, or he could find a new niche in Council Bluffs.

As he walked down the main street, Levon Dai looked at the familiar store faces with the emotion of one seeing them for perhaps the last time. It surprised him to realize how fond he had grown of the place. Then all at once he saw something that proved, Hadji said, that he was forever destined to good fortune. In the window of an inconspicuous dry-cleaning shop was a sign: FOR SALE. A vision suddenly entered his mind — of himself transformed into Mr. Kingsley's most prosperous rival, standing at the counter of the most beautiful dry-cleaning shop in all Council Bluffs.

Now, Hadji said, other men might still have trembled and clutched the bank book and taken the next train East. But not Levon Dai. First, he learned that the present owner of the shop was asking $3000 for his equipment, and from this he surmised — quite correctly — that this man, who was old and ailing, and had been open for business only sporadically, would not only come down to $2000 but would ultimately accept $1500.

It became a matter, then, of raising a thousand dollars, and this money Levon Dai was able to borrow from the bank, with the help of Mrs. Slater and Mrs. Portlemaine, who for once got together and eagerly undertook to back his loan — especially when they heard that the shop was equipped with a small back room which would be ideal for Levon Dai to sleep and cook meals in.

There was one thing to be said for the good ladies — once roused, their enthusiasm ran wild. When Levon Dai confided to them his dream of one day beautifying the shop, they immediately gathered together some of the ladies of the Auxiliary (tactfully omitting Mrs. Kingsley) and collected all manner of stray draperies, odd chairs and unwanted lamps, and even a nice old plum-colored carpet. Before very long it was obvious that his was to be the most inviting shop in Council Bluffs, if not in all of Iowa.

When Levon Dai had made his one trip back East, he had described with tears in his eyes the moving sight that struck him when he went to his door on the morning he opened his shop for business. There, stretching as far as he could see, stood a queue of ladies bearing quantities of clothing. They all, apparently, had a grudge against Mr. Kingsley's dry cleaning. Some had consistently lost buttons, while others had had woolens shrunk. It was all Levon Dai could do to keep from kissing each of the ladies' hands as they came in.

Levon Dai found himself so busy from the first that he was forced to hire two helpers after only a week. Even so, the ladies had to wait, sometimes, but they rarely minded this because there were Mrs. Slater's old chintz-covered armchairs to rest in while they sipped the Turkish coffee Levon Dai invariably served. His profits grew and grew; and it became obvious after a few months that Mr. Kingsley's business was suffering drastically.

The sinus-troubled manager of Mr. Kingsley's shop had left for Arizona, Levon Dai learned. There followed a succession of managers, and then the owner was reduced to managing all his three shops himself. After a few more months Levon Dai heard that Mr. Kingsley was ill.

It was a year after Levon Dai had first opened shop that Mr. Kingsley, rasping, wizened, and looking very pale, drove up to his door. He was sick, Mr. Kingsley told him. "Bad heart. Arf."

"I'm sorry," said Levon Dai, feeling a stab of pity for the old man, despite himself. "Is there something I can do to help you?" Mr. Kingsley, between wheezes, and stutters about incompetent help, managed to convey his message: he, Abner Kingsley, was about to make Levon Dai a munificent offer. Would Levon Dai become the manager of his three stores? The compassion in Levon Dai melted instantly.

"I'm sorry," he said, "I cannot neglect my shop to manage yours. Not unless I am to be compensated by receiving a portion of the profits. In addition to my salary, naturally."

Mr. Kingsley reacted with a violent coughing attack. "Wasting m' time!" he shouted, growing alarmingly purple.

"Quite so," said Levon Dai. "I should waste no more if I were you, sir."

But that was not quite the end of it. Within a week Mr. Kingsley dispatched his lawyer to see Levon Dai. This gentleman tried, at first, to prey on Levon Dai's sympathies. He was speaking for an old sick man who probably had not long to live, he said. He was begging Levon Dai, as a humanitarian gesture, to accept the job and save an old man's life. But Levon Dai could not see what charity had to do with it. If they wanted him to take over, he would do so on his own terms, and these he considered perfectly just.

"You're a hard man!" the lawyer said with admiration.

"Eh, I am only in business," said Levon Dai deprecatingly.

One could say, I suppose, that Mr. Kingsley and Levon Dai became great friends, and that as he grew more frail the old man began to look on Levon Dai as the son he'd never had. One could say this, but it would be pure fiction. For Mr. Kingsley became a very testy, unreasonable old man indeed, and in nowise did he develop an affection for Levon Dai.

During the last years of his life Mr. Kingsley's wife and his lawyer were finally able to maneuver him into selling out his stores, one by one, and eventually the dry-cleaning plant itself.

"But not to *that* curmudgeon!" Mr. Kingsley shouted each time.

"Now, Abner," the lawyer would say, "who else is there who can afford to pay your price?"

"And that is how it was that Levon Dai got rich," said Hadji to Satenig, who was the only one left who was listening.

THAT NIGHT, after the honored guests had gone, I lay in bed listening to the family's voices from the living room:

"I had a feeling he was not coming. I had it right here."

"That's your diaphragm, Hadji, you must have a psychic diaphragm. It's quite common among *hadjis*."

"Ahh, but a good day, still."

". . . beautiful girl, and so *dandigin!*"

". . . coming for certain in July."

Just before I drifted off to sleep it occurred to me that the voices of Kelesh, Dikran and Marta-mama were conspicuously missing.

SPRINGTIME varies in New York from street to street. Around Gramercy Park the trees and bushes were sprouting, virgin-green and hopeful. Window boxes in the brownstone houses showed spotty signs of colored buds. But our house was pervaded with gloom those days after Easter, after the initial heady optimism had evaporated and all that was left was the memory of disappointment. Only Marta-mama seemed untouched, and this very resignation, so alien to her, was an added concern. As she sat by her window she no longer even pretended to watch the street below. She was waiting, she said, if you asked — she no longer spoke of dying. She contested hardly at all when my mother announced that she had arranged for Little Menush to stay all the time with her. Dwarfed Little Menush, the happiest of souls, with the energy of a colt and a strength that made full-sized men flinch. She loved to clean, and all day she scrubbed and waxed, dusted and washed. It looked as though life was a big bucket of suds to Little Menush, and I wondered at her, lovingly, for there was not only the stunted little body to contend with but the ugly, swollen scar on the back of her neck, and the leathery burnt skin that never faded; mementos of a blunt sword and a year's wandering in the deserts. She never spoke of that time. How she had survived or reached America no one knew.

She brought some cheer to Marta-mama, but there was little enough of it at our house. Kelesh came and went like a gaunt shade, while Boghos moved his easel around restlessly. Here the light was bad; here, too much glare. Too many people around. Nobody to talk to. He spent much of his time quoting cynical Armenian proverbs. " 'What does an ass know about almonds!' "

"You and Levon Dai have grown up like brothers," Hadji said. "It is sinful to talk so of a brother. God in heaven should not hear you."

" 'If a brother were a good thing God would have one,' " Boghos quoted another, by way of reply.

"But Levon Dai is coming in the summer; he said so."

"There is an old proverb," said Boghos, " 'Ere the fat become lean, the lean are already dead.' "

From Newark, Azniv peppered us with rumors that Mr. Sulyan was fraternizing avidly with the Karpajians. The news put even good-natured Dikran into a glum mood. Meantime, Levon Dai was producing tremors among us with passing references in almost every letter to social involvements, charming Iowans (sex unspecified) and the fact that he was not getting any younger. To make matters worse a day hardly passed without Hadji's hearing of somebody's son or daughter running off with a non-Armenian. The culture was in danger of evaporating. Boghos declared: "We are only a handful now; in twenty years you won't hear the language spoken by anyone under fifty. Songs, literature, history — three thousand years of it. Pfffft — gone." He swept one palm against the other by way of illustration. There was never any answer to this gesture of finality. It succeeded in leaving us staring at one another in dour resignation.

Uncle Pousant was a perfect ogre these days. It seemed as though all the insensitive barbarians in the city had taken it upon themselves to patronize his restaurant. Never, said Uncle Pousant, had he thought that he would be subjected to such downright spiritual torment. He sent so many customers to Charlie's Saloon — with the hope expressed in Armenian that they choke on their sandwiches — that Charlie must have been making a pretty penny.

Uncle Pousant fanned his distemper by renewing his feud with the janitor in the apartment building behind his restaurant. His relations with this gentleman had been deteriorating for many years, and at this point their feud was concentrated on the question of who was to sweep the courtyard outside the kitchen door. This was a rectangular area which faced the rear of a six-story apartment building apparently tenanted entirely by families who owned no garbage cans. Setrag had been sweeping it each afternoon until the day came when Uncle Pousant decided that the courtyard was the janitor's responsibility. "Setrag," he said, "you are forbidden to sweep that courtyard any more."

Setrag smiled deliriously. "Ho-*kay,* boss!"

In a very few days the courtyard was littered with bits of paper, orange peels, broken beer bottles, and several thousand cigarette butts. Hadji was threatening to clean it herself, one afternoon, when the janitor appeared at the kitchen door.

"Jahnee*tor!*" cried Uncle Pousant, gesturing wildly at the yard. "That yard is a disgrace to my establishment!"

"You're right — it's disgusting," said the janitor. "I came here to tell you to get after it. It ain't my garbage."

"Are you a statue that you cannot attend to your tasks, you indolent son of a ne'er-do-well father and a slothful mother who should be looking down in shame?" Uncle Pousant had switched to Armenian, but the janitor caught the tone of his remarks.

"Watch your language, buddy," he muttered, and walked away, kicking at a tin can lying in front of the door.

"I'll just go out this once and the man will feel ashamed," said Hadji, easing her way toward the door with a broom.

"*Shamed!*" cried Uncle Pousant. "How can you shame such a donkey? I will not give in. *I* would be shamed!" He took the broom from her hands. "Pigs!" he said, referring to the untidy neighbors. "May they spend all eternity cleaning the ashes from the hell fires."

"We will have mice," warned Hadji, but Uncle Pousant was now deep in thought. In a few moments he slapped his thigh.

"*Eshalah!*" he exclaimed. "I am afraid that I shall have to take this matter to the highest authorities. I shall write to the *Board of Health!* Go, get some paper and write what I will tell you," he said to me.

I ran to the cash register and came back with a pad and pencil.

"Translate this well," said Uncle Pousant. "'My Honored Sirs —'"

I interrupted. "My teacher says you begin, 'Dear Sir.'"

"Your teacher comes from peasant stock," said Uncle Pousant.

"Also, she was not considering that you would be writing to the Board of Health. Write as I tell you. 'My Honored Sirs.'"

I wrote:

My Honored Sirs:

Forgive me for crossing upon your noble paths with my small problem. Your work is of the Highest Order and may your two eyes never grow cold in the performance of your duties.

"In English this sounds silly," I said.

"Write!" said Uncle Pousant. "This is poetry, not prose!"

Fourteen years have I stood upon your glorious soil and breathed your free air. Fourteen years have I labored in the restaurant business — Pousant's Armenian Specialties, 57 Lexington Avenue — in your land of purity and sunshine. Fourteen years have your inspectors found fit to smile upon my spotless kitchens. But now misfortunes are creeping to my very doors. Darkness is coming upon me and a blackness is beginning to engulf my establishment. I implore your aid.

May the lights always shine in your eyes to the great glory of the United States of America. May I remain, always, your obedient servant in the restaurant business.

Pousant Tekmekian, Proprietor
Pousant's Armenian Specialties

I read it to him when I had finished.

"It has not the beauty of the Armenian," said Uncle Pousant, "but what can you do? It's their language."

"You haven't told them about the yard," I said, "or the janitor, or the orange peels, or anything."

"My girl," said Uncle Pousant, "this is the Board of Health. Do you have to say 'one and one is two' to the Board of Health? Go on, send it." And he went back to his artichokes.

I was having dinner in the restaurant a few evenings later when a policeman, a mild-looking soul, entered and asked to speak to the proprietor. All he wanted, he said, was to sell some chances for the

Police Force Relief Association, but Uncle Pousant might have been confronted by the President himself. He bowed several times and, in his excitement, spoke entirely in Armenian. "You honor me, sir," he said.

The policeman looked puzzled and, since there was no one to help out, I volunteered. "You honor him," I told the officer.

"For what?" asked the policeman.

"For what?" I asked Uncle Pousant, in Armenian.

"For *what!* For doing me this honor, as a representative of the government. For coming to my aid. I, who came to this country fourteen years ago . . ."

It began to dawn on me that Uncle Pousant believed the officer had been sent by the Board of Health.

"He wants to sell some chances," I broke in. But Uncle Pousant had raised a cup of coffee and was heatedly toasting the officer, the Board of Health and the United States of America. Then he rushed the bewildered officer to his own seat, shouting all the while for Setrag, who ran to fetch linen and set a new place.

"Tell him thanks, but I've got to be getting along," the officer said to me. I conveyed this message but Uncle Pousant laughed knowingly, taking these pretexts as mere politesse.

"He has not yet seen the yard," he whispered to me in Armenian. "He thinks he is intruding on us tonight and must return on his health business in the morning. We must show hospitality."

"He's selling some lotteries," I said.

"He is?" said Uncle Pousant. "Then I must buy some. It is the same in every country; a man must earn a little something extra if he has a large family to support. Tell him I will buy three books."

"He wants to buy three books of chances," I said to the officer, whose face lit up immediately.

"Three just happens to be what I've got with me," he said. Apparently relieved beyond words at the transaction, he shrugged his shoulders and started to eat the *sarma* which had been set before him. We all watched expectantly.

"Say, this stuff's all right!" he said. Uncle Pousant immediately put the entire platter before him and waved to Setrag to bring on the *shish-kebab*.

An hour later, when Boghos came to fetch me, Uncle Pousant was teaching the officer an old Armenian toast, while the policeman stared incredulously at Hadji's tattoos.

The next morning was Saturday, and I stopped by at the restaurant on my way to Caroline's. Uncle Pousant was in a splendid humor. He nodded his head and smiled when I asked him about the policeman. "My girl," he said, "have you looked at the yard this morning?"

I ran to the kitchen and looked out. The courtyard was perfectly clean. Uncle Pousant surveyed the scene proudly.

"Who swept it?" I asked.

Uncle Pousant became impatient. "Who swept it? Who *could* have swept it? Last night, I show it to the officer. This morning when I look out, it is clean! That is the United States Government for you — action! Ah, how that janitor must be smarting! Perhaps they even threatened to put him in jail!"

A few moments later Hadji came slowly down the stairs. She looked somehow as though she were anticipating our news.

"Have you seen the yard this morning? Look!" said Uncle Pousant.

"I saw, I saw," said Hadji. She added, "From the window, of course." And to me, "Your uncle is a genius."

"Genius!" said Uncle Pousant. "Although most Armenians, I must admit, do not know how to handle these matters."

"Of course not," said Hadji, avoiding my eyes.

The reply from the Board of Health came a week later. I read it over to myself:

Dear Sir:

We are in receipt of your letter of May 2, and suggest that you contact your Light and Power Company representative for help in solving your problem.

Yours very truly,
James B. Simons, Complaint Department

"What is it?" asked Uncle Pousant.

"Oh, just an advertisement," I said.

AFTER the first of June, everyone's spirits began to revive, even Kelesh's. He came home more and more often with a bureau scarf or a nut dish which he shyly presented to my mother, and went so far as to announce, one evening, that he was ready to buy a ticket on the next Irish Sweepstakes.

We were all looking forward to a Fourth-of-July picnic Mr. Sulyan had organized for the Armenian Conservative-Democratic Federation. It was to take place at Indian Point, and we would travel there and back on the Hudson River Day Line. Subconsciously it had become a goal in our minds. After the Fourth of July, Levon Dai would be coming. If Satenig Sulyan was still free, hope could be renewed, while Boghos might still submit to Levon Dai his plan for a lecture tour, and Kelesh might approach him about financing the yogurt factory.

At nine o'clock on the morning of the Fourth, we set out with our food baskets. When we reached the dock, it was swarming with Armenians and also, it appeared, with Local 53A of the Pipefitters Union, who were prancing around with banners, preparing to share the boat with us for their Annual Frolic. As we descended from the taxi we could see Uncle Pousant and Hadji surrounded by more food baskets and boxes of every size and description.

We rushed aboard the boat just as the whistles began to sound. The elders dropped, exhausted, onto folding chairs that were jammed side by side on the deck. The motors churned and the Day Liner belched forth a series of salutes over the hubbub of shouting, while the noisy pipefitters' band struck up a resounding march.

Uncle Pousant was counting food bundles while Mother counted relatives.

"Twelve baskets," said Uncle Pousant. "'Nine boxes, four jars yogurt. Where's the beer?" Nobody was listening.

". . . eleven, twelve, thirteen," Mother said, "or perhaps I should count the children separately. Ah — *there* is Mr. Sulyan."

On the other side of the boat the pipefitters' band struck up "East Side, West Side."

"Pipefitters!" said Mr. Sulyan, jerking his thumb. "I have nothing against pipefitters. For all I know there may even be Armenian pipefitters, but you must admit their music is not calculated to relax the nerves, hah!"

"Oh, I don't know," Mother said. "Nobody seems to be minding it very much."

Hadji was asleep in her deck chair, and Uncle Pousant was keeping time to the music with his umbrella, while surveying the sky. Mothers of daughters more eligible than attractive were walking them along the deck in search of acquaintances with sons. Mrs. Asvazian was persistently guiding her snaggle-toothed daughter, Pergouhie, in our direction and Mother tried vainly to lean across Hadji and catch Dikran's eye, to warn him.

"Hello, hello, hello," Mrs. Asvazian said. "Oh, *hello,* Mr. Sulyan. What a splendid outing." She turned to my mother. "And how your little girl is growing, Maryam! Before long she will be rivaling my Pergouhie." The daughter giggled. "And who is *this!* Not Mr. Dikran! Oh, I am very angry with you, Mr. Dikran. Now that you are among the high and mighty photoengravers you forget your promises to visit us, eh? Here, take Pergouhie for a walk and explain yourself to her; she is young enough to be more charitable than I." Pergouhie giggled again, and Dikran resignedly walked her away.

"Look at that," said Mr. Sulyan sadly after Mrs. Asvazian had gone. "Not half a dozen young men in this entire crowd. These bargain hunters had better go look over the pipefitters market."

Everyone but Mr. Sulyan seemed intent on enjoying himself. The only trouble was, there was so much to do! When we reached Indian Point, it was hard enough getting off the boat with bundles and children intact. Then there was the task of finding enough adjoining tables to keep everyone together. The pipefitters had made a beeline for the gangplank and, having a head start to the picnic tables, had selected them haphazardly, making it necessary for the rest of us to fit in wherever we could, cut off from one another by members of Local 53A.

Our table was groaning with anchovies, *pasterma,* salad, tomatoes, olives, *sarma* and half a dozen loaves of bread; and the group rallied around. Uncle Pousant put on his chef's hat and began passing out the plates.

"Just look at that," he said in a choking voice indicating the pipefitters' table next to ours, "peanut butter, probably. Disgusting, isn't it?"

Our second course was *lahmejoun,* a sort of meat pie. Then came pilaf, *shish-kebab,* cheese, bread, eggs, chicken, yogurt, watermelon, *halva, paklava,* cookies, cake, ice cream. When we were all through there was soda pop, and then came the snacks: sandwiches, hot dogs and hamburgers for those who were still hungry.

All through our meal five or six pipefitters' children with traces of jelly around their mouths stood by and watched us eat. Their eyes traveled from plates to mouths and back, and they didn't seem to get bored, even after the first few courses.

"Eat bread," Hadji kept saying to us. "Do you not know it is a sin to eat meat without bread? It is a sign of gluttony." She herself, like all of her generation, ate a slice of bread for every bite of meat. "Eat eat eat, this is a picnic. Can we afford to waste all this food? Eat eat."

"I can't!" I wailed. "I can't eat another bite." Bloated with overeating, all but the very smallest children groaned and spread themselves on the grass in various attitudes of lethargy. Uncle Pousant returned from a stroll during which he had apparently been inspecting our friends' tables. He flung himself on the grass and covered his face with his straw hat, so that only the handle-bar mustache showed.

"How goes it, Pousant?"

"Quantity, but no quality," said Uncle Pousant from underneath his hat. "Aintabtzis' pilaf is greasy, as usual. The Mareshtzis never fail to overcook their *sarma.* One can see it without tasting. Even their cheese is the color of dirty laundry." And, contented, he slept.

Gradually, as lunch wore off, the party revived. Someone unearthed Kosrob Pesa — what would a picnic be without him? — and began coaxing him to sing. *"Yerk,* Kosrob! Sing!"

"Not today. Stomach too full," laughed Kosrob Pesa, but they dragged him out, pulling at his sleeves, his coattail.

"*Yerk,* come, Kosrob Pesa. *Yerk!*"

"Just one then, which will it be?"

Shouts of: "*Im Chinaru Yaru,*" "*Hayastan,*" "*Sirouhis.*"

A space was cleared. No one was asleep now. Even the pipe-fitters looked on, curiously.

"Let it be '*Sirouhis,*'" said Kosrob Pesa. He turned to the pipe-fitters. "I am going to sing now Armenian folk song," he said gently, almost apologetically. "Perhaps you like to listen, too. It is called 'My Love.' Young man is singing about his sweetheart. It is beautiful song. I hope you enjoy, too." The pipefitters clapped politely, and the others turned to one another and smiled. How *like* Kosrob Pesa, their eyes implied, and they beamed with pride as he sang their songs, one after another, with a tenderness that went beyond the limits of his aging voice.

There were some inevitable tears, and much applause, and shouts of "Encore! Encore!"

"Say, how about 'Danny Boy,' pop?" shouted one of the pipe-fitters. "You know any Irish songs?"

"How about '*Otchi Chornya!*'" shouted another. And so Kosrob Pesa sang "Dark Eyes" and "Danny Boy" and "When You and I Were Young, Maggie" with everyone joining in on the choruses, before he was finally allowed to rest.

"Look there, over there." Suddenly, spontaneously, the folk dancing had begun. One or two extroverts at first, while the others clapped and chanted the jerky rhythm from the sidelines: "*Hoy-na-ra hoy-nar, HOY-nar-naa.*"

"Go on, Pousant, get up and show how it's done. *Barré, barré!*"

Uncle Pousant was in the center, waving his arms, twirling, crouching low, jumping into the air, snapping his fingers. "*HOY-na-ra HOY-nar . . .*"

"Get in there, Dikran. Atta boy!"

"Come, Satenig, *barré, barré.*"

The ladies were joining in. The men made a wide circle and tapped their feet and clapped the rhythm while the women whirled and weaved sensuously. Satenig Sulyan, true to Marta-mama's prediction, had lost her reserve and abandoned herself charmingly. Dikran grabbed her for his partner and a space was

cleared while she wove and pirouetted around him, then he around her.

"*HOY-na-ra hoy-nar* . . ." Why, the pipefitters were joining in, too!

"Come, come, we show you. Come, *barré, barré,* it means dance. Come!"

"Barray, barray!" shouted the pipefitters. "HOT cha cha!"

"Here. This way. You understand? You wiggle the shoulders. So. Yah, yah, so! Good! Ha-ha! You real good *jumbuzji!*"

"Here, have some raki. Good for the feet. *HOY-na-ra HOY-nar* . . ."

"*Barré!*"

The boat whistles were sounding. Mr. Sulyan leaped to his megaphone and began announcing in English, for the benefit of everyone, that the boat was ready to leave. There was a mad scramble for baskets, jugs and children.

There was no more pretense of segregation on the ride home.

The pipefitters' band struck up "Hail, Hail, the Gang's All Here," and sounds like *"HOY-nar"* filtered up from the lower deck where the more energetic continued the dancing. With Hadji, I walked down the deck searching for Dikran.

"Ah, here they are!" Dikran was guiding Satenig in our direction.

"I thought we lost you on the battlefield," muttered Mr. Sulyan, who came bustling toward us. "You must be exhausted, Satenig. Come, we will try to find some seats, if such a thing is possible."

"I'm not a bit tired," said Satenig. "In fact, Mr. Dikran and I are thinking of going downstairs to dance a little more."

"You certainly produced a highly successful picnic, Mr. Sulyan," said Dikran, beaming. "Everyone is saying it is the liveliest they have been to in years."

"It is true," said Hadji. "You should be thankful when we can bring non-Armenians into the culture, even if it is merely to teach them our songs and our dances."

10 Two weeks had passed since the picnic, and every day a letter was expected saying that Levon Dai was on his way. The last one he had written had contained a mixture of hope and foreboding. He was relieved to know, Levon Dai said, that Marta-mama was well. He hoped surely to visit her after the Fourth of July. Meanwhile, the pressures of business, together with some new and very pleasant developments in his social life, kept him busier than ever.

Hadji's psychic diaphragm was working overtime. There were only a limited number of ways to interpret "new and very pleasant developments in social life." She could have put these interpretations to the test by opening the cards, but she frankly admitted that she was afraid of confirming them. She should have been amply forewarned, she said later, but even so it was a shock when the letter finally came.

Hadji was alone in the restaurant when I stopped by; Uncle Pousant had gone shopping. "Any lemonade around?" I asked. Hadji looked up. The letter lay on the table, and she pointed to it.

"So. He is betrothed," she said. "It's all over." She sounded as though someone had died.

"To *whom?* What's her *name?*"

"Agh, how should I know? I cannot pronounce their ridiculous names."

Levon Dai had written, for him, a long letter, detailing the virtues of his young lady, whose name was Shirley Adams. The engagement had not yet been announced, but Levon Dai promised that as soon as it appeared in the newspaper he would send a clipping, and a picture. He ended with assurances of his joyous state of mind. There was no word about his coming East.

"Just how does he think we are going to tell Marta-mama?" Hadji asked herself bitterly.

Everyone but Marta-mama and Dikran, who had no telephone had learned the news by the time the second letter arrived. Kelesl was relegated once again to hopelessness. He had scarcely spoker all week, except to express his sympathy for the unfortunate couple. Azniv had been called on the telephone and, after countless exclamations of disbelief, offered to close the shop and rally to the family's support at this moment of crisis. She was told that there was nothing, alas, that she could do.

"Another step down the sorrowful path of cultural extermination," said Boghos. "I give it ten years." Everyone was consumed with compassion for Satenig Sulyan.

Levon Dai enclosed in his second letter a picture of his fiancée. Mr. Levon Levonian, the accompanying clipping said, who owned the Kismet dry-cleaning plant on Kelmer Avenue and who had recently been installed as Commander of the North Gate Lodge Number 2, Royal Star Masons, was engaged to Miss Shirley Adams, daughter of Mr. and Mrs. Calvert Herkimer Adams, also well known, of Council Bluffs. Miss Adams was noted for her "exquisite collection of miniature glass animals." The picture showed a pixie face, smiling. Shirley was slender and blond.

"Very pretty," said my mother without enthusiasm, "but all her features point upward. It is not a sign of intelligence."

"Did you say animals, of glass?" said Uncle Pousant.

"It says so," Mother said. "Small ones."

"I wash my hands of him!" said Uncle Pousant. He ground his cigar butt violently in the ash tray. "What sort of foolishness is this! Commander!"

"Shiran Edemus!" said Boghos. "What kind of a name is that!"

Mother explained that the name was Shir*lee,* not Shir*an.* "The wedding is to be on October twenty-eighth," she said. "They will come East on their honeymoon."

"They can stay where they are," said Uncle Pousant. "They can go West, North or South. They have no obligation to fulfill here. They need not come East to please *me!*"

"They are not coming East to please you. They are coming on a honeymoon," said Hadji.

"I don't care for what imbecilic reason they are coming. They can go in some other direction," said Uncle Pousant. "I hardly think that is asking too much!"

"He says," Mother continued, "that his fiancée's parents are

coming to New York in two weeks. He asks us to entertain them."
This was too much for Uncle Pousant.

"You write and tell him," he said in a shaking voice, "to send
his future relatives someplace else. They can go to Myemmy! They
don't have to come *here!* What is he trying to do, kill me?"

"We can drink to the occasion," said Mother sadly. "It's the
least we can do." Hadji went to the kitchen, returning with a
decanter of raki and six small glasses.

"To the Commander of Iowa culture and his future bride, she
who collects animals of glass," said Uncle Pousant. He drained his
glass in one gulp and slapped it on the table.

"May they be blessed with long life and myriads of children,"
Hadji said quickly.

"Hee haw," said Uncle Pousant. "She hardly looks as though
that were possible."

"It is a figure of speech," said Hadji. "May they also be blessed
with wealth, and yet not forget the values of the spirit."

"There is only one thing left to do," Mother said. "Someone
must tell Marta-mama." She looked at Hadji.

"I will go, in the morning," said Hadji resignedly.

"This is going to be a very difficult thing to do," Hadji said as
we climbed the stairs the next morning. We could hear Little
Menush singing over the sounds of splashing water.

"Who is here, Marta-mama! You have guests! Oh, we were
waiting! What do you say, Marta-mama! They are here!"

Marta-mama turned from the window. "Yes, we were waiting,"
she said. Her hands were folded in her lap. It seemed strange not
to see them busily crocheting. "Agh, Hadji, why do you bring so
much food? What news have you? None from Levon Dai, I suppose?" Hadji took the letter from her purse. "Thank God!" said
Marta-mama. "I was afraid he might be sick. Is he well?"

"Very well," said Hadji. "He has written a long letter this time.
He says he has been very busy again. He sends a check."

"There is no need to send so much money," said Marta-mama.
"I have spent hardly half of last year's money. Does he not say
anything else?"

"He is getting lonely there," said Hadji, pretending to read. "He thinks perhaps he ought to be looking for a wife."

"About time!" said Marta-mama. "He was thirty-six years old last December. Why shouldn't he come look for a wife? Does he say when he is coming? That Sulyan girl would be a fine choice."

"He says he has met some very nice ladies right where he is. One, especially, he says is a real *dandigin*. He sends you her picture to see how you like her." Hadji handed the picture to Marta-mama, who held it with a shaking hand and tried to study it carefully through her glasses.

"Eh, it's hard to tell from a picture," she said at last. "So, he has made a choice! Good for him! Does she look bright enough?"

"Very intelligent," said Hadji.

"What did you say her name was?"

"Shirlan Edemus."

"Edemus," said Marta-mama, "Edemus. Greek name, isn't it?"

"It must be," said Hadji, looking down.

"Eh," said Marta-mama, "we cannot be old-fashioned. The Greeks are fine people. They cook much the same way we do."

Hadji looked relieved. "We are all very happy for him," she said brightly. "He is going to be married on October twenty-eighth. Then they will come here to see you on their honeymoon."

Marta-mama had her eyes closed and she was rocking gently from side to side. "Agh, so now he has made his choice," she said again. "Now he can settle down and be happy. I am at peace, dear Lord. I have nothing more to wait for now."

11 AT NINE fifteen on the morning of August 25, 1929, a bystander at the information booth at Grand Central Station would surely have turned to look a second time at the nervous group of oddly assorted people who stood shifting from one foot to the other, glancing now and then at the clock. That medium-sized man with the celluloid collar and the grotesque mustaches would be Uncle Pousant. The glazed look in his eyes is because he is wondering how he came to be here, over his own dead body. Kelesh is the hollow-cheeked mournful-looking one who keeps running long disjointed fingers through his wild black hair. Boghos, there, pacing the floor, is not mumbling the multiplication table, he is practicing in English what he expects to say in a few minutes: "Mr. and Mrs. Edemus? We, the proud living relations of our mutual Levon Dai, welcome and greet you."

Mother is looking quite elegant in her new georgette print, although slightly warm and harassed, in contrast to Hadji, who appears sensibly cool in the gray monk's cloth which is so loose that the air circulates all around inside it. In my bright-red silk dress with matching bow in my hair I am peering into everyone's face, wondering if it could be *they*.

"They are late!" Uncle Pousant said at precisely nine thirty. "I see no reason to stand here waiting all day." Hadji reminded him quietly that the train was not due until nine thirty.

"Well, where is it? Where is the train? That is what I am telling you, woman, they are late!" Levon Dai had asked that we stay right beside the information booth where, armed with very adequate descriptions, Mr. and Mrs. Adams could not fail to spot us. All of us except Uncle Pousant were completely ignorant of the Adamses' appearance. Uncle Pousant, though, knew exactly what they would look like. She would be thin, wizened, blond. She would giggle. And *he!* A buffoon. Flat jokes, loud coarse laugh. But cowering at his wife, mind you! "Yes, hooney. Yes, dorlink, yes, my sveet, yes, doll bebek! Just don't bring them in *my* restaurant!" Uncle Pousant finished, shouting.

Hadji turned to my mother. "Well, then," she said, "what do you say we take them to Pilafian's Pilaf House for lunch?"

Uncle Pousant drew a noisy breath. "Boghos, my boy," he said slowly, as though each word were a stab at his heart, "you see that woman there? *She is trying to kill me!* You want my inshuras polsy? So take a knife and stick it in my chest. Go on, go on. Pi-LAF-ian's PI-laf House! *Tu!*"

"Look here," said Hadji, "we are not talking to you. If you would like we will move someplace else and talk there."

"Stay where you are!" shouted Uncle Pousant. "So, you are going to take those two *zavalluhs,* who have come a thousand miles, tired, hungry, but eager, mind you, ignorant but eager to learn, mouths watering. You are going to create a reputation for your *race,* woman! So, you disgrace us. *Tu!*"

"Their *pulaki* isn't bad," Hadji said.

"Not if you like garbage sprinkled with olive oil. Go ahead, disgrace us. What does it matter what they think of us! *Tu!*"

"We'll have to take them *somewhere,*" said my mother.

At twenty minutes to ten, a round, dimpled, white-haired lady, who looked as though she could pose for an ad for Mother Adams' Home Baked Pies, approached Uncle Pousant. Boghos took a step forward, "Mr. and Mrs. Ed — ?"

"You must be Mr. Tek*make*-ian!" Uncle Pousant nodded, his face frozen. "I *knew* it! Didn't I tell you, Calvert? I said, 'That is surely Uncle Pousant, right over there.'"

Mr. Adams introduced himself and pumped Uncle Pousant's hand. He was a short, gray-haired, ruddy-faced man with a generous smile. "A pleasure to meet you, sir!"

"And *this* is Hadji!" cried Mrs. Adams, embracing her first, and then the rest of us. (Uncle Pousant was obviously startled to see her so demonstrative. Americans, he had always maintained, were strictly cold soup.) "Levon described you all *perfectly!* Didn't he, Calvert? Oh, it's wonderful meeting all of you at last!"

"You must be tired," Mother said. "We'll go right home and let you rest up." But the Adamses protested they were brimming with energy and would love to see something of the city.

Once six of us were wedged inside a taxi — Boghos and Kelesh were taking the subway home — my mother plied the newcomers with questions about Levon Dai and Shirley. Levon looked very well, Mrs. Adams said, though he was working too hard. He and Shirley were both radiant right now, naturally. They had known each other for about a year. Met at a Country Club dance, and before you knew it they were a regular twosome. Levon had been quite the hopeless bachelor until then, said Mrs. Adams.

We dropped Uncle Pousant off, still fairly grumpy, at the restaurant with Hadji, and proceeded home, where the guests unpacked. Boghos shrugged when Mother asked what he thought of Levon Dai's parents-to-be. "We'll see yet," he said.

Several hours later, on top of an open-topped double-decker bus, Boghos, quite out of breath, was remarking to me with admiration on the Adamses' inexhaustible energy. We had taken them for a brisk tour of the Woolworth Building, Wall Street, Chinatown, Greenwich Village and the Flatiron Building, mostly on foot and in the space of three hours. We were now on our way to meet Hadji and my mother at Marta-mama's house, and were going from there to Uncle Pousant's restaurant for supper.

I had never seen Boghos look so contented, for the Adamses had captivated him by unwittingly bestowing the finest gift they could have conjured, that of their own rapt attention. It had begun at luncheon. Boghos had been displaying his customary boredom, since the conversation did not concern his interests, until Mr. Adams chanced to remark that he was anxious to learn about Armenians. "Just where *is* Armenia?" he had asked.

"I thought," Boghos said with a touch of sarcasm, "Levon Dai told all about Armenia. He gives lectures, does he not?"

Mrs. Adams laughed. "He did something like that when he first came out. Nobody knew just what he was talking about, I understand, but they took quite a shine to him. It's one of his favorite jokes. But please, won't *you* tell us about Armenia, Cousin Boghos?" Both she and Mr. Adams turned eagerly to Boghos, whose expression bespoke gratitude although, like a hungry man presented unexpectedly with a menu, he didn't seem to know quite where to begin.

"All right then," he said finally, laying aside his fork and glaring at my mother, who was busily urging helpings on the guests. "I shall summarize quickly. Before the days of Alexander the Great Armenia was a kingdom north of Babylonia and west of Persia, where now you find parts of Russia, Turkey and Iran."

"More salad, Mr. Adams?" Mother asked.

"Please," Boghos said in Armenian, "try not to interrupt. I am teaching them something! Now, it is said we were descended from the ancient Urartu people who lived thirteen hundred years before Christ, near Mount Ararat. You did not know this, hah?"

"Had no idea," said Mrs. Adams. "How fascinating!"

Exhilarated by their polite concentration, Boghos plunged on. "Did you know, Mrs. Edemus, that our nation was converted to Christianity in the year 303? At least eight years before the conversion of Constantine. . . . Did you know, Mr. Edemus, that our written language was one of earliest, how you say it — phonetic — writings? . . . Did you know . . ."

His recital became inspired. With gestures, he described the heroic stand of Vartan the Bold against the Persian armies. He ran to his bedroom and brought forth his dusty paintings, illustrating the fields of Vartan, Mount Ararat, the Sea of Marmara, the Bosporus, bathed in all stages of solar light. Then the coffee was brought in, necessitating a pause.

"Why, Cousin Boghos," said Mrs. Adams, "you really should come out to Council Bluffs and speak to the Auxiliary!"

"You think — they would be interested?" Boghos turned, flushed, from one to the other.

"Of *course* they would! It's all terribly interesting. I must speak to Shirley. She's been very active in the Auxiliary."

"That would be nice," Mother said. "Some cream, Mrs. Adams?"

Nice! My feet danced with excitement under the table.

So it was that after lunch Boghos volunteered with genuine enthusiasm to conduct the Adamses on a flying tour of downtown New York. They were unusual people, he told Mother as we were leaving. That devil Levon Dai! Even when falling into the clutches of foreigners, he was incredibly blessed by the kindest fate.

There was much commotion when we arrived at Marta-mama's. Little Menush must have spent the entire week washing, waxing, polishing. She was leaning over the stairwell, shaking with excitement. She ran, screaming, into the apartment, fluffing pillows in agitation. Hadji and my mother had already arrived. They were smiling slyly, as though they knew something we didn't.

"But *look!*" I cried. "Look at Marta-mama!" Little Menush was doubled over with laughter.

"Surprise, surprise, I *knew* you would be surprised! You can't believe it? Ha — *ha,* I told you, Marta-mama!"

"Vy!" Even Boghos was amazed. Marta-mama was on her feet, smiling radiantly and walking toward us, holding out her hands in welcome to the guests. Only a week before, she would have had to be carried. And her dress! I had yearned since I was very small to see her in something bright. "For your wedding," she had once said, laughingly, "I will wear a bright-red dress." And here she was, not in red, but in orchid. With violets at the neck.

"You like her dress? I picked it out yesterday. Isn't she beautiful? And young? Forty-five, Marta-mama, I *told* you!" Little Menush danced with glee. The guests could hardly understand the excitement, but they were enchanted with Marta-mama. She patted Mr. Adams' cheeks, and stroked Mrs. Adams' hair and led them to the sofa, motioning for them to sit down.

"Ninety-seven?" said Mrs. Adams. "I just can't believe it. *You are a very wonderful lady!*" she said, shouting slightly, and articulating each word. *"Levon Dai sent you a kiss. Here!"*

"Yah? Yah?" Marta-mama grinned. She had understood. "Agh, how is he? And the bride?"

Mrs. Adams took out a bundle of snapshots from her handbag. *"Pictures. See? Shirley."*

"Oh! Yah!" Marta-mama took them eagerly and squinted carefully over each one. "Tell them," she said, "that I love their daughter like my own. She is very beautiful. She must be kind and warmhearted as well, like her parents." She sighed. "If only," she said, "I could at least speak Greek, to tell them myself." No one, fortunately, translated her wish.

UNCLE POUSANT was civil enough during the evening at the restaurant. He was host, after all, but he arranged his face so that those of us who knew him would be aware of his displeasure. One could see, however, that this pained endurance was becoming increasingly difficult to maintain. He could scarcely avoid grunting his appreciation when Mrs. Adams said, over the *media,* "Why, this is the most *exquisite* thing I ever tasted. Shirley will just have to learn to cook some of these things." And when Mother translated Mr. Adams' remark — "Man, you ought to write a cookbook. I'm willing to bet you'd make a fortune!" — Uncle Pousant, forgetting himself for a moment, smiled outright.

"Setrag!" he shouted. "Bring the raki!"

12 How STRANGE and unfamiliar it was in those weeks before Levon Dai's wedding to wake up to smiles and sunny dispositions; especially to the unfamiliar sound of Boghos singing in the bathroom. Uncle Pousant seemed able to tolerate most anything these days — even his customers. "Welcome, welcome!" he shouted now when *odars* — non-Armenians — came into the restaurant.

It was oddly disquieting, after being inured to pessimism, to have everything going so smoothly. Dikran was about to take his oath of citizenship, and in a few weeks he would become a full-fledged apprentice in the photoengraving trade — no longer a mere plate washer. His future was assured.

Even Kelesh's luck was turning. After six years of waiting, his permanent visa had been granted, and he was planning to go to work. He accepted congratulations with the brightest smile I had ever seen him yield, and instead of the crossword puzzle or the horse-racing page, he turned now directly to the want ads. There were hundreds of jobs to be had, but there would be no more trusting to luck: he was going to study the employment problem scientifically, Kelesh declared, without rushing into the first thing, willy-nilly. The yogurt factory was still his dream: it was merely the method of achieving it that had been revolutionized.

And then, early one morning, Little Menush ran in, incoherent with hysteria. Father threw his suit over his pajamas, grabbed up his small black bag and rushed out the door. He returned dragging his feet and gravely confirmed that Marta-mama was dead. She had died quietly, he said, in her sleep.

We sat around the table that evening, dry-eyed, disbelieving. She had almost died so many times before that the fact of her death could hold no reality for the moment. The truth was that she had never been so alive as in these past few weeks, wearing her orchid dress, her fingers busily crocheting the border for the wedding quilt.

No one could bring himself, quite yet, to talk about her. Boghos blew his nose and recalled Marta-mama's husband. "How old was he when he died?"

"Forty-six," someone said.

For fifty-one years, then, Marta-mama had postponed joining him for one reason after another. The thought hung in the air above our heads and a knot rose in my throat.

Hadji was crossing herself. "May God bring peace to the living," she was saying.

"Amen," the others said.

13 MARTA-MAMA would have been pleased at her funeral. The Archbishop himself conducted the service, lending with his dignity and rank a real grandness to the occasion. Parseghian, the undertaker, stinted nothing in making the funeral arrangements; he even insisted on a brassbound coffin for the price of the plain one Hadji and my mother had chosen.

With his wedding so imminent, no one questioned the fact that Levon Dai did not come home. Even Uncle Pousant understood, and refrained from criticism. And so, as Marta-mama was befittingly laid to rest, Levon Dai returned to grace. Preparations for a grand celebration in New York to coincide with the festivities in Council Bluffs, which had been interrupted by Marta-mama's death, were taken up again although in a more cautious spirit.

On Monday morning, just a week before the wedding, Boghos was seen to the train with many blessings and "God willings." He had been beside himself with excitement when Levon Dai wrote asking him to be his best man and Shirley wrote (enclosing round-trip fare) extending an invitation to speak to the Ladies Auxiliary of the First Presbyterian Church. He wore a crisp brown suit and carried a shiny black Gladstone bag; new, all new, from the brown fedora to his tan-and-brown sports shoes. Hadji crossed herself ceaselessly until the train pulled out of sight.

On the day of the wedding the kitchens both at home and at the restaurant were once again in full operation, bursting over with the sounds of chopping, sizzling, bubbling, and Uncle Pousant's verbal whiplash over Setrag's groans of exertion. Everyone was coming — Azniv and Dikran, the Archbishop and Little Menush, the Sulyans and Parseghians, Harutune Sohokian the poet, the sculptor Khutumian and Kosrob Pesa of the glorious tenor. Not one *zavalluh* would be left out on this occasion.

"I need another pound of chopped onions," said Uncle Pousant. "Can't you chop any faster, man? Here, you children help him." He handed Caroline and me two paring knives and we pulled up chairs to the long wooden table. Caroline had filled out considerably since the spring, and Uncle Pousant liked to believe it was his feeding of her between meals. He took a proprietary interest in her weight and she, in turn, had grown quite fond of him and, unlike Setrag, no longer jumped when he shouted at us. Uncle Pousant had even begun teaching Caroline Armenian. "I think that girl has gained another few pounds," he said kindly. "How you say onion, girl?"

"Sogh," said Caroline.

"A-tta girl!" Uncle Pousant returned to the stove, his mustache twitching with pleasure. Every now and then he shouted over his shoulder, "How you say chair, girl? How you say eggplant, watermelon, overcoat? — *A*-tta girl!"

"What are you talking about?" said Hadji. She had just come in, loaded down with shopping bags, flushed and panting from her walk to the markets. "Ouf, I am dying from my feet. My, my, my, I have news! My! My! My!"

"Can't you ever tell something without all these preliminaries?" Uncle Pousant exclaimed. "So, you have news. So, give your news! Do you ever see the newspapers starting with 'my, my, my'?"

"Just a minute until I catch my breath," said Hadji. She sank into a chair. "Well, I was passing the trolley-car stop," she said slowly, with relish. "I had these three big bundles and they were slipping around. Whew! I was glad to get them home intact. And who should I see getting off the trolley car but Azniv!"

"Thank you," said Uncle Pousant. "That is news? Women!" He turned his back.

"So — " Hadji continued, looking out of the corner of her eye at Uncle Pousant, who was now making a loud racket over his pots and pans " — she gave me the news. *Dikran is getting engaged!* And will you guess to whom?"

Uncle Pousant had stopped stirring. *"Dikran? Vy,* Dikran, *vy!* Who is the unfortunate woman?"

"Satenig Sulyan!" said Hadji.

"What do you say!"

"My! My! My! What a celebration we shall have tonight!"

"Good for Dikran!" shouted Uncle Pousant. "He has his eyes fixed rightly in his head, and his wits, too. *Vy,* Dikran, *vy!"*

"Azniv heard it from those Karpajians in Newark," said Hadji. "Can you imagine that? My, my, my!" She slapped her thigh. "Leave it to that devil, Dikran! Courting her behind all our backs! I'll never forgive him. Never."

"Come!" Uncle Pousant clapped his hands together. "Business first now. We can celebrate tonight. Do you realize it is five o'clock? They will be starting to come in another two hours."

"Five o'clock," mused Hadji, "that means in Council Bluffs they are about to begin the wedding any minute now." She crossed herself. "God willing."

THE WEDDING party was to be in the restaurant. Shortly after six o'clock, Kelesh, Azniv, Mother, Father and I entered to find Hadji and Uncle Pousant standing just inside the doorway, waiting to greet the guests. Uncle Pousant's mustaches were ferociously twirled and waxed; his deep celluloid collar pinioned his neck, giving him an air of inflexible formality. Hadji, too, looked appropriately uncomfortable. In honor of the occasion she had discarded her monk's-cloth garb for a new creation of her own design:

navy-blue silk decorated with immense red cabbage roses. On the door of the restaurant hung a sign: RESTAURANT CLOSED, it said. PRIVATE PARTY IN HONOR OF MR. AND MRS. LEVON LEVONIAN OF COUNCIL BLUFFS, IOWA. JUST MARRIED. Silver papier-mâché wedding bells were fastened to each of the four corners of the sign. Inside, crepe paper and balloons hung in multicolored profusion from the ceiling. The tables were arranged in a great horseshoe, with a tremendous five-tiered wedding cake set squarely in the center.

Little Menush was the first guest to arrive, on the stroke of seven, escorted by her famous brother, the garbage man, who put everyone to shame with his almost-new tuxedo and high silk hat. It was surely the biggest night of her life. "Oh, if only Marta-mama could see this!" she kept saying. "God bless her good soul. Ohhhh, this is so beautiful!"

"Oho, look who has come!" Hadji cried. Satenig and Dikran were welcomed and embraced while Mr. Sulyan stood by with a self-satisfied grin.

"Dikran! You never said a word!" Dikran was still too dazed to say much, preferring to fasten his eyes on Satenig. Was she not beautiful? Undeniably, everyone agreed. And how radiant she was, with not a trace of shyness left. She took Uncle Pousant's hands and waltzed him around the floor. "Hey giddy hey!" cried Uncle Pousant. "I have found myself a bride tonight!"

The room was almost filled when a messenger boy delivered a telegram from Boghos, which my father read aloud: "THE MARRIAGE IS A SUCCESS. WE IN COUNCIL BLUFFS SEND RECIPROCAL FELICITATIONS. PEOPLE HERE FRIENDLY LIKE ARMENIANS. REMAINING TWO MORE WEEKS."

Everyone broke into cheers, and then the Archbishop pronounced a blessing on the marriage, and Uncle Pousant pulled the shades and locked the door while Setrag and two helpers who had been recruited for the evening began serving the wine.

"To the bride and groom," said Hadji, raising her glass. "Long life, happiness, and a dozen dark-eyed children."

Everyone drank: to Levon Dai and Shirley, to Dikran and Satenig, to Boghos, to the Edemuses, to all the citizens of Council Bluffs, to the United States of America and the Board of Health.

"A toast," said Uncle Pousant, "to the memory of Marta-mama."
Everyone drank to her memory and her husband's. To the late
Mrs. Sulyan who baked *paklava* unexcelled, and Father Nishan
who sang the Mass as it could never be sung again, and Agpar the
Pastry Man, and Katchig the Blind, and Bulb-nosed Toros who
told funny jokes. The waiters came in bearing aloft huge platters
of snowy pilaf to inaugurate the feast, and still the toasts went on.

"Bravo to Kelesh, future citizen of the U.S.A.!"

"Bravo, Effendi, good luck!"

And a toast to Kosrob Pesa; he would actually be giving a con-
cert in a few weeks. *"Yerk,* Kosrob, *yerk!"* someone shouted.

"Hcy giddy hey!" Uncle Pousant was whirling Satenig around
in the center of the horseshoe.

"Come, Kelesh, *barré, barré!"*

In the midst of these familiar faces and surroundings, suddenly
it came to me that *something* was different. . . .

And then I knew. There were no *zavalluhs* — no lonely ones —
in the room this night.

14 I AM writing this in Iowa. Levon Dai has a spacious
home, shaded with elm trees, and he has graciously
turned the library over to me. There is a loving cup on the mantel-
piece presented to him by the Chamber of Commerce when he
was elected Man of the Year. Next to it is a trophy his son,
Frederick Torcom, won at Yale for wrestling. And next to that are
Marta-mama's husband's fez, and his water pipe. They go, somehow, with the nice thick Oriental rug on the floor.

In the walled garden back of the house Levon Dai has planted
a grape arbor, covering it with sheeting in winter: it produces
some fine grape leaves. He still cooks exquisite *sarma*. He has made
a batch today, in honor of my finishing the book. Shirley is quite
an expert herself at making pilaf and *shish-kebab*. Tonight, we
will have a thoroughly Armenian dinner and drink to Uncle
Pousant's memory, may God illumine his soul. In fact, we will
drink to them all.

Boghos is a guard now, at the Freer Gallery of Oriental Art in

Washington, D.C. Perhaps you have seen him there, giving little lectures, especially on the ancient Armenian Bibles. He says that Americans are the most receptive, intelligent people he has ever known anywhere in the world.

Hadji closed the restaurant when Uncle Pousant died, and she lives with my parents now, in the old brownstone. It is the only one left on that block, and, if you should happen to pass, please stop in and tell her you know her — she'll understand — and I'll wager there will be some *paklava* and Turkish coffee ready.

Kelesh is there, too. He finally got a job in a factory making artificial flowers, but the factory folded in the Depression. So Kelesh worked in Uncle Pousant's restaurant until Uncle Pousant died and Hadji closed it. Then Kelesh went through a long, tormented period when he felt responsible for every calamity that happened to anyone. You can imagine how he felt when yogurt began coming out on the market!

Right now he is in good spirits because he has had a wonderful idea for frozen *shish-kebab*. He got some really good lamb from Azniv — she still has the butcher shop (Prospect Street, Newark, just left of the drugstore) — and he had Robert, who is Dikran and Satenig's oldest son and a doctor, take a sample of the prepared *shish-kebab* to his hospital and quick-freeze it to see how it would taste after several months. It was delicious! The only difficulty is the financing. Levon Dai is willing to put what he can into it, but it would apparently take a great deal more. Kelesh fears that meantime one of the big companies will steal the idea. So please keep it to yourself because someone might readily pounce on it and, aside from what it would do to Kelesh, it could easily taste terrible if it is not made properly, like so many other things.

You would like Levon Dai. He is as American as can be, except for his nose, and his eyes, and his speech, and his sentimentality, and his superstitions. When I showed him my book, he said, "*Vy vy vy,* you cannot possibly be thinking of ending it on the thirteenth chapter! It is bad luck and it would be *destined* to failure. Please! Listen to me and add another chapter." And so I have.

Marjorie Housepian

MARJORIE HOUSEPIAN was born in that section of New York City she describes in *A Houseful of Love*. Her father, a doctor, was an Armenian who emigrated from Syria, while her mother's family came from Turkey. With the exception of one year spent in school in France when she was ten, and two years at Smith College, she was educated in New York City, graduating from Barnard in 1944.

During her last year of college she was married to a Navy lieutenant and spent the next several years following him from coast to coast. A son, Stephen, was born just after the war ended.

Since then she has lived in Virginia, Maine and southern France and has traveled over most of Europe and the Near East including, most recently, Moscow and Soviet Armenia. Travel is her hobby, she admits, for it has given her a splendid opportunity to know and like a most incongruous variety of people. She lives in New York and is a member of the public-relations staff of Barnard College.

Illustrations by James Alexander

THE THREE FACES OF EVE

A condensation of the book by

CORBETT H. THIGPEN, M.D., and
HERVEY M. CLECKLEY, M.D.

ONLY one slight figure sat in the doctors' office, only one tongue spoke, only one pair of blue eyes flashed or wept. But the two eminent psychiatrists who treated Eve White soon realized that in this timid, modest housewife they were dealing with *three* distinct personalities, each struggling to control her life.

This amazing true story of a multiple personality has the excitement of a suspense novel, the fascinating intimacy of a case history. If the patient's sanity was to be preserved, two of the three conflicting personalities must be destroyed. *But which two?* The outcome is totally unexpected and deeply moving.

"The authors, who are hardheaded clinical observers, present their astonishing experience as would a highly skilled novelist. . . ."
— Dr. J. McV. Hunt, past President of the American Psychological Association

"The story of Eve White's triple personality reads quite as absorbingly as Stevenson's *Dr. Jekyll and Mr. Hyde.*"
— Ashley Montague in *The Saturday Review*

CHAPTER 1

HE DID not at first appear to be an unusual or a particularly interesting patient. This neat, colorless young woman was, she said quietly, twenty-five years of age. In a level, slightly monotonous voice she described the severe headaches from which she had suffered now for several months. Unlike some patients to whom the elastic term *neurotic* is applied, she did not say that the pain was "unbearable," or "as if an axe were splitting my skull." She described the attacks without dramatic emphasis.

We shall call the patient Mrs. Eve White, though that was not her real name. There was no suggestion of anything that the layman might think of as *nervousness*, as she sat in our office, her feet close together, speaking clearly but in soft, low tones. Her hands lay still on the arms of the chair; her head and shoulders drooped just a little. Her dark hair and pale-blue eyes were distinctly pretty, though she seemed too retiring and inert to be very clearly aware of her potential attractiveness.

Her local physician had sent her from her home in a neighboring town for psychiatric consultation. Ordinary physical examinations, X ray and laboratory studies had disclosed no cause of the headaches.

Without evasion or fanaticism, but with real perplexity, she discussed her situation. Six years ago she had married a young man who was a faithful Catholic. As a serious Baptist, she had had misgivings about the commitment she had made before marriage, promising that her children would be brought up as Catholics. Now that her daughter, Bonnie, was three years old, she could not bring herself to turn the child over to an institution that seemed ever more alien to her. She had stubbornly refused to have Bonnie baptized in the Catholic Church. As time passed she apparently had tended to identify all her husband's faults and all sources of contention between them with his church.

Mrs. White did not, however, hold her husband alone responsible for the difficulties of their marriage. In fact, she took pains to defend him, and only reluctantly gave some details of the quarreling that had become habitual. Her husband, she said, had often seemed irritable or sarcastic toward her during the last few months. Sometimes she could not tell what had offended him. She finally admitted that on one occasion, quite unlike himself, he had struck her. Though it was apparently only a light slap, administered perhaps inadvertently in pulling his arm away from her detaining hand, she had felt deeply hurt. He had gone out then, and later that same night, while alone with little Bonnie, the patient had suffered a distressing miscarriage. Since then, she said, the marital relations which had been difficult for a long time had grown steadily worse. She had felt a coldness toward her husband, a deep alteration of her feelings which she could not influence. It was shortly after this experience that the headaches had begun.

It was almost impossible to imagine this gentle, unvengeful little woman participating aggressively in a personal argument. Something about her suggested the admirable qualities implied in the Christian principle of turning the other cheek. Surely it must be an unusual man who would lose his temper with her. What were the grounds for his anger?

"I am not quite sure what it is I do that aggravates him so." She hesitated, then sadly admitted, "I've never seemed to make him happy."

He had apparently lost most of the sexual interest he had once felt for her. Never, she confessed with regret, had she been able to reach any sort of exciting fulfillment in their marriage relations. Lately she had found physical contact with her husband distasteful.

The joy this couple must have felt in each other when they

planned to marry had, so far as one could tell, disappeared entirely. Little closeness or sharing of interests had grown between them during their marriage. It was plain that Mrs. White saw no hope of happiness with her husband. It was equally plain that she did not want a divorce. Her failure to have her little girl baptized a Catholic seemed to augment her determination not to break another vow. Fear of what divorce might do to her child also convinced her that she must continue the marriage. Behind Mrs. White's restrained expression and her almost stiltedly decorous posture, indications of deeply felt grief and bewilderment and an almost desperate love for little Bonnie became ever more apparent.

Mrs. White spoke of blackouts which followed her severe headaches. At times she referred to these spells as though she simply fainted; at other times the examining doctor felt she might be describing more complicated periods of amnesia, or loss of memory. Neurologic examination revealed no indication of organic disease that might cause periods of unconsciousness. There was no history of convulsive disorder, such as epilepsy.

So this is how the patient, Eve White, appeared in her first psychiatric interview. Her personal problems were complicated and serious, but her clinical symptoms were not unusual. Nothing about her led the doctor to suspect that from this colorless little person would emerge manifestations so challenging that eventually her case would be presented at a meeting of the American Psychiatric Association as something almost unique.

OVER a period of several weeks, Mrs. White returned for a few more interviews, sometimes accompanied by her husband. Then, and throughout our treatment of her, most of Eve White's interviews were with Dr. Thigpen, but often in consultation with Dr. Cleckley. Henceforth the terms "doctor" and "therapist" can be taken to refer to either of us — Thigpen or Cleckley.

During this early period Eve White made gratifying improvement. She still had occasional headaches but they were less severe. She no longer reported blackout spells. The doctor had tried to help the Whites resolve their difficulties, and relations between them were apparently much better, though there seemed little hope the marriage would ever be really happy. Her husband, Ralph White, confirmed in general the history as given by the patient. He admitted that at times she showed peculiar changes of mood, but he regarded her, nevertheless, as a patient, industrious wife and a devoted mother.

"It's hard to believe, Doctor, that such a sweet, steady woman could ever aggravate anybody. Maybe that is why I lose my temper once in a while. You get accustomed to what she's like and you don't know what to make of . . . of anything different. It must be a sort of little erratic streak that comes out just every now and then." He spoke also of occasional forgetfulness that had caused misunderstandings between them.

In retrospect it seems remarkable how little emphasis Ralph White put on these points, how little detail he gave.

Several weeks passed without news from Mrs. White. Then a discouraging letter from the husband was received. The severe headaches had returned. Seated in the office again a few days later, Eve White seemed very tense and dejected and in considerable pain. She was concerned with a dream which had recurred several times.

"I am in a tremendous room," she said. "Toward the center of this room is a pool of stagnant green water. On the edge of the pool stand my husband and my uncle. I am in the water with Bonnie. We both seem to be drowning, but I must not take her out where she will be near the others. Despite all I can do, I put her directly into my husband's hands. Then my uncle, whom I love dearly, tries to push my head under the slimy water."

As she seemed unable to relate this dream to the events of her life, the doctor suggested that she undergo hypnosis. She agreed, and in this state was asked to repeat the dream and told that on awakening she was to endeavor to determine what it might reflect of her actual situation.

Awake, she stated without hesitation that the room seemed to represent her existence, the stagnant pool her husband's church. In the dream, as in reality, she was trying to escape its influence, especially for her child. Her husband stood aside, refusing to help

alexander

her in this struggle. The uncle who stood with him, unlike her parents and other relatives, had encouraged her to fulfill her promise and have her daughter raised as a Catholic.

This interpretation revealed nothing she did not already consciously know. Discussing it, however, seemed to help her bring out some previously restrained emotion connected with these problems. The headache, to her surprise, suddenly ceased. She left the office more nearly relaxed and cheerful than the doctor had yet seen her.

For almost a year after this the patient got along fairly well. Little was heard from her until her husband called to say it was urgent that she return for help. A quarrel had caused deep disturbances in the marriage. While visiting her cousin Flo, who lived fifty miles away in Columbia, Eve had apparently enjoyed herself so much that she had stayed longer than planned, failing, however, to inform her husband that she would do so. When she did not return on the expected date, he telephoned her. In curt tones she told him she would come home when she was good and ready. Disturbed, he at once drove to Flo's house, where Eve received him antagonistically, shouting that she was not going home. After a truly violent scene both husband and wife had announced the end of their relationship. Ralph White had then gone home and waited for his wife to return for her personal possessions.

When she came he was astonished at her smile, at her gentle voice. She kissed him lightly on the cheek, then casually began her routine household tasks as if unaware of any problem. Though puzzled, he was relieved by her apparent reversal of feelings, and decided not to risk precipitating another crisis by referring to their quarrel. For several days relations between them seemed at their best. Then one evening he found Eve packing her suitcase. She was calm and matter-of-fact. Cautiously he asked why she was doing so.

"Why, I'm getting ready to go and visit Flo," she told him. She seemed at a loss, wondering why he should ask her this. Before the recent trip, they had often discussed Eve's spending several days with her cousin Flo. Now Eve could not understand what she took to be her husband's unfamiliarity with the well-known project.

Nor could Ralph convince her that she had already paid the visit.

When she came to the office she told the doctor that she had not the slightest recollection of the period Ralph said she had spent with Flo and her husband, Jack. This, the doctor decided, was an impressive amnesia. Hypnosis was easily induced and then Eve found it possible to recall the visit to her cousin in considerable detail.

What she and the congenial cousin had done — shopping expeditions, going to the movies, playing canasta — became quite clear, and was retained after she was awakened from hypnosis. Her host and hostess reported later that Eve had been in wonderful spirits during the visit, showing at times a gaiety and liveliness they had not seen in her for years. She had so many plans and engagements that she was seldom at the house.

About the quarrel with her husband, though she said that she remembered it, Eve's remarks seemed to the doctor not quite satisfactory. Flo and her husband later confirmed Ralph's account of his wife's participating in the fray with all the fury of a tigress. Though Eve denied nothing of this, something suggested that her memory acknowledged the experience as lacking in some dimension of reality. Sensing that Eve became more and more tense as the quarrel was discussed, the doctor refrained from pursuing the subject.

Later she expressed alarm at having suffered such a lapse of memory. However, she seemed to gain some reassurance in the explanation that unacceptable events are sometimes unconsciously repressed from memory, and left the office in good spirits. Her period of amnesia, as far as could be determined, was now clear. She seemed free of any intention or impulse to withdraw from her marriage.

A number of days passed. Then came the following letter:

Tues —

Dear Doctor,

Remembering my visit to —— brought me a great deal of relief, to begin with.

Just being able to recall the trip seemed enough, but now that

I've had time to think about it and all that occurred, it's more painful than I ever thought possible.

How can I be sure that I remember all that happened, even now? How can I know that it won't happen again? I wonder if I'll ever be sure of anything again.

I can't even recall ———'s color schemes and I know that would probably be the first thing I'd notice.

My head hurts right on top. It has ever since the day I was down there to see you. I think it must be my eyes — I see little red and green specks — and I'm covered with some kind of rash.

baby please be quite dear lord don't let me lose patience
with her she's too sweet and innocent and my self-control

Though unsigned, most of the message had plainly been written by Eve White. Had some child scribbled those additional words on the uncompleted page and, perhaps as a whim, mailed it in an already addressed envelope? Could Eve White herself have decided to disguise her characteristic handwriting and add this inconsequential note? And if so, why?

Within a week her husband called requesting another appointment for her without delay. He seemed at his wits' end. Eve, he said, had gone downtown without consulting him and had bought a great array of expensive clothes. Moreover, nothing now seemed to relieve her headaches, and there had been more blackouts.

Sitting in the office again, Eve quietly but positively denied having sent the letter. She said she clearly remembered beginning a letter to the doctor, but she had not finished it. For the new clothes which had so angered her husband she had no explanation.

"I never saw them, Doctor," she said, her light-blue eyes puzzled and intent. "I never saw them until Ralph took me to the closet and showed them to me."

Their income, though sufficient for ordinary expenses, would not pay for such extravagance. Eve made most of her own clothing. When she had looked in the closet and seen half a dozen luxurious evening gowns, several pairs of I. Miller shoes, the new coat, the lingerie, she had stepped back aghast, her equanimity profoundly shaken.

Tues.

Dear Doctor,

Remembering my visit
brought me a great
_____ to begin with.
_____ able to recall
_____ but _____ to

on top. It has ever since
the day I was down there
to see you. I think it must
be my eyes. I see little red
& green specks. and I'm covered
with some kind of rash.

baby please be quite dear lord
don't let me lose patience with her
she's too sweet and innocent and
my self-control

Telling about it now, her voice lost its monotonous calm. For the first time her doctor saw Eve's eyes grow moist. As if in apology, she mentioned her headache, saying it was now quite severe. Then she looked silently at the man from whom she sought help as if there were something she *must* say, though strong forces seemed to work against it. The doctor involuntarily took a deeper breath.

"Doctor . . ." the young woman said. She lowered her head a little as if to avoid something she dare not face directly. Her unfailing composure was at last broken. Her small hands, lying as usual on the arms of her chair, knotted slowly into tight fists.

"If you hear voices . . . what does it mean . . . ? If you really hear it . . . with no one there . . . ?" She sobbed briefly. "I know what it means." Her posture tightened. "Madness!" she gasped. "The State Hospital . . . Bonnie . . ." Her voice was scarcely audible. "My little Bonnie . . ."

Auditory hallucinations are indeed alarming. Eve White was right in concluding that they plainly indicate psychosis, serious mental disorder.

"For several months," she finally admitted, "I've heard the voice occasionally." Now she could not escape it. It was always a woman's voice and somehow familiar. It spoke jauntily, often using vulgar phrases.

The doctor was struck by several points. Psychotic patients who experience auditory hallucinations are sometimes terrified at what the voices say, but seldom find the experience of hearing them alarming in itself. They almost never regard the hallucinations as an indication of mental disorder.

Eve White's reactions were those of a normal person to what, theoretically, could happen only to a person with a grave psychosis.

The physician was able to assure her that he did not consider her psychotic. But Eve White was clearly frightened and baffled. Speaking softly again, in her characteristic steady voice, she returned to the episode of the clothes. Clerks at the stores where she tried to return them had insisted it *was* she who had bought them. She spoke again of the voice she had heard. She hesitated. There was perhaps a minute or more of silence.

The brooding look in Eve's eyes became a dazed stare. Suddenly her posture began to change. Her body slowly stiffened until she sat rigidly erect. The lines of her face seemed to shift in a barely visible, slow, rippling transformation. Closing her eyes, she winced as she pressed her hands to her temples, twisted them as if to combat sudden pain. A slight shudder passed over her entire body.

Then the hands lightly dropped. The blue eyes popped open. There was a quick reckless smile. In a bright unfamiliar voice the patient said, "Hi, there, Doc!"

With a soft intimate syllable of laughter, she crossed her legs, carelessly swirling her skirt, and settled more deeply into the cushions of the chair. The constrained posture of Eve White had melted into buoyant repose. One foot began a small, rhythmic, rocking motion.

Still busy with his own unassimilated surprise, the doctor heard himself say, "How do you feel now?"

"Why just fine — never better! How you doing yourself, Doc?"

Eve looked straight into his eyes. Her eyelids flicked and opened wide again. She tossed her head lightly, flirtatiously. Her face was fresh and marvelously free from its habitual signs of underlying stress. She seemed barely able to restrain laughter.

"She's been having a real rough time," this girl said carelessly. "I feel right sorry for her sometimes. She's such a dope though. ... What she puts up with from that sorry Ralph White — and all her mooning over the little brat!"

She leaned forward. "Would you give me a cigarette, please, Doc?"

He handed her a cigarette and then, lighting it, said, "Who is 'she'?"

"Why, Eve White, of course. Your saintly little patient."

"But aren't you Eve White?" he asked.

"That's for laughs," she exclaimed, a ripple of mirth in her tone. "Why, you ought to know better than that, Doc!" An impish smile flickered over her childlike face as she said softly: "I know you *real* well, Doc . . . and I kind of like you. I bet you're a good dancer, too."

Disclaiming any special talents for the dance, the doctor said,

"Can you tell me anything more about those dresses that upset your husband so much?"

"I ain't got no husband," she replied promptly and emphatically. "Let's get that straight right now." She grinned broadly.

"Well, who *are* you?" he asked incredulously.

"Why, I'm Eve Black," she said (giving Mrs. White's maiden name). "I'm me and she's herself. I like to live and she don't. . . . Those dresses — well, I got out the other day, and I needed something fit to wear. I like good clothes. Not those prim little jobs she has. So I just went downtown and bought what I wanted. I charged 'em to her husband, too!" She began to laugh softly.

Instead of the gentleness and restraint of the vanished Eve White, there sparkled in this newcomer a rippling energy, a greedy appetite for fun. She spoke casually of Eve White and her problems, always using *she* or *her* in every reference, always respecting the strict bounds of a separate identity.

It was also immediately apparent that her voice was different, as was the basic idiom of her language. Perhaps because of the easy laxness of this girl's posture and her more vigorous movements, she seemed somehow more voluptuously rounded than Eve White. A thousand minute alterations of manner, gesture and expression all argued that this could only be another woman. We cannot even say just what all these differences were. But they profoundly distinguished from Eve White the carefree girl who had taken her place. This was a vivid mutation, a seeming example of rare dual personality.

In contrast to her predecessor, talking was easy for Eve Black. "What can you tell me about Eve White?" the doctor asked.

"I can tell you plenty, Doc," she said, childishly eager. "I know lots and lots of things about her she don't know herself. For one thing, she's sick of that husband. She and her fine airs about always having to do the *right thing* even if it kills her."

"Is it because of little Bonnie?" he asked.

"Little Bonnie, little Bonnie, little Bonnie! That's all she can think about. Oh, the kid's all right most of the time. But why should a girl fret all the time about a four-year-old child?"

"Don't you *love* your daughter?"

"My daughter! I don't *have* no child, Doc. Not me. I like to have a good time — like to live. Bonnie's *her* child."

When asked if Eve White's all-absorbing devotion to Bonnie was genuine, she hesitated for a moment. "Yes, Doc, I reckon you'd say that's real. . . . But it's silly. . . ."

Eve Black did not deny that the body from which she spoke was also the body of Eve White, or that from it the little girl had been born. But she still insisted that she herself was not a mother, that she was not married to Ralph White "or to anybody else either."

"Where were you when the baby was born?" the doctor inquired.

A triumphant flash of mischief crossed her face. "Now, Doc, that's one for you to answer! There's an awful lot I don't understand. But I do know I'm not her and she's not me. Now, Eve White would worry about all those questions you've been asking, but not me."

"*Is* she worrying about them?"

"That's one trouble she's got she don't know about! She don't know anything about me. . . ." She broke off suddenly and a flash of defiance lit her eyes. "And don't you go and tell her either! When I get out I do like I please and it's none of her business. Lately I've been getting out a lot more, too."

She could not tell the doctor what happened to Eve White when she herself "got out" and went on her merry way. She was able to maintain awareness, she claimed, of nearly everything Eve White did, and had access most of the time to her thoughts and her memory. She did not, however, always take advantage of this. Often she found the other's thoughts and activities so boring that she withdrew her attention for long periods and occupied herself with plans and fancies of her own. On the other hand, Eve White had no suspicion of Eve Black's existence.

Eve Black could not, she admitted, emerge at will to express herself freely in the body of the sober and retiring housewife. Until about a year ago, when Eve White had had a miscarriage, it had been only at long intervals that Eve Black was able to gain control and then, with one exception which she did not discuss, only for brief periods.

The doctor was aware that Eve White's headaches and blackouts had begun soon after the miscarriage suffered a few months prior to her first interview.

"What gave her those headaches," the new Eve said, "was trying to keep me from getting out. She didn't know what was going on but when she tried to stop me, her head would give her hell."

Sometimes, but not always, after Eve Black had been "out" Eve White was left with the memory of a blackout. There were occasions too when she had been left with other consequences of her unrecognized twin's activities. With a flashing roll of her eyes this bold girl began to laugh. "About a week ago I was out dancing nearly all night and got right well polluted. You ought've seen her when she woke up the next morning and found herself with the hangover! It was a dilly. She didn't know what it was and she was scared half to death."

"But didn't you feel the hangover yourself?" the doctor asked.

"Me? *Of course* I didn't feel it! I wasn't out then. I wouldn't have cared to be out."

This lively Eve told of several other occasions when she had slipped back into retirement, leaving the other, innocent Eve to face various puzzling and unpleasant consequences. She could sometimes, but not regularly, do this of her own volition. At other times Eve White would replace her spontaneously. Thus she explained the outcome of the visit to Eve White's cousin Flo in Columbia. She had succeeded in emerging and had stayed "out" most of the time. When Ralph White called up and told her to come home, she not only refused but gave this man she disliked a piece of her mind, a mind that had nothing in common with that of his self-effacing wife. She herself had had a wonderful time in Columbia, where, as a stranger, she was able to do nearly anything she chose without any risk of being mistaken for Mrs. White. During this period she had entertained hope that she might "stay out" indefinitely, typically ignoring the difficulties that would arise. But despite her efforts to maintain control, the other Eve had reappeared and returned to Ralph.

The doctor, who was thinking that it was little wonder that Ralph White sometimes lost his temper, now asked Eve Black what she would do should Eve White become aware of her presence and do everything possible to keep her "in."

"I'll fight," she said with vehemence. After a moment's pause, she added, "I'm getting stronger than she is. Each time I come out she gets weaker."

The doctor asked what would happen if this continued.

"Then the body will be mine," she replied with assurance.

She talked freely, often expressing disdain for Mrs. White and for Ralph, who also, she said, knew nothing about her. When she was asked if she herself had ever had physical relations with Ralph, her eyes flared with indignation. The quick reply snapped out, "Definitely not!"

Then the doctor asked: "If it was you in Columbia with Flo and Jack, why didn't they recognize you? How did they go on believing it was Eve White?"

"Well, for one thing, they don't know about me. And when I have to, I can put on a pretty good job of acting like Eve White — even to saying dopey things and being real mousy, like I generally do if I happen to run into Ralph. Naturally I try not to come out if he's going to be around. It's a real strain, I tell you, but I couldn't very well act like my own self around her family, could I?" She chuckled to herself. "Flo and Jack did seem to feel she was mighty lively and happy, at that. They talked about it several times."

On rare occasions, she told the doctor, she actually had purposely precipitated herself into the family circle to quarrel suddenly with Ralph, scold Bonnie, or indulge in a tantrum. At such times she quickly subsided, often being extinguished by forces which she could not successfully resist or clearly describe.

During her longer periods "out," Eve Black said that she regularly avoided the family and friends and sought only the company of strangers. At the doctor's request she now demonstrated her skill in playing the role of Eve White, imitating the other's tone of voice, gestures and attitudes. She seemed to take a childish pride in this accomplishment.

About the voice that had so alarmed the other Eve she said, "It was just me. I've never been able to influence her thoughts or make her do a thing I wanted her to, and not till the last week or so was I ever able to make her hear me like that. It seemed to help me when I wanted to get out. She'd get so upset she couldn't do much to stop me. You really ought've seen her the other day. Ralph was giving her hell and I got kind of sick of it. Before I knew it I shouted to her, 'Knock the old creep's block off!' "

"Did Ralph hear you?" the doctor inquired attentively.

"Of course not, Doc! But *she* heard me all right."

CHAPTER 2

Dᴜʀɪɴɢ this first hour's interview with the capricious woman who called herself Eve Black, the doctor had often reminded himself that Ralph White was outside in the waiting room. Eve White's auditory hallucinations established beyond a doubt the deep gravity of her illness; the doctor thought she should enter the hospital connected with the local University Medical School. For this her husband must give his consent, but would he believe the doctor's strange and disturbing report?

It was decided that the husband must meet Eve Black in person. Otherwise he might lose confidence in the doctor and, perhaps, refuse to let his wife be admitted to the hospital.

With this in mind he asked the patient, "What do you think we ought to do now?"

"Lord, Doc," she said smiling amiably, "watching you work with her so long I've got to kind of like you. I'm willing to try most anything you say."

He asked if she would be willing to talk with Ralph White.

"Why should *I* talk with him, Doc?" she answered, a little startled. "I don't want nothing to do with him."

The necessity of Eve White's going into the hospital was then carefully explained. The girl listened politely but made it plain that she did not relish the idea of finding herself on a "bughouse ward," and showed little concern about Eve White's prognosis.

"However loony she may get," she insisted blithely, "it won't have nothing to do with me."

The doctor then told this girl that the auditory hallucinations, no matter how one might account for them, suggested that, without proper treatment, Eve White might become much worse. If she became profoundly irrational, she might have to remain confined in an institution for many months, perhaps years. Because of her husband's limited financial resources, commitment to the State Hospital would be her only choice. With Eve White confined thus, there would be no place for Eve Black to go, nothing very interesting to do when she emerged for her "times out."

As the point about confinement sank in slowly, the debonair girl was forced to agree that her own future would be jeopardized if Eve White grew worse. "I think you got something there, Doc," she said reluctantly.

She agreed then to having the co-tenant of her body go into the hospital, and promised not to disrupt treatment. She also agreed to refrain from whatever she did that (according to her) resulted in Eve White's hearing voices. But despite the doctor's emphatic warnings, she would not actually promise to do all she could to relieve the other's headaches.

"Why, if I did that, Doc, I might not ever be able to get out again."

Eve Black did, however, agree to reveal her identity to Ralph White.

Sitting with the husband in another office, the doctor wondered how he should prepare this deeply worried man for what he was to encounter. Any effort to account for his wife's puzzling behavior through the assumption of "another personality in her body" might well impress him as a farfetched phychiatric theory. Also, any preliminary discussion might make it impossible for him to be an unbiased observer.

So it was decided to let Ralph first *see* this woman who called herself Eve Black. He had lived with his wife for almost seven years. Certainly he should be able to recognize her through any disguise; though it may not be possible for strangers to tell one identical twin from the other, the husband of either seldom has difficulty. The recognition is probably achieved through thousands of small items of perception, data from the dim edge of awareness.

When this husband was brought into the presence of Eve Black he was, of course, confronted with an infinity of physical detail that had long been familiar. Contradicting all this came the brash, unfamiliar voice in which Eve Black said that she had never married him, that she was not Bonnie's mother. Anatomically this was the face Ralph knew, but all that it expressed was alien. The small involuntary movements through which a countenance reflects feeling were not those he had ever seen in the face of his wife.

At the beginning of the interview, it seemed to the physician that Ralph White, though amazed and genuinely distressed, clung to the idea that nervous instability and emotional stress had led his wife to adopt this unfamiliar attitude. Patiently he tried to reason with her as one might with a child in a tantrum. Finally, despair and something akin to awe seemed to possess him. Grasping for what he knew to be his wife's deepest feelings, Ralph White slowly said, "Bonnie ... our little girl ... what about Bonnie ... ?"

"Why ask me?" Eve Black interrupted him carelessly. "I got nothing to do with your child — or with you either." Her eyes drifted from him. She leaned forward a little and absent-mindedly began to rub a knee.

"These darn nylon stockings she puts on! They always make me scratch!" She turned to the physician, arching her dark brows. "How long, Doc, does all this have to go on?"

AFTER leaving the room with the physician Ralph freely granted permission for the patient to enter the hospital.

"The longer I looked at her," he said, "the stranger she seemed to me. It's just as though I'd never seen her before in my whole life. ... But this does bring some kind of sense to a lot that just didn't fit together before."

Returning to the office where Eve Black, sitting relaxed and apparently unperturbed, awaited him, the physician was faced with another problem: to "locate" the patient who was to receive treatment. Perhaps if the present Eve could be hypnotized the other personality might somehow be brought out. This girl said she had no objections, but several attempts to hypnotize her were unsuccessful. Though Eve White was subsequently put under hypnosis on many occasions, Eve Black always remained refractory.

After some discussion the girl suggested that the physician call Eve White by name. Then she fell silent. Quite immobile, she appeared to concentrate, in some way to make herself coöperative in the attempt. Her eyes closed as the name "Eve White" was called.

A moment later they slowly opened, now quiet, cautious. This face wore the habitual expression of Eve White, a delicate poise almost masking the faint lines of tension. Her legs assumed a more sedate position, with knees and feet together.

She gave the impression of one whose attention has been momentarily distracted, who suspects she may have missed a few words of the conversation.

"What happened?" asked the physician.

"I don't know," she said in her slow, precise voice. "Was it anything very much . . . ? I might have had a blackout . . . but I'm not sure."

She smiled as if just becoming aware of something pleasant. "My head, Doctor, the pain has all gone."

The physician now talked with Eve White at some length, trying to stir some latent awareness that might serve as a link between the two manifestations. Finally he asked:

"Do you ever have the feeling that deep down in you there's still somebody that you used to be, somebody you can't quite reach?"

She looked up at him with puzzled eyes. After pondering a few moments, she said, "I . . . I don't know what you mean."

He suggested then that she enter the hospital and noted that her reactions were those of one who had heard nothing of what he had said on this subject a little earlier to Eve Black. She seemed deeply relieved at the prospect. "I don't believe I could do otherwise, Doctor," she said. "Somehow, I dread the thought of being alone at home."

No hint of the brashness of the submerged Eve could be detected in the slender sedate little figure that left the consulting room for the Hospital Admitting Office. The tired, delicate body even gave the doctor the illusion of weighing several pounds less than the boisterous, teasing girl who called herself Eve Black.

DURING many years of experience in psychiatry we had both often encountered manifestations that the layman would find astonishing. Why, then, did we find ourselves regarding this patient (or should one say these patients) with such uncommon interest?

The psychiatric manifestation called *dual* or *multiple personality* has been extensively discussed over several decades. The concept was hardly novel when Robert Louis Stevenson in 1886 published his story of *Dr. Jekyll and Mr. Hyde*. In this eerie novel impossible bodily alterations accompanied the process by which an evil presence gained ascendancy in a hitherto benevolent person. But throughout the story we find a thread of reality that cannot be dismissed. Much of the effect of the tale lies in the definite implication that in each of us similarly malign forces perhaps lie dormant.

It has been presumed for many years that so-called dual personalities arise through the dissociation, or breaking into parts, of an originally integrated entity. Everyone, no doubt, becomes aware at times of inconsistent tendencies within himself. The ordinary person endeavors throughout life to suppress impulses and traits that prompt him toward unacceptable behavior. There is reason to believe that some inclinations, rejected from one's awareness, maintain an existence not suspected by their possessor. The development of a secondary personality has been explained as coming about through the mobilization, organization, and eventually the emergence of what has been thus discarded or dissociated from consciousness.

Dual personality, however, is not commonly encountered — a careful survey of professional literature on the subject reveals only seventy-six cases that have displayed this disorder fully — and it is scarcely surprising that practical psychiatrists today should hold a skeptical attitude toward such marvels. There is no doubt that the concept at once arouses suspicions. If Eve White is an unhappy wife, restricted by her moral standards from seeking various pleasures, what could be more convenient for her than to simulate a dual personality? She can live it up as Eve Black and then return, untroubled, to her status as innocent wife and mother.

Neither of us, at the time our quiet little patient changed so spectacularly in the office, had ever seen anything that even remotely resembled a dual personality. Nor had we ever met another psychiatrist who had seen such a patient. Yet whatever one might choose to call what we witnessed when this patient became Eve Black — deliberate pretense, somnambulism, hysterical dissociation or dual personality — it was a performance or manifestation that demanded attention and study.

It seemed plain that Eve Black's activity played a major part in our patient's illness. How should treatment be planned? After some deliberation we decided against using electric shock or insulin coma treatment, measures which had for years proved helpful in dealing with psychotic disorders of many types. Though in textbooks dual personality is often classed under the familiar term *hysteria,* neither of us felt that this patient should be so labeled, or that she would be likely to react as is usual in that common disorder. There was about this woman something that made us distinctly aware of the limitations of our knowledge, of the immense mysteries of human entity and of life.

We decided to feel our way as best we could, there being no distinct or reliable path that we could see to follow. Our experience had led us to be skeptical of the currently popular psychodynamic processes by which, through the manipulation of analogies and symbols, it is possible to arrive at easy, and almost identical, explanations of all cases. But we remained deeply impressed with the value of communication between patient and doctor.

With Eve White in the hospital, we hoped to give her relief from an acute situation and we planned to establish a helpful relationship which would encourage her to talk about her life and feelings. Should Eve Black reappear, we hoped to communicate with her also. But it was the tense, serious little wife and mother, and she only, whom we saw and talked with during the first few days in the hospital. No faint suggestion of Eve Black slipped out during this period when her docile alternate was under constant and carefully planned surveillance. We considered it important to learn what she might do when alone and, so far as she could know, entirely free from scrutiny. Nurses and others reported no change in her even demeanor, no rift in the orderly routine of her days.

Often she sat alone in her room reading a copy of Palgrave's *Golden Treasury,* or verses clipped from newspapers and magazines which she had over the years pasted into a scrapbook. The poems she liked best were those dealing with the basic values and virtues often regarded by the sophisticated as simple or even banal.

Like most of her personal interests this pleasure in verse had remained a solitary preoccupation, not discovered by us until she was in the hospital where it could be observed that she turned to it as to a familiar refuge. Formally and quietly she discussed her preferences. Among the favorite lines committed to memory that she often dwelt on silently, she mentioned this stanza from Tennyson's *In Memoriam:*

> *I held it truth, with him who sings*
> *To one clear harp in divers tones,*
> *That men may rise on stepping-stones*
> *Of their dead selves to higher things.*

In the hospital environment Eve White seemed to feel some degree of security or protection. She freely discussed the early years of her life. Her father, a farmer and country storekeeper, had been able to provide a comfortable living for the family but very few luxuries. So far as she recalled, she had felt wanted and loved. Yes, she supposed she could say that both her mother and father seemed warm and understanding. They were not arbitrary about discipline, nor did she remember them as pampering any of their children.

"As a child," she said, "I must have been very sensitive to criticism and punishment." She felt quite sure that her parents had not punished her too frequently or severely. "Perhaps it was because they did it so seldom," she suggested, "that it sometimes hurt my feelings and I couldn't understand." Most of the scoldings and punishments she received had been given by her mother. The father was away at work nearly all day. She believed that her mother had been fair and not unduly strict.

Important in her memory of early childhood was the birth of twin sisters when she was about five years old. She recalled this event as chiefly pleasant and exciting. She must have felt jealous of the twins sometimes, she supposed, but she could recall no enduring sense of rivalry, no tragic sense of displacement. Though she was an only child until the twins were born, she had always enjoyed the close companionship of Flo, her cousin who lived nearby.

A long time before the twins had been born, she had experienced a good deal of apprehension about an incident she still remembered vividly. There was a large ditch of stagnant, slimy water under a bridge in the woods nearby. The woods, particularly in twilight, seemed mysterious and beautiful but haunted with danger. A man had drowned in this ditch one night. Eve White believed she had been present when his body was dragged out next day, for she recalled her horror and fear at the sight, and her vague but powerful new realizations about death.

What she actually saw as a small child soon became entangled with overheard snatches of conversation, with elaborate fantasies spun by older children to shock the hearer. One way or another, she had come to believe for a while that a malign and dangerous monster dwelt in the stagnant waters of the ditch. She recalled dreams and daylight fantasies in which the monster threatened and pursued her. The deadly thing was pictured as a great scaly reptilian form, larger than a grown man, with baleful and merciless eyes.

But on the whole Eve White felt that her childhood had been happy; even the dangerous inhabitant of the ditch, she now felt, probably had afforded more interest and excitement than distress.

During this period of observation nothing was observed in Eve White that suggested a masked or incipient schizophrenia, the familiar delusionary mental disorder. Her restraint and propriety reflected only normal timidity, not the chill and glassy aloofness, the inexplicable withdrawal from life of the schizophrene.

After much consideration, we decided to seek another audience with Eve Black. Though we felt confident that Eve White should know more about her alternate, both of us felt some reluctance at simply confronting our coöperative and insecure patient with a forthright account of Eve Black, of whom she appeared entirely unaware.

On two occasions when Eve White had been hypnotized, amnesia for the period of "sleep" had been obtained. Hypnosis was therefore induced again. While the demure little patient sat with eyes closed, Eve Black was called by name and asked to speak.

The eyes opened promptly. Even before they moved, or so it seemed to us, there could be no doubt about whom we dealt with. Almost instantaneously the figure relaxed into the buoyant ease of Eve Black.

"Well, Doc," she said in the husky, brisk voice so unlike that of the other, "what you did just now sure made it easier for me to get out. I think it made it easier on her too."

Her bright eyes roved briefly about the hospital room as if in amused curiosity.

"I know what this place looks like all right," she explained, "but I just thought I'd like to see for myself." She smiled, her affable face at ease, and then said casually, "She's really feeling a lot better. She's still scared, all right. I can tell that. But nothing like what she was a week ago."

This Eve was at first a little negative to the suggestion that the other be informed of her existence. She questioned the influence this might have on her own ability to "come out" and be herself. There was a way, she admitted, in which her alternate could oppose her and prevent her getting out. Just how this power worked Eve Black could not explain, but it varied with the other Eve's state of health and security. "She don't really know what she's about, either, but just struggles hard to keep herself from what she thinks of as going to pieces."

In Eve White's recent improvement this Eve had found added difficulties. She had, she admitted, tried unsuccessfully to "come out a couple of times for just a little while" and investigate the psychiatric ward.

The physician then suggested that, with Eve White aware of her, there might be some lessening of the peculiar conflict. She was, however, requested to avoid conduct during her periods of ascendancy, or pressures while submerged, that would damage the other; and she was again reminded of the dangers to herself should Eve White become psychotic.

The confident girl before us was not immediately compliant to all these suggestions. She did not seem in the least cruel or vengeful, but rather stood in the role of a disinterested observer.

"I got nothing against her," she said, speaking of Eve White. "I don't wish her any bad luck. But I got myself to think about, too; I can't keep my mind on her and her worryings all the time."

When Eve Black did agree to behave with reasonable discretion, her words of compliance seemed a little too glib to rely on, but she finally gave wholehearted consent to the doctor's explaining about her to Eve White.

Then, mentioning several minor flirtations she had enjoyed in the past few months, she began to laugh with warm amusement. Lively and extremely contagious little gusts of mirth interrupted her as she explained how she had successfully evaded the consequences of each adventure.

"Her face will be a sight to see if you tell her about the time I was out at the Lido Club," she said finally. "Had some champagne cocktails with a fellow there. I like to sing, you see. Well, about two o'clock I got out in the middle of the floor and really let 'em have it. They liked it, too. Everybody stopped dancing. The orchestra quit. I got better and better. The pianist started up again to accompany me. They kept on clapping and stomping and cheering. I put some charge in it when I got to 'Rockin' and Rollin' ' — *Rockin' and rollin' / All night long....*"

With a little toss of her head she carried a snatch of the tune for a moment. "But what really sent 'em," she said, "was when I stood there in the middle of that dance floor with the spotlight on me and let 'em have 'Sixty Minute Man.' "

IN OUR attempt to tell Eve White about the other personality we proceeded circumspectly. She seemed confident that the blackouts of which she had complained were probably nothing more than brief fainting spells caused by the severe headaches which preceded them. Sometimes when she had come to our office, however, shortly after suffering a blackout, she had seemed uneasy, less assured that they had lasted only a few moments. She had not checked with watch or clock to obtain evidence of their duration. Had there been some vague inner feeling, warning her that doing so might add to her stress and bewilderment?

From her parents we learned that many years ago she had suffered from periods of stupor or delirium that varied in length from a few minutes to an hour or more. The patient herself remembered being told by them that during early childhood she often walked in her sleep. She recalled no particular uneasiness about her sleepwalking on the part of her parents. It must have begun very early, a few months after the twin sisters were born. After a year or two it gradually disappeared. It did, however, recur once or twice in her early teens. Once she had walked out into the living room where her parents were sitting. Next day when they told her about it she asked them to tell her exactly what she did.

Her eyes had been open, they said, and apparently she could see what she was doing, for she avoided objects that lay in her way. She had turned toward them when they addressed her, and indeed spoken in reply. Her gaze seemed inattentive to the immediate surroundings, but not troubled or unnatural. She seemed not so much sleeping as incompletely conscious. They had told her she was responsive to persuasion. After being led back to bed she had slept on through the night. Next morning she was unable to remember anything about it at all.

Would she be upset, she was asked, if such an episode should occur during one of her blackouts? Eve seemed to give this possibility little thought, but said she found nothing particularly alarming in what she remembered being told about her sleepwalking

long ago. No attempt was made to hurry the patient toward any concept of serious personality dissociation. What she remembered of her somnambulism was utilized in discussions of the varying degrees of consciousness in commonplace situations, such as concussion. She accepted without undue apparent apprehension our statement that during her blackout in the office, just before coming to the hospital, more than an hour had elapsed. With what seemed to be well-controlled surprise she listened as we told her she had spoken and had opened her eyes soon after losing consciousness, that her manner and voice had changed considerably and that she had seemed remarkably free from worry about her problems. She was encouraged to think of the lapse as having some points of resemblance to the sleepwalking of her childhood. Our experience with several patients who had carried on activities during brief periods of amnesia was then discussed.

Characteristically laconic, Eve White seemed to react with mixed feelings. To be faced with evidence that during periods of unconsciousness she had behaved in ways unknown to herself was disquieting. On the other hand there was an advantage in the patient's having now some explanation for the disturbing events which heretofore had seemed an impossible paradox. Could she, for instance, actually have gone downtown to the stores and heedlessly bought all those lavish clothes while in such a state? It was as if with one hand she seemed to grasp for relief in such an explanation, while with the other she pushed it away as fantastic, and in some new way bizarrely terrifying. Her pupils had dilated, giving her intent eyes a darker hue. "Really, Doctor," she said in a low, serious tone, "there wasn't one of those dresses in which I could have felt . . . well . . . like a decent woman."

During the following days the performance of acts without apparent volition was discussed. Encouraging examples of recovery from serious cases of amnesia and automatism were cited. Gradually emphasis was shifted to the striking differences in manner, appearance and behavior of those manifestations often referred to as *alternating consciousness* or *dual personality*.

We did not, at this point, use those expressions, feeling that they were more likely to distort the patient's ideas than to clarify them, likely, even, to provide her with a scapegoat. If the situation we confronted was indeed the result of dissociation, then it seemed logical to believe that help might lie in the direction of bringing together the unalike elements.

Though Eve White came to accept the fact that behavior incomprehensible to her had taken place during periods of amnesia, she seemed instinctively to evade some aspects of realization. If real progress were to be made, might it not be necessary for her eventually to regard whatever occurred during blackouts as of her own doing, whether or not she might, in the ordinary sense, be held responsible?

During this period we also had a number of interviews with Eve Black, hypnotizing Eve White to obtain the other's presence. Without reluctance this debonair girl now agreed to help in the attempt to acquaint the other with herself. She had, as we have said, claimed to be responsible for the objectively unreal voice that Eve White had fearfully reported. Perhaps, through this hallucinatory form of communication, this Eve might manifest herself to the other convincingly. Good-naturedly she agreed to try. Some moments after Eve White had been summoned, Eve Black was addressed by name and requested to speak directly to her alternate.

The response was immediate and impressive. Eve White's familiar face went suddenly blank. The deeply ingrained control shattered like an eggshell. The habitually guarded eyes shone luminous. Absence of all expression was followed by naked astonishment. Catching her breath with a scarcely audible sigh she slowly whispered, "It just can't be."

The patient was profoundly shaken and disturbed. Her doctor remained with her the rest of the afternoon, reassuring her and helping her adjust her feelings to a realization that she found weirdly terrifying.

CHAPTER 3

Eve White remained in the hospital for approximately two weeks. She received no specific treatment other than the psychotherapy we have described. She seemed to gain steadily in strength and confidence and to make general improvement. After a brief period of consternation on hearing the alternate announce herself, she seemed to benefit from having an explanation, however strange, for the voice which she had heard previously, and found in it relief from the fear that psychosis was impending. She never again heard Eve Black's voice or in any other way came in contact with her directly.

During long interviews each day we were gathering further detail about Eve White's career. As time passed she became increasingly articulate, and it seemed helpful to her to express herself. Despite this, one felt that she was in some important respects a person for whom real intimacy was peculiarly difficult.

During this period we were able to interview Eve White's parents several times. When Ralph White had first attempted to describe their daughter's condition to them they had come promptly to the hospital, at first skeptical and a little distrustful of the doctor. But after they had visited her and, later, interviewed Eve Black, their point of view changed. Through them, through Eve White's sisters, her cousin Flo and other members of the family, we were able to obtain valuable historical detail of the patient's life. At that time, as was to become our practice generally, we made extensive tape recordings of all that the parents could tell us.

We had both been surprised and doubting when in an early interview Eve Black told us she had enjoyed an independent life ever since Eve White's childhood. We had felt that she was probably a product of the patient's recent emotional stresses, but she told us freely of episodes twenty or more years ago in which she had allegedly emerged, usually to engage in acts of mischief or disobedience. She explained her ungrammatical speech, so unlike her alternate's, by saying she had never bothered to pay attention while Eve White was in school.

Since Eve White, whose word on any matter always proved good, had no access to the other's current awareness or her memory, it had been impossible through her to check directly on Eve Black's stories. She was able, however, to confirm reports of certain punishments she had received in childhood for deeds unknown to her but described to us by Eve Black.

Several of these stories were substantiated through the parents. Eve White's parents impressed us as sober, conservative citizens of a small rural community. Throughout their daughter's long struggle to regain her health, they were faithfully coöperative and always loyal to her, even in situations which they must have found totally bewildering.

The parents both clearly recalled that once they had had to punish their ordinarily good and conforming six-year-old daughter for having disobeyed their specific rule against wandering through the woods to play with children living approximately a half mile away. On her return Eve had received a hearty whipping despite her desperate and persistent denials of wrongdoing and disobedience.

Almost as surprising as disobedience and lying in such a good child was the daring with which she had wandered home through the darkening woods. Eve was timid and had for some time shown abnormal fear about going near the ditch under the bridge where the man had been found dead. This evening she had been seen to loiter there boldly.

Eve Black had previously described this incident to us in some detail, expressing amusement about having been able to withdraw and leave the other Eve to appreciate the sensations of the whipping. Though Eve Black, when "in," preserved indirect awareness of the outer world through Eve White's thoughts and perceptions, she insisted that she was then totally immune from any physical pain or other sensations experienced by the latter. The adult Eve White recalled this punishment and several others which she had had no way of understanding and which had sometimes deeply confused her in her relations with her parents. Even after being told in detail what had occurred, she was never able to gain memory of the experiences of Eve Black for which she was punished, though extensive efforts were made, both with hypnosis and without, to bring this material to awareness.

There were other incidents related by Eve Black which the parents confirmed. For example, she admitted to having felt annoyance with her twin sisters, which she once expressed by biting their toes hard enough to cause wild yelling. Though Eve White recalled no unkindness on her part toward her younger sisters, she had been punished several times for cruelty to them during their infancy.

When our patient was five or six years old, her cousin and close companion, Flo, was given for Christmas a doll which seemed to Eve inexpressibly lovely. As an adult she recalled in detail her longing for it, and a peculiar sense of emptiness or of rejection in finding not herself but Flo blessed with its possession.

When her reserve had been lessened under hypnosis, Eve White sometimes spoke at length about this early experience. Once or twice her eyes brimmed with tears. Revival of the old longing for this doll was a clue that could open and expose her present devotion to her actual child, an emotion she usually found it difficult to express freely.

When the doll belonging to Flo was found smashed to bits, evidence pointed to Eve as the culprit. Though she denied guilt, she was punished. The adult Eve White denied any recollection of breaking Flo's doll.

About this she wrote to us later as follows:

> Why I made such a scene in your office over the china doll Flo had as a child is beyond me. I hope that outburst will be forgiven. You wanted me to bring back all I could remember of it. As well as I recall it was a china doll with golden hair and blue eyes. It was lovely.
>
> Perhaps I envied her having it. When I look back I enjoyed just looking at it as she held it in her arms and rocked it as one does a baby. When it was broken it hurt me as much as it did Flo. To the best of my knowledge mother punished me because for some reason she thought I had broken it. I'm certain I didn't. That's all I can remember of it. I hope it is what you wanted to know.
>
> Sincerely yours,
Eve White

Before this letter was mailed Eve Black, during a brief period "out," found it. On another sheet of paper she typed a comment of her own which she sent with the other:

Hi Doc,

Our brain child has a way with them big words, huh? You know, of course, I broke the china doll. I'd do it again. They thought Flo was so much. You should have seen her flaunting her pretty doll in my face. Sure I broke it and if *I* had gotten the tanning for it, which I didn't, I'd still be glad I broke it. I can't type so fancy and all like Eve White, but, hunt and peck and what have you, I can type too. If I said I was grateful for the patience you shown with me you'd sure as fire faint, so I won't say it. You know you're cute, remind me to tell you. Guess I'd better sign this thing one way or another, heck, I'll do it like madame.

Sincerely yours,
Eve Black

During the interview referred to above, and apparently suggested by the discussion of the doll, Eve White mentioned a blue china cup. She remembered playing with it in the company of her cousin Flo, when she was about five years old. The incident seemed to hold some sharp flavor of the past for she kept coming back to it. An unaccustomed animation came into her voice as she tried to find some association that would bring recollection of surrounding events. Despite continued attempts nothing further emerged. Eve Black denied any memory of the cup.

As we talked with Eve White's parents, it seemed more and more likely that the division between the two personalities must have been much less sharp during the patient's childhood and adolescence, the contrast less consistent and spectacular, the disturbances brief and rare. They ceased entirely after Eve White's marriage and did not recur until after the miscarriage which has been mentioned before.

BEFORE our patient left the hospital Eve Black had emerged spontaneously on several occasions. A young man, admitted about a week previously to recuperate from a relatively mild alcoholic episode, had, during his first hours of discomfort and remorse, found in Eve White a soothing, uncritical and maternal figure to whom to turn. Recovered from his illness and dejection, one day

this man sat alone with an open book in a small recreation room
Glancing up, he saw what at first he took to be a familiar figure
Eve Black had playfully tiptoed into the room. Now like a child
who has succeeded in startling an adult by saying "boo," she broke
into soft warm laughter. In flagrant contrast with the frail, retiring
Eve White he thought he saw before him, this woman pulsated
with energy. Catching and holding his glance with bold bright
eyes, she took a few buoyant steps forward and casually sat on the
arm of his chair.

"How you doing, boy?" she asked.

Then like an energetic kitten she was up, swinging with a strong
supple step to the phonograph across the room and putting on a
record. Turning toward her companion she stood for a few seconds
her shoulders and hips responding just perceptibly and perfectly to
the rhythm. Her whole face lit with a fresh inviting smile.

"Come on, boy . . . dance with me," she urged softly.

A minute or two later the floor nurse came in. Having known
only Eve White, she was astonished and delighted to find this quiet
and troubled patient throwing herself with such spirit into the
dance. After brief observation she decided, however, that it was
time for Mrs. White to return to her room.

Nothing unseemly had occurred, the nurse reflected, but she felt
a sense of uneasiness at the incredible change in Mrs. White. For
Mrs. White — of all people! — had in some inexpressible way
seemed stimulating and provocative.

Later, Mr. Smathers, the male patient, talked at some length
with an intern on the psychiatric section about his personal re
actions. Looking back, he didn't know how to describe the peculiar
feeling he'd had. Well as he knew Mrs. White, he found himself
thinking someone must be impersonating her. But instead of an
impersonation this just wasn't like her at all! It seemed for a
moment that he was about to lose his grip on himself. For, abruptly
the idea got hold of him that he was with somebody else . . . some
body else altogether!

It was summer and a number of medical students were working
as attendants in the hospital. One of these took up duties on the
psychiatric section a few days before Eve White was dismissed. He

hours began after supper when medical duties were few. He was thoughtful and sympathetic and liked to talk to the patients and help make the evening pleasant for them.

Though he was uninformed about Eve White's history, his attention was at once drawn to her, this delicately attractive young woman in whom he felt an inarticulate need for friendliness. Each evening he spent some time talking quietly with her. He found that she was familiar with some poems and music that held a personal significance for him; soon he began to feel he knew the essential qualities of her character.

Walking along the corridor late one night he scarcely noted that Eve White's light was on and the door ajar. She often read at this hour. A low, surreptitious whistle caught his attention. She was standing just inside the doorway. The rich slow voice that asked him for a cigarette made him suddenly tingle with surprise. Though Eve White had never smoked, it was not remarkable that she might decide to do so. She invited him to come in and talk for a moment.

Soon afterward he was at the telephone calling the resident physician. He could not precisely state what had happened. Mrs. White had neither said nor done anything in the least irrational. He had never seen her so happy or so energetic. But something extraordinary had come about. Of that he was sure. His scalp seemed to prickle with the strangeness of what he had encountered, as he tried to frame for the resident his report on the profound impression of difference that had come over him.

WHAT DANGERS would be in store for our patient when she left the hospital? There seemed little reason to believe that Eve Black would not continue to emerge from time to time. It seemed evident that she was not a genuinely evil or vicious manifestation. But it had become plain that she could not be relied upon to fulfill a promise and that, when it suited her, she would lie in the reckless spirit of a child who almost feels that saying so may make it so.

Though her voice and manner flaunted sexual challenge and promise, she apparently had no real inclination to consummate any of the adventures she took such joy in starting. To dress conspicuously, to speak and move provocatively were ways to attract attention and promote the atmosphere of frolic and commotion that Eve Black inevitably sought. As the study of her reactions continued through subsequent months, our conviction grew that, despite all her vitality and sensuous challenge, this manifestation was limited by a deep and specific frigidity.

We had no assurance, however, that Eve Black would not involve herself and Eve White in minor indiscretions and misdemeanors. Our hope now was to learn better how Eve Black might be mollified and indirectly persuaded toward coöperation, through the responses of Eve White.

As the patient left the hospital with her husband, happy at the prospect of seeing Bonnie again, it seemed as if some ground had been gained. Ralph could now more wholeheartedly help her. Believing, in a limited but really meaningful sense, that it was not she who had reviled him in Columbia, that she had not simply lied to him about the clothes in the closet, he was now able to modify the blame he had heaped on her in the past.

When he had first met Eve Black two weeks earlier in our office, after watching her for a while with spellbound eyes he had said: "Why, that's exactly the way she looked — the way she was — when she threw those dishes at my head. That's who it was!"

On our first encounter with Eve Black we had asked ourselves at once how such a manifestation could have gone unrecognized, even for a minute, by the husband or parents. Eve Black had occasionally come out in their presence, but they had not really discovered her until she agreed to reveal herself to them in the physician's presence. Now it was evident that these people had been forced, for want of any other explanation, to think of those odd, wayward moments in Eve White's career as fits of temper, rare quirks of mood in a habitually docile, considerate woman. Who in their position, having in mind no trace of the multiple-personality concept, would be likely to suspect such a situation as that voluntarily revealed to us by the patient?

FOR ABOUT two months after the patient's release from the hospital, improvement continued. Eve White returned from time to time for interviews. She was free from headaches and had suffered no more blackouts of which she was conscious. Occasionally there had been a lost lapse of time, brought to her attention by the clock or calendar, which indicated that her alternate had been in command.

Sometimes the telephone would ring and some strange male voice would ask for Eve Black. Occasionally she awoke in the morning with a taste like dry ashes in her mouth. Once she had found a small bottle of pungent perfume, a vivid red dress, and a few other small items of feminine apparel carefully hidden in a closet. Checking, she found that a relatively small amount of cash was missing from the drawer where she kept a little money saved for extras from housekeeping expenses. She winced at the thought of being seen in the dress, and her first impulse was to throw the things away at once. Remembering, however, that her counterpart had shown consideration (or caution) in limiting her purchases, she decided to leave everything as it was, hoping that coöperation to this degree might limit damages.

Usually the transitions occurred smoothly enough, for Eve Black seldom came out except when Mrs. White was alone or among strangers, and now Eve White was almost never left in unfamiliar surroundings or perplexing situations by her alternate's withdrawal. She told of one notable exception, however, when she had suddenly found herself on a busy street corner engaged in conversation with an unknown young soldier. Wide awake and in possession of all her faculties, she had concluded immediately that the alternate must have come here, must have been talking with this man for some time.

Eve White soon caught the gist of what had been going on. The man was expressing strong indignation, as if he considered himself unjustly misled. His new companion found it necessary to say very little. The contrast of her quiet dignity with the argument that must have been in progress seemed to affect him almost at once. His anger seemed to dissolve in bewilderment, and he soon mumbled some final expression of courtesy and hurried off.

Despite these inconveniences and tribulations, Eve White felt encouraged. Ralph had been very patient and seemed better able to express his affection. It was a joy to see little Bonnie happy. It was characteristic of this considerate woman to be grateful even for small things. She cherished every little item on which hope might be founded.

Now that Eve White knew about the other manifestation it was no longer necessary to induce hypnosis in order to summon Eve Black. This was done with the patient's acquiescence each time she came for an interview. Eve Black, too, was on the whole encouraging in her reports. Mr. and Mrs. White were getting along a little better, she thought, though not as well as Eve White tried to tell herself. She herself wouldn't put up for five minutes with Ralph or with any of his ways. She had not meant for the other Eve to find the few simple things she'd bought for herself. She insisted she had a right to a little life of her own. She admitted that the money she took did not belong to her; but, with a shrug, casually maintained that she had to get along somehow. When asked if she would like to earn money that would be unquestionably her own, she replied in an amused playful tone:

"Now, Doc — you're always bringing up something like that. Sometimes you talk the way she thinks. Why would I want to fret at some piddling job? That ain't living."

About the soldier with whom Eve White had been confronted, Eve Black at first calmly professed ignorance. On being accused of lying, she was petulant, then with a warm smile said, "You can't believe just anything she tells you, Doc. She may try to act like a fancy little saint but she's human in her way, like the rest of us."

Finding that this explanation made no impression, she shifted her position in the chair. Crossing her legs, she gave her head a little toss and began to laugh softly.

"The poor scary thing couldn't have slept, I bet, if she hadn't told you about that. Of course, I know that fellow. Met him once before at a dance in Columbia. Just a crazy kid. Seemed to like my singing and the way I danced. When I ran into him the other day I told him I'd go out with him that night. Then he got a little tiresome. Wanted it to be just the two of us — and right then. He kind of lacks finesse," she confided with blended naïveté and quasi worldliness. "I wasn't born yesterday, Doc."

The young man had continued to urge her, increasing the vehemence of his persuasion as she tauntingly evaded him. She might have had to make a little disturbance to settle the affair, she admitted, with a kind of childish pride in the interest she had aroused: "I was just getting ready to tell him off, even if it took some shouting and might attract a crowd."

Then another and simple solution occurred to Eve Black. Let Eve White do it! It would save a lot of bother and unpleasantness. Besides, there was something extremely amusing in the prospect of her prissy associate's having to handle the situation. Sometimes, not always, she could fade away like this by choice and leave the other to face her problem. This time it had worked precisely. Her lively eyes shone with fresh delight as she boasted innocently of her achievement.

The relatively tranquil period subsequent to Eve White's hospitalization did not last. Soon, like a poorly rooted plant, the basic relationship between Mr. and Mrs. White seemed to wither steadily. They could offer each other only the lifeless shadow of companionship. As Ralph's frustration and discouragement increased, and he began to spend more time seeking diversion away from home, Eve became more remote. Her determination to preserve the marriage, however, did not alter.

Manifestations of Eve Black grew more troublesome. She gained control more often and flaunted her freedom with increasing boldness. On rare occasions she emerged deliberately before Ralph White to taunt and deride him. During interviews the doctor found her more openly determined to have her own way at any cost. Several times she took over and absented herself from the house when Bonnie had counted on her mother's being at home. The little girl had been carefully instructed to go next door and stay with the neighbors if she found herself alone. Usually no difficulty arose on this score, but neither parent found it possible to explain satisfactorily to the neighbors why they could not give regular notice of when Bonnie was to come. Nor could they make Bonnie understand why her mother would sometimes disappear after promising to read to her or cut out paper dolls. The child was told, of course, that her mother had spells of sickness, that she would get better, and everything would be all right. But why certain things happened that frightened and bewildered the little girl — who could explain this?

Several months earlier, while the presence of Eve Black was still unsuspected, Ralph had brought his wife to the physician, insisting that the night before she had threatened to kill Bonnie. She had, he explained, actually put the cord of a Venetian blind around the child's throat and had seemed to be trying to strangle her. He had stopped her and in the ensuing quarrel had struck her lightly. Eve White, though distressed and bitterly hurt, had firmly denied his accusation.

It seemed preposterous to consider that Ralph would arrantly fabricate such an accusation. To the doctor it seemed perhaps even more difficult to conceive that this woman was lying or that she would ever under any circumstance harm her child. But he could not believe that Eve White was psychotic, or that she had been so. Could the husband, in all the stress under which he labored, have honestly misjudged his perception? There seemed to be no satisfactory answer.

Sometime after Eve Black had revealed herself, she was questioned about this episode. At first she denied it, insisting that Ralph was a liar. Some days later, however, her volatile mood had changed and she told a different story:

"Sure, Doc. I was just trying to tone down the little varmint. She got to bawling and fretting. And I hadn't been out in a long time. I was working out some plans, and if the kid wasn't quiet it might mess me up."

Unabashed by the admission, she said casually that she would not have actually harmed the child. Because of the absence of serious malice in this scamplike entity, we were prepared to believe her, that she had meant to threaten dramatically and punish a little.

With this incident in the background, both Mr. and Mrs. White were especially apprehensive about any intrusion on the part of Eve Black into the life of their daughter. Once when Bonnie had been left alone the neighbors were not at home. Frightened by the approach of darkness, she had run wildly back toward the empty house. Tripping, she had fallen and skinned a knee. Ten minutes later Ralph came in from work. How long had this little girl been crying in her helplessness? How seriously was she injured? It was only a superficial abrasion but Ralph, in growing indignation, could not accurately estimate its gravity. A little later when his wife appeared, still clad in the flashy red dress Eve Black had put on earlier that afternoon, he had lost the last secure hold he had on himself and was swept willy-nilly into a tide-run of honest wrath.

Large and small troubles continued to accumulate. After no word had come from the Whites for a longer period than usual, a short note was received by the doctor. It was signed with the initials E. B. In a careless scrawl was written:

Doc,
I think I ought to let you know. E. W. is quite sick. She tried to kill herself this morning. I was able to stop her. Ralph don't know about it. She's promised herself that nobody must ever know. I know you should. I'm not sure she won't try it again.

A telephone call was made. Eve White agreed to come for another interview without delay. She denied all knowledge of the note but admitted that she had been desperately unhappy and had thought of suicide. Because of Bonnie and because of her religious convictions, she felt that she would never take such a step. Then with painful reluctance she said that she had at last reached a decision to separate from her husband. She realized she could not look after her little girl adequately until she got better. So she had decided to give up her child, forever if necessary, in order to protect her.

It was arranged for Bonnie to go and live with Mrs. White's mother and father, in the distant rural home where she herself had been born. Ralph was going to a city in another state with the intention of starting over in his business. Since living expenses would be increased by these moves, Eve strongly felt that she should find a job and provide for the major needs of herself and her daughter.

After the interview with Eve White, the other Eve was summoned. She first expressed pleasure in the plans for separation. "Maybe the poor old gal will get some sense in her yet," she said with an easy half-interested smile. No, she had not exaggerated what she wrote about in her note. She had been aware of her alternate's thoughts as they progressed to the awful resolution.

"She must have been half dazed, I guess," this Eve said, now a little more intent than usual. "She started into the bathroom and was so worked up she could hardly find her way. I could tell she was going after the razor and was going to cut her wrist. She was going to kill herself. *I* knew nobody'd be back for an hour or two to do anything about it. She'd be dead by then." Pausing now, she added wistfully, "And that would have meant I'd be dead too."

During the struggle to "get out," Eve Black said, it had seemed for a while that she might fail. "Something awful was on her mind, something I never was up against before." Shaking and uncoordinated but with unswerving resolution, Eve White had banged open the medicine chest.

"She'd already grabbed the razor when I finally got out," Eve Black said. "I think she meant business, Doc."

That Eve White had not remembered this incident might be explained by something Eve Black had told us during an earlier interview. Then she had said that Eve White's memory was sometimes erased during short periods when she was still in control but struggling against her alternate in an unusually difficult, and for the time being indeterminate, contest for consciousness.

Approximately a week later, the household having been disbanded, Eve White moved to our city and began work with a large corporation located only about fifteen miles from our offices. Behind her lay considerable experience in typing and bookkeeping, and for a short time in her teens she had operated a small telephone switchboard. She found a room in a modest boardinghouse which she planned to share with another girl.

Was this merely progress from the frying pan into the fire? In her present condition would she be able to hold a job? For weeks Eve White had been steadily losing initiative and vitality. Was it possible that Eve Black, freed from the restraining influence of the Whites' home, might "come out" to stay? A bright, unworried butterfly would no more certainly perish.

On the other hand, Eve Black might become more coöperative. If she was representative of unrecognized tendencies in the other, then changes in Eve White's routine or freer expression of her emotion might soften the forces invisibly rebellious far within her. Or would appeasement serve chiefly to incite the rebellious drive? Would Eve Black, encouraged and emboldened, merrily cry havoc and loose the dogs of total war?

CHAPTER 4

DURING the next year we kept these two personalities under close observation. The patient usually came twice a week for an hour's interview with her therapist. Occasionally there were interviews that lasted throughout a whole afternoon. With the permission of both ladies, tape recordings were made of each as she worked with the doctor. Over many months the attempt was made with each Eve to work back step by step into early childhood. Eve White and Eve Black each took various psychological tests. Their handwritings were studied and compared by a qualified expert. Though he was considerably impressed by consistent and significant differences between the two, it was his opinion that an expert could establish sufficient evidence to show both were done by the same human hand. Each Eve consented to our making moving pictures. Our first pictures were on silent film but we later obtained a study with sound. By this means they were for the first time, one might say, able to see each other.

Eve Black, because of her access to the other's thought, had, of course, an approximate idea of her alternate. Watching the film with obvious amusement, she commented from time to time when Eve White expressed an opinion or straightened herself in the chair, "Wouldn't she, now!" When the film showed Eve White get up and walk across the room, the disdainful observer murmured, "Mincing!"

Eve White, on the other hand, studied the film with solemn gravity. When it ended, embarrassment showed in the faint pink spots on her cheeks, in the withdrawal of her eyes. She sat silent for a few moments as if seeking her customary outward poise. We had never heard Eve White speak unkindly of another. Not in sarcasm, but humbly and in the truest spirit of charity, she at last found herself able to say in a low serious voice, "I suppose . . . I mean one could say there's a lot about her that seems fresh and . . . really . . . right attractive. She does seem so young."

The Rorschach test, in which the patient tells what he sees in ten standardized ink blots, as well as other projective tests, revealed nothing important about either Eve White or Eve Black that was not already known. It is, however, interesting to note that the Rorschach record of Miss Black was interpreted by the clinical psychologist as "by far healthier than the one of Mrs. White." On the Wechsler-Bellevue intelligence scale Mrs. White's I.Q. was estimated as six points higher than that of her alternate. Of each, however, the psychologist reported:

> There is evidence that the native intellectual endowment is well within the bright normal group. . . . In Mrs. White's case anxiety and tenseness interfere, in Miss Black's superficiality and slight indifference as to achievement are responsible for the lower score.

These technical tests did not bring us any understanding of how or why the manifestation called Eve Black had emerged; nor did they help explain how Eve Black had access to Eve White's thoughts and memory while Eve White remained unconscious of the other's entire experience.

With deepening emotional relations between the patient and physician and with repetition, the process of summoning the absent personality had progressively become simpler. Relatively early in the course of treatment an effort had been made to promote some sort of blending by calling out both personalities at once. These attempts had caused headaches and emotional distress, and were abandoned.

During the many months of observation each Eve, with remarkable consistency, played her own role. No mingling or blending of their characteristic traits was even momentarily observed. In

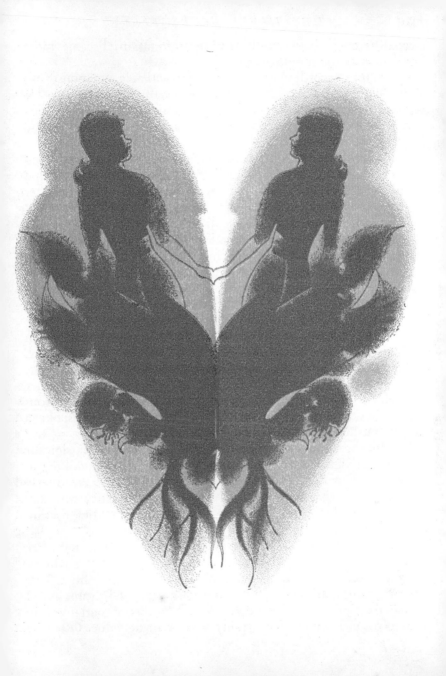

fact, differences between the two manifestations became more impressive as the months passed.

Eve White, according to her employers, was able and industrious at her job; serious, and unfailingly courteous, she made an excellent impression. During her interviews with the doctor she tried to veil her fear and the sorrow that she endured in the separation from her beloved daughter.

The routine of her days was seldom varied. During working hours she kept her mind on the job. She often smiled at jokes that circulated from desk to desk, but never seemed to join in the banter of the others. After work, she spent much of the time in her room. Skillful at needlework, she made all of Bonnie's clothes and many of her own. Each day she wrote a letter to Bonnie.

She sometimes took a walk in the little park near the boardinghouse, alone or with one of the other girls. At night she often read until bedtime or occasionally played cards with the group downstairs. She attended church regularly, taking an inconspicuous part in its activities. Over this year of close observation Eve White showed no important change. Her new environment, freedom from the routines of housekeeping, the diversions of a city much larger than she had previously lived in seemed to alter her habits and attitudes very little if at all. The little pleasures that came her way she accepted quietly. Evidence of enthusiasm or vigorous initiative was never displayed, though her industry bespoke a deeply felt purpose in providing for her child.

Eve Black, meanwhile, showed little or no real compassion for this mother's grief in the separation from her child. In talking to us about all matters past and present her emotions were utterly free. She bore the other no ill will. Amusement, saucy vexation, eager anticipation, a fresh, childlike delight in trivialities, fleeting anger, naive vanity, all flashed in her volatile face.

Efforts to interest Eve Black in helping Eve White with her problems were continually frustrated by the playful Eve's whims. She owned to no attachments, accepted no responsibilities. The doctor occasionally was able to enlist her support in some novel remedial aim directed toward Eve White. Sometimes attaining in her even an attitude of neutrality was of great value. Often by ingenious lies she misled the doctor to believe that she was co-operating when her behavior was particularly detrimental to Eve White's progress.

One valuable means of influencing her, which had been partially used before, remained. As has been said, sometimes the adventurous Eve could "get out" and sometimes not. Since Eve White had learned of the other's existence, it had become plain to us that her willingness to step aside and, so to speak, to release the imp played an important part in her alternate's ability to appear. The therapist now used this fact again for bargaining with Eve Black for better coöperation. When she avoided serious interruptions of Eve White's work and refrained from pranks that caused difficulties, she was rewarded with more time "out."

Despite occasional brief eruptions of her alternate during the hours of work, Eve White held her first job for approximately two months. Perhaps Eve Black was influenced more than she admitted by recognition of the fact that her sober partner must maintain a source of livelihood if she herself were to subsist. Usually the flamboyant one restricted her longer excursions into the outside world to week-ends or to evenings. A couple of weeks after Eve White began her first job, however, Eve Black decided to visit her office. "I just thought I'd like to see for myself what it was like there," she explained to the doctor later with a tranquil smile. Lacking Eve White's skill with the typewriter she soon made a series of mistakes; then, vexed or bored, she awkwardly spelled out the words of a risqué joke. Amused at the incongruity of this offering in a serious business report, she tried her hand at filing, leaving a good deal of confusion for the other Eve to deal with.

After that she slipped "out" every now and then in the office. Having no incentive for work, she seldom interrupted her colleague very long. But even when present for only a few minutes, she sometimes created strange impressions, coming out spontaneously with some wisecrack that was in astonishing contrast with everyone's concept of the sober Mrs. White.

More rarely, estimating that she would be able to hold the stage for a considerable period of time, she would leave the office to seek a more congenial environment. When this occurred she sometimes offered the excuse of headache, but by no means always. Once Mrs. White was observed to disappear from her post without giving notice. A few hours later the office manager was passing by a moving-picture theater. A jovial shout hailed him by name. Though he knew Mrs. White only casually, this bold, vigorous girl, strolling out of the theater lobby, somehow brought her to his mind.

"Glad to see you out getting a little fresh air, boy — might do you good," the astonishing apparition called to him loudly. Her eyes flashed straight into his face for a moment and she gave him a warm smile. Then she turned and was lost in the crowd. The manager wondered if he had lost his senses.

On several subsequent occasions Mrs. White was left with the uncomfortable task of accounting for a peremptory departure. Except for these peculiar episodes, she was so consistent and conscientious that Eve Black's occasional pranks were tolerated by her various employers for a long time before their cumulative effect caused her to lose the jobs. Sometimes Mrs. White herself resigned, after learning by inference of some humiliating exploit of her alternate. It was occasionally necessary for the physician to intercede for her in regard to these difficulties.

During this period of approximately a year she moved several times, finding it less difficult to seek a new boardinghouse or a new roommate than to attempt excuses or explanations. In a rapidly growing metropolitan area inhabited by almost a quarter of a million people, Eve White found it possible to obtain new jobs and to make fresh starts in neighborhoods far from the scenes she had fled. But again and again she was forced to start over somewhere else at a minimum salary. Surely this career could not continue indefinitely.

Eve White found herself severely handicapped in establishing simple friendships or in participating in little plans for diversion that other girls at the boardinghouse suggested. Even when Eve Black was relatively coöperative and undramatic, her brash voice and impish exuberance seemed like such a formidable eccentricity that Mrs. White's acquaintances often withdrew in bewilderment.

Thus limited, Eve White dearly cherished what companionship

she found available. Having recently moved to a new boarding-house, she often sat on the porch for a while after supper with her landlady and a few older couples. In this little group were an elderly, retired English teacher and his wife who showed her many pleasant little attentions, both seeming aware of the unexpressed sadness in this quiet timid girl.

The former teacher noticed that Eve White occasionally sat reading an anthology of poetry on Sunday afternoons. Subsequently finding himself on the porch with her, he mentioned the book and spoke of his own interest in it. She was at once responsive, and spoke a little to him, in her guarded manner, about the poems she liked best. At her timid request he finally read aloud to her from her favorite volume on several Sunday afternoons.

She had expressed to the doctor her pleasure in finding these two older people and particularly her gratitude and respect for this gentleman who took pains to bring something like understanding into her semi-isolation. When she spoke with regret of a change in his attitude, she as well as the therapist had little difficulty in surmising what must have happened.

Some weeks after denying any knowledge of what might have affected the former teacher's attitude toward Eve White, Eve Black with twinkling eyes told this story.

Having "got out" one evening just before supper she lost no time in getting her own clothes from the closet and wriggling into them. Before the mirror she archly lined her eyebrows and put mascara on her lashes. With her own vivid lipstick she made over her mouth. She then decided to take a stroll. Tripping through the front door, she paused at the cordial greeting offered her by the elderly gentleman who rose from his chair. Though she knew about him, she had not, as she put it, been sufficiently interested in his conversations with Eve White to pay much attention to him. Now her childlike vanity was arrested by the attention he plainly offered. Surprise and pleasure grew in his eyes. He assumed at once that his melancholy and demure little friend must have been touched by a happy miracle to be so gaily bedecked.

"Why, dear child," he said, "you look lovely this evening."

Distractible as a kitten, Eve Black came over and sat on the porch railing near his chair, overbalancing as she did so. "Oops!" she gasped, flashing a playful glance at him as she carelessly smoothed the dress which had flurried about her knees.

After one or two perfunctory remarks her companion fell silent. Then, trying to orient himself, he caught at the memory of his last conversation with Eve White. They had both tried to recall some lines of verse which subsequently had come to him. Now, seeking a path to familiar territory, he said them aloud in his grave, well-trained voice.

With a sweeping roll of her eyes and a soft exclamation of laughter, Eve Black rocked over the banister, clapping her hands together. "Now Pops, I do think that's right cute." Ready to join in any game, she arched her brows for a moment of concentration. "I know one too! Listen, Pops, I bet you goin' to like it." Then she recited:

> *"They call him a lovin' man;*
> *He sure ain't got cold feet.*
> *He can make you warm inside,*
> *And your heart do the boogie beat."*

She swung herself off the porch railing with a brave swirl of ruffles, touched her immobile companion cordially on the shoulder, and was away toward the street. When she reached the sidewalk, Eve Black turned, waved cordially, and with a smile called out, "Nite-tee — now!"

PERHAPS the reader will grant that we were justified in fearing what might happen to such a creature as Eve Black during her nocturnal adventures about the city. We could conceive of no way to control her directly except by sending Eve White to the State Hospital. As weeks passed and we saw that the venturesome Eve repeatedly extricated herself from crisis after crisis, we began to feel that beneath her naive recklessness there must exist a real shrewdness, perhaps some reflex pattern of action by which she unfailingly saved herself. It became steadily clearer to us that she was attracted not by sin or depravity but rather by the trappings with which they are so often garnished.

From time to time she would call from some night club, disturbing the therapist's sleep with childlike requests for help in a situation that threatened to become serious. More rarely she called at some late hour on an impulse to share with him a little of the festivity she was enjoying, or to sing over the telephone a bar or two of some song with which she was enlivening her surroundings.

One day the physician was surprised to find that Eve Black had come to the appointment in Eve White's place. She agreed to cooperate in calling forth her alternate, but maintained that before the interview ended she should be restored to the state in which she had come to the office. This was agreed upon and after the interview with Eve White, who also admitted that the arrangement was just, Eve Black was called "out" again and allowed to go her way.

Aside from the basic question of fairness in such a complicated situation, there were other reasons for not interfering with the balance of power these two had worked out between themselves. Should Eve Black be deprived of her period of freedom she might be provoked into extremely rebellious behavior. There was reason to fear Eve Black's ill will and opposition, whether outwardly expressed in damaging mischief during her freedom, or from within in the ways that had once caused Eve White's headaches and blackouts and contributed to her anxiety.

From this time on it was occasionally the second Eve who came to fill the appointment Eve White had made. In the waiting room she at once made herself happily at ease. Talkative and irrepressible, she soon engaged everyone in conversation. Though much of her speech consisted of unoriginal slang, her own fresh and superficial feelings bubbled through so gaily that even these words took on an April flavor. Soon there was no question in our secretary's mind about which Eve to announce.

On one occasion Eve Black attracted particular attention in the waiting room. It was the eve of St. Valentine's Day and she had taken some pains in decking herself out appropriately. Into her luxuriant dark hair that now hung free at shoulder length, she had woven dozens of small red roses, carefully forming a vivid heart shape, an elaborate and resplendent floral valentine. Her eyes eager and jubilant in anticipation of the applause she was sure would be forthcoming, she took her chair.

The doctor decided it would be inadvisable to call out Eve White and thus inflict upon her this vision of herself. Later, in commenting on how she had felt when she had emerged at home and found herself in this capricious adornment, Eve White said, "Even a woman accustomed to playing parts on the stage wouldn't have gone out on the streets looking like that."

AFTER a year of employment Eve White had gained ground in some respects. She was working efficiently in the best position she had yet obtained and had held it for a longer period than usual, despite occasional minor interruptions by Eve Black. A raise in salary and her careful management had enabled her to save a little money. The headaches and blackout spells had not troubled her for many months. She had become a little more hopeful of eventually reaching some acceptable relationship with her husband. Though sadly missing her child, she found some comfort in her successful efforts to provide for her. She had made a few friends in the once strange city.

Meanwhile Eve Black had in general been causing less trouble. Being bored with all regular work, she seldom "came out" any more to indulge in complicating pranks while the breadwinner was on her job. Though in leisure hours she often indulged in boisterous amusement, her demure and conventional counterpart, lacking knowledge of these peccadillos, was spared humiliation and distress.

At this point Eve White's headaches and blackouts suddenly returned. They grew more severe and more frequent. The other Eve denied having any influence in the new development. She did not experience the headaches, but, surprisingly, seemed now to participate in the blackouts and could give no account of what occurred during them. Apparently a little uneasy about these experiences she said, "I don't know where we go, but go we do."

Two or three times the patient was found by her roommate lying unconscious on the floor. This, so far as we could learn, had not occurred during the previous blackouts. It became difficult for her to work effectively. During interviews she became less accessible, while showing indications of increasing stress. The therapist began to fear again that a psychosis might be impending.

Sometime after the return of the headaches and blackouts, a very early recollection of a painful scalding was being discussed with Eve White. As she spoke her eyes closed sleepily. Her words soon ceased; her head dropped back on the chair. After perhaps two minutes, her eyes opened. Blankly but calmly she stared about the room, looking at the furniture and the pictures as if trying methodically to orient herself. Her eyes finally met those of the therapist. Slowly, with immeasurable poise, she said, "Who are you?"

From the first moment it was vividly apparent that this was neither Eve White nor Eve Black. She did not need to tell us that. Quietly she continued her survey of the surroundings. Her calm face showed neither fright nor bewilderment. After a few minutes the doctor asked, "What is your name?" With no evidence of embarrassment, she replied, "I don't know."

For a while she said nothing more. Then she asked, "How long have I been here?" As the doctor told her briefly what had preceded, she occasionally asked a pertinent question. She had the manner of someone who needs time to absorb each new item of experience. She denied even the slightest knowledge of any such person as Eve White (or Eve Black) and at first appeared to find nothing remarkable in what the physician told her of her relationship to them. Everything, she admitted, was new to her. She denied consciousness of any life or experience prior to the moment she had opened her calm, steady eyes a few minutes ago. After considerable conversation, she was again questioned about her identity, and said, "My name is Jane." Of how she knew this, or why she made such a choice, she could tell nothing.

ONLY in a superficial way could this new woman be described as a compromise between the two Eves. Jane's impressive command of language no more suggested the pinched, laconic reserve of Eve White than the ebullient slang of Eve Black. She looked no more like circumspect Eve White than like that shallow, boisterous

scamp, her willful alternate. Though Jane's eyes never flashed with the vivacity characteristic of Eve Black, they seemed to reflect a disciplined vitality, an ease, and a range of feeling and interest beyond the reach of Eve White. Jane's face had its own alert and thoughtful expression. Unlike Eve White she could laugh, and her smile was fresh and lovely. Just as Eve Black gave the illusory impression of having a more rounded figure than Eve White, so Jane seemed a little taller when she stood, more lightly erect, more capable of command. Her gait and movements were her own, unobtrusively graceful and perfectly feminine. There was far more of woman and of life about this third personality than might be expected from the two Eves with their faults and weaknesses eliminated and all assets combined.

Neither Eve knew for some time that a third manifestation had emerged. From her initial appearance, however, Jane enjoyed access to each of the other's consciousness during its periods of prevalence. Within a week she had, so to speak, accompanied Eve Black to the dance halls. She had also attended Eve White at work and followed sympathetically this mother's longing thoughts about her daughter; she had appreciated, without sharing personally, her gentle courage and her sense of impending doom. She soon learned a good many details of Eve White's work. This did not bore her as it did Eve Black. And she reported with utter detachment, but with tolerant amusement, various rowdy witticisms and lusty incidents that occurred when Eve Black was out for the evening.

"You know, Doctor," she said seriously, "I'm beginning to believe that girl actually has a sort of talent. I haven't had long to observe, but it seems to me that people in night clubs are often bored and worried. Eve Black puts real excitement and hilarity into any little song or bit of horseplay. Soon other people forget their own moods and seem also to be having more fun."

After considerable acquaintance with Jane, the therapist decided to make her existence known to Eve White. Jane agreed to do what she could to convey to the other a sense of her friendly presence. It was decided that she make this effort at the moment when the physician was informing Eve White about her.

Jane was described to Eve White as a capable and intelligent entity, one in whom she might find a powerful and sympathetic ally. In an intangible brief expansion of awareness, Eve White seemed to obtain some convincing realization of Jane — not as part of her own being, but as a proximate entity, unperceived but for the moment somehow intimate. Before the wonder and astonishment had faded from her pale face, Eve Black burst out suddenly and unbidden.

With a vehement toss of her head she sprang from the chair and strode across the room. With her back to the physician she stood for a moment with a hand on each hip. Turning, she approached him, wrath and indignation on her face.

"What in hell's this all about?" she shouted. "I might've knowed you and she'd cook up somethin' fishy.... You and her and all your fine honorable airs!"

The peak of her anger passed quickly and a little of her habitual cajolery returned. "All right now, give me the straight of it," she demanded. "What about this Jane business? I've got the right to know!"

Though she became somewhat mollified as her questions were answered, it was plain that she disliked the new situation. Eve White was a well-known rival with whom she felt she could cope. This was a stranger whose thought and action lay outside the scope of her awareness.

During the eleven months in which all three carried out their separate careers, Eve Black was never able to displace Jane's consciousness. Jane could not be called out by the therapist nor, as a rule, could she emerge voluntarily when Eve Black was present. (On the one or two occasions when she apparently did accomplish the latter, Eve White may have momentarily replaced Eve Black to provide the means of outlet for Jane.)

Jane soon found herself spontaneously alternating with Eve White, at first without volition or forewarning. A little later she often found it possible to "come out" intentionally. Her knowledge expanded rapidly. Though unable to command the memory of either Eve, she was told of incidents in their past and used this knowledge skillfully to orient herself. Neither the present nor the past experience of either Eve, however, impressed her as belonging to herself.

Despite her unfailing poise, Jane often showed a naïveté quite her own. Her reactions suggested that all experience was new and fresh, and even the most commonplace glowed with novelty and charm. Her rapid acquisition of knowledge, however, suggested that beyond or beneath the limits of her awareness lay considerable resources which bit by bit would become more available. Small items of direct experience, like keys to secret doors, seemed to give her access to additional material.

Though at first George Washington's name held no significance for her, a few sentences of information about him brought within her grasp a good deal more about the American Revolution and its chief figures than had been told her. In some respects she seemed like a person who fifteen years ago in college had mastered Latin but since that time had never thought of it. Such a person, if called upon, could reacquire the lost knowledge with facility.

Much of Jane's information seemed to emerge from resources not available to either Eve. Her interests, viewpoints, tastes, all consistently indicated a being whose experience remained apart. On her first appearance expectation naturally arose that in Jane there might be some fusion of, or even a mere compromise between, the two Eves. But it immediately became difficult to fit her into such a concept. She appeared to us with increasing clarity to be another entity. She coöperated with warmth, judgment and originality beyond that of the others. All her behavior was constructive and socially acceptable. In contrast with Eve White she displayed ingenuity, humor and confidence. In her active coöperation she often wrote down comments on the situation and sent them to the doctor.

A few months after her first manifestation, Jane, emerging on Christmas Day when Eve White was at the home of her parents, set down these reflections.

MY FIRST CHRISTMAS

I think I have missed much, not having had a childhood period. Bonnie Baby is a very happy little girl today and is so fortunate to have a mother like Eve White who devotes her all to the happiness of one little person. Her baby must never know the sorrow and insecurity suffered by her wonderful mother. I know I could not be big enough to give so much so freely to a family that had neglected me as she must have been neglected as a child. This has caused her to develop an illness from which she may never recover.

Her eagerness to offer gifts to those she loves brings a reward: a joy and happiness to her in knowing they are pleased. They, perhaps for the first time, have given serious thought to buying gifts for her. I wonder if they have ever done this before. I doubt it, because she cried so humbly this morning. Has no one ever loved her, or deeply cared if she was happy? It takes so little to make her happy — a smile or a kind word from either of her parents.

I feel depressed and unhappy. I don't know how to live. I understand almost nothing of the meaning of love and security. I know I must have both to be happy. I have little idea yet of my purpose, of what I may be searching for. I can never feel satisfied, for there seems to be some further point, some goal . . . where?

Jane, who at first had felt herself personally free from Eve White's responsibilities and attachments, steadily developed an affection and compassion for the industrious and devoted mother. She soon took over many of Eve White's tasks at work and at home in efforts to relieve and assist her. Her feelings toward Eve's little girl appeared to be those of a wise and richly compassionate woman toward the child of a family not her own, complicated by the deep conviction that she must not in any way come between the distressed mother and her only child. During the first few months of her separate existence Jane became stronger and more active. As time passed she stayed "out" more and more.

Almost any observer would, we thought now, find it obvious that, if Jane could remain in full possession of that integrated human functioning we call *personality,* our patient would probably regain full health, eventually adjust satisfactorily, perhaps at a distinctly superior level, and find her way to a happy life. It would have been easy to say that the only rational solution to this astonishing problem was for Jane to survive, and Jane only. But we did not judge ourselves wise enough to make this decision. It is plain that, even if we had this wisdom, the responsibility was not ours. Would any physician order euthanasia for the heedlessly merry and amoral but nevertheless unique Eve Black? Certainly none who had ever felt the inimitable identity of her capricious being.

A surviving Jane, though it seemed very unlikely that she would ever return to Ralph White, would provide for Eve White's half-lost little girl a maternal figure of superb resources. But would her feelings toward the child ever be the unique feelings of deep love that sustained Eve White in her struggle to give the child a chance for happiness? It may be said that Jane *was* the little girl's real mother. The child was, after all, born of her body. But *was* she her mother? Those who had known Eve White would find it hard to accept simple affirmation as the whole truth. This whole truth can be better sensed in direct feeling than conveyed by explanation.

We did not wish to exert pressures arbitrarily and perhaps play a part in the extinction of valuable qualities if they could be integrated into more responsible patterns of behavior. We believed there was some choice open to the psychiatrist as to which personality he should try to reinforce, but that he must work along with developments within the patient rather than make full and final judgments.

We felt that therapy had played a part in the emergence of Jane, but we did not consider her merely our creation. Our influence seemed to have been more catalytic than causal. We could not predict the outcome with any great confidence, but as Jane continued to grow in influence we became hopeful that some reasonably good adjustment might work out through the capacities she contributed.

Jane, who appeared to have some grasp of this whole matter not available to either of the Eves, shared our sharp reluctance about participating in any act that might contribute to Eve White's extinction. The possibility had occurred to Eve White. Too restrained ordinarily to speak freely about such a matter, after hypnosis she offered, in tones of immeasurable conviction, to accept this extinction if it might win for Jane the role of mother, in which she felt that she herself had failed Bonnie.

It has been said that a man must first lay down his life if he is to find it. Was it possible, we wondered, that this mother might, through her very renunciation, somehow survive and find a way back to the one and dearest thing she was ready to leave forever?

At about this time Eve White, anything but a physically bold or instinctively active person, was challenged suddenly by an event which for her was momentous. Of this Jane, deeply moved, wrote to the therapist:

> Today she did something that made me know and appreciate her as I had not been able to do before. She must not die yet. There's so much I must know, and so very much I must learn from her. She is the substance of, *This above all, to thine own self be true*. I want her to live — not me!
>
> She saved the life of a little boy today. She darted out in front of a car to pick him up and take him to safety. But the moment his baby arms went around her neck, he became her baby — and she continued to walk down the street carrying him in her arms.
>
> I have never been thus affected by anything in my four months of life. There seemed only one solution to prevent her possible arrest for kidnaping. That was for me to come out and find the child's mother. Eve White had her baby again for a short while this afternoon; and I'm so happy for that.
>
> I still can't feel Eve Black. I can't believe she's just given up. *I feel inexpressibly humble.*

AFTER approximately seven months of experience with Jane and more than a year and a half with the two Eves, we prepared our report of this case for the American Psychiatric Association meeting, and also a longer article, published later in the *Journal of Abnormal and Social Psychology*.

Some who read our report no doubt concluded that we had been thoroughly hoodwinked by a skillful actress. It seems possible that such an actress after assiduous study and long training might indeed master three such roles and play them in a way that would defy detection for an hour, perhaps for several hours. But could any person consciously dissimulating over a period of months avoid even one telltale error or imperfection?

Others may have asked if we were not being taken in by what was no more than superficial hysterical tomfoolery. Or could not such a presumed disintegration into three manifestations of personality be regarded as schizophrenic? Even if the process was akin to schizophrenia, it must still be noted that not one of the three personalities showed any symptoms suggesting the presence of that disorder.

It seemed of some importance to us to learn how other observers would react to what we had so long been studying. All three of the ladies agreed readily to appear before the Dugas Journal Club, a group of approximately forty physicians, psychologists, physiologists and chemists from the Medical College of Georgia, the University Hospital and the local Veterans Administration Psychiatric Hospital. Eve White was presented first. When Eve Black was produced an audible intake of the breath brought this group to rapt attention. Jane was presented last.

For approximately two hours the three ladies answered questions, each displaying the characteristics so distinctly her own. In this sober setting of scientific inquiry a sense of drama steadily grew. Not one of the characters could be thrown off balance by any ruse. From none emerged a word or gesture inconsistent with her separate identity. One experienced clinician who asked Jane about an event that had occurred almost a year previously received this reply, "But, Doctor, you forget that I am only seven months old!"

Another questioned Eve Black about Eve White's reactions, implying they must after all be her own. When this was denied he said, "But surely you share some of her feelings. You are, in a sense, twins, aren't you?"

With a quick snap of her eyes, she replied emphatically, "But not *identical* twins."

SOME WEEKS after Jane emerged electroencephalographic studies of the three patients had been conducted. An electroencephalograph, often used in the diagnosis of brain disorders, is an instrument for recording minute changes in the electrical activity of the brain. In summing up, the report said:

> . . . The greatest amount of tenseness is shown by Eve Black; Eve White is next and Jane least. . . . Eve Black's record also shows evidence of restlessness and muscle tension. Eve Black's tracing is definitely distinguished from the other two and could be classified as borderline normal. Eve White's tracing probably cannot be distinguished from Jane's; both are clearly normal.

Now our three personality manifestations were each for the first time given the semantic differential test, a relatively new exploratory device suggested to us by Dr. J. McV. Hunt, editor of the *Journal of Abnormal and Social Psychology*. Charles E. Osgood and Zella Luria, who devised this test, carried out the blind analysis of the material we obtained separately from the three personalities. They knew only that they were dealing with a case of triple personality; that the patient was a married woman with a child; that she had a job. We had no direct communication with our co-workers; Osgood and Luria did not know who was treating this patient or in what part of the country she was located until after their results were submitted for publication.

The test contains fifteen significant concepts: LOVE, CHILD, MY DOCTOR, ME, MY JOB, MENTAL SICKNESS, MY MOTHER, PEACE OF MIND, FRAUD, MY SPOUSE, SELF-CONTROL, HATRED, MY FATHER, CONFUSION, SEX. The patient places each of these items in a series of scales indicating judgment between two contrasting evaluations, or opposites, such as *valuable–worthless, soft–hard, active–passive,* etc. There are ten pairs of these evaluations. Each scale gives seven choices of degree between the two extremes as shown in these examples:

MY FATHER   active __ : __ : __ : __ : X : __ : __ : passive.
MY MOTHER   soft __ : X : __ : __ : __ : __ : __ : hard.

The results of the test led Osgood and Luria, whose report has since been published in the *Journal of Abnormal and Social Psy-*

chology, to estimate Jane and Eve White as "socialized" personalities. They differ chiefly from each other in their responses to the concepts ME, MY SPOUSE and SEX, Eve White's reactions suggesting a negative critical attitude, Jane's suggesting acceptance of them as positive values. "Eve Black," they report, "shows gross differences on almost all concepts . . . clearly the most deviant and disordered personality." Her test analysis says in part: "What are positive values for most people — CHILD, MY SPOUSE, MY JOB, LOVE and SEX — are completely rejected as *bad* and *passive,* and all of these except CHILD are also *weak.* . . . LOVE and SEX are closely identified, both as *bad, weak, passive* things."

Osgood and Luria tentatively infer that, of the three, Eve White is "most in contact with social reality and under the greatest emotional stress." She is described as "accepting the mores or values of others (particularly her mother) but continually criticizing and punishing herself. . . . If this case came to the psychotherapists with a voluntary plea for help," Osgood and Luria conclude, "then it seems likely that Eve White was dominant at the time."

Eve Black is described as accepting socially disapproved attitudes as "perfectly legitimate," as seeing "herself as a dominant, active wonder-woman" and as "in no way self-critical." Osgood and Luria also say, "Like a completely selfish infant, this personality is entirely oriented around the assumption of its own perfection."

To our surprise, interpretation of the test indicated Jane as "the 'original' personality, in the sense of being most characteristic of the woman her friends and relatives knew. . . ." She also appeared to be "the most puzzling of the three personalities." She is described as "superficially . . . a very healthy personality: 'all's well with the world and I'm getting better and better.' " Some points, however, indicate that through self-deception she may have "woven a web of repression as to the state of reality," that the promising features in her performance may be misleading. Two interpretations of Jane, according to the test, become possible, one offering much hope, the other strongly suggesting that what is most encouraging about her may be quite insubstantial.

If we keep in mind the fact that Osgood and Luria had no information at all about this patient except the few items mentioned above, some of these estimates, based solely on what each of the personalities scored in the test, seem remarkably accurate.

The uncertainty about Jane and her potentialities which the test results bring up is a point of great significance. Would the qualities we have surmised in this manifestation, after all, prove to be little more than a blind mimicry of life? If we were wrong about Jane, the prognosis for our patient became poor indeed.

Here, we had thought, was an ally whose strength might be added to Eve White's apparently dwindling resources. Here too, it seemed to us, were signs of a response to life through which might occur some reconciliation of the conflict between the two Eves. Since Jane had vastly more capacity for fun and humor than Eve White, might not the shallow hedonistic impulses of Eve Black find through Jane more acceptable outlets and more mature goals?

It was still impossible to estimate with any confidence what would next befall our engrossing patient, but her situation did improve for several months. Eve Black for a while was less ambitious in her exploits. Minor incidents, however, continued to indicate her activity. One morning Eve White telephoned in agitation from the department store where she had been working.

"What's wrong with her?" she sobbed over the telephone. "She goes around telling lie after lie. Doctor, it's so embarrassing I can hardly stand it. She's been telling customers that this and that piece of merchandise will be in the next day when she must know we don't even carry those things. I've tried to believe she isn't really bad — maybe in some respects a nice person — but I don't see how she can be anything but hateful."

Such a loss of patience was not characteristic. Eve White usually succeeded in restraining her tears even when large misfortunes befell her or when tragic events portended. Perhaps the never-ending repetition of annoyances would eventually undermine her remarkable self-control. If this defensive barricade could not be kept intact, would Eve White rapidly deteriorate? Or would she become less constrained and eventually better able to survive?

During this period Jane wrote in her diary:

Eve White seems to think she is slowly dying. She is constantly trying to arrange everything so it will be easier for her successor, whoever that may be. The doctor seems to feel that I will be the successor. If it should be me, I hope the day may come when Eve White will know the fulfillment of her desires, especially for Bonnie, through me. It confuses and depresses me to feel that if I am to live it must be through the "death" of one so fine. We seem to be moving toward a climax, toward something I cannot foresee. Drifting as we are is not building strength. I do not need to say here that I'm frightened. I am scared to death....

CHAPTER 5

Eve White kept her job at the department store until several months after our study of the case was reported, with fictitious names, at a meeting of the American Psychiatric Association. Eve Black took great interest in the newspaper stories that followed this presentation. Indeed, she seemed to be fascinated by her anonymous fame. During her midnight revels she sometimes hinted that she was a woman of renown and, perhaps, a sort of genius, voluntarily disguised in the role of a carefree girl to avoid recognition. The stories varied with her mood. There is reason to suspect that at least once she convinced a tipsy dancing companion that she had achieved distinction in Seville as a female matador.

Eve White asked permission to leave her work early one afternoon because of a minor physical indisposition. Approximately an hour later the manager of the department store received a telephone call from someone who gave as her name that of a nationally known woman journalist. The manager was asked if Mrs. Eve White was one of his employes. The caller explained that she had come to the city to write an account of Mrs. White. She briefly discussed with the busy executive some points about multiple personality, implying that in some respects at least it was to be regarded as a rare gift.

The attitude of the inquirer soon convinced the department-store manager that he was the victim of a practical joke and he hung up. This, however, led to inquiries about Mrs. White's work.

Despite a generally good record of efficiency, her immediate superiors reported that, particularly during recent weeks, she had often seemed listless and unhappy; then again she would be overconfident and careless, chattering boisterously on irrelevant subjects. As time passed these erratic episodes became more troublesome and finally Eve White lost this position.

Eve Black later admitted her part in the proceedings. She had been motivated by criticism of her work by the manager on one of her occasional periods "out." Jane further interpreted the telephone call as Eve Black's means of bringing to the manager's attention the fact that she was a person who had stirred interest in places afar.

Though Jane, with increasing experience, was now able to help Eve White more and more often at work and sometimes to emerge on critical occasions, she had, so far, found no way to bring about any satisfactory compromise between the deeply conflicting aims of Eve White and Eve Black. Sometimes and in some way Eve White was within reach of Jane's wordless counsel or support, but, when Eve Black obtained control, Jane still could not in any way exert an influence either directly or through Eve White.

Some months after the separation Ralph White had become distinctly attentive to his wife, coming often to see her on weekends and urging her to return to him. She had left him with the understanding that she was to live alone until she had improved sufficiently to decide confidently to renew their relations. Under Ralph's attempts to woo his wife back her stress and perplexity mounted until it became necessary for the therapist to intervene and re-emphasize to Ralph White the terms of his agreement. Jane, who maintained an impersonal attitude toward Ralph, spoke more freely than Eve White did about the situation. It was her opinion that the wife was increasingly affected by repugnance at the prospect of returning to him. She tried to tell herself, according to Jane, that this was a feature of her illness, something she could hope might eventually subside.

Now, after almost a year of separation, Ralph came to the city apparently determined to take more positive steps. Telling his wife that he was unable to see that *she* had made any progress, or that *they* had made any progress, he strongly urged her to give up her present plans and return with him to Jacksonville, Florida, where he was employed temporarily. Maybe they could soon take Bonnie back to live with them.

Eve White firmly and repeatedly declined. He then asked her to go away with him for the week-end. She continued to shake her head. Finally Ralph became angry and a serious quarrel broke out. After making remarks that led his wife to fear he might take legal steps to gain custody of Bonnie, he returned to his hotel.

Sitting there in disappointment, remorse and intense frustration, he took a highball hoping that this might afford some relief. After about an hour there was a knock at the door. Opening it, he beheld, with astonished eyes, the woman whom he had so recently left in bitterness and sorrow.

Or *was* it his wife? Eve Black for a moment tried to pretend that this was so, saying she had changed her mind, but this time she did not deceive Ralph. He made this known to her at once.

"All right," she said, "so what of it? She don't want to go with you, but maybe I do. She don't like you. But . . . well, I'm beginning to think you're right cute."

She came nearer and took him by the hand. Except when she was mimicking Eve White to preserve her own secret, Eve Black had always confronted Ralph with scorn and derision. He had never before experienced the gaiety that she so freely dispensed to others. The inviting eyes that turned upon him now, apparently with warmth and excitement, stirred his feelings.

Ralph did not doubt that his wife had a strange and serious psychologic illness. Could this be the improvement everyone had been hoping and working for? Would it not be wise for them to try being together for a week-end? That was precisely what he had attempted to persuade his wife to do hardly more than an hour ago.

Behind the serious hopes that shaped this thought there could scarcely fail to be an exciting appeal in the prospect of spending the week-end with a girl who looked like this and seemed to be in such a mood. The amazing differences between this girl and the woman he had known as his wife must have made him feel, however illogically, that the intimate relations she offered might constitute an act of marital infidelity. Yet he was married to this woman.

Ralph soon found himself urging and coaxing Eve Black to go with him to Jacksonville. Apparently surrendering, then coyly withdrawing, she played with gusto the elusive role of the nymph pursued. Ralph became more confident and expansive in his wooing. The event must be gala: there should be a celebration; he spoke of a corsage. She pointed out that she had at hand only the dress she wore. Why then, he would buy her fitting raiment for the splendid occasion.

Before we learned that our patient had left the city, a picture post card from Jacksonville brought this news.

Hi Doc!
   Having more fun! People believe anything!!!! Did you know I'm the latest thing from the West Coast? I'm singing at the Viennese Petticoat nightly at $50.00 a night. A bluff will soon wear off so I agreed to sing three nights. See you next week —
                                        Eve B.

The fact that Ralph White had a night job in Jacksonville, Eve Black told us later, had played an important part in tempting her to spend the week-end there with him. She was doubtful if she would have gone through with her scheme to get new clothes had it been necessary to spend the evenings with Ralph. Since he did not get back from work until long after midnight, she devoted the preceding hours to visiting the liveliest spots in and about the city. At one of these places, she claimed to be a professional entertainer who had worked steadily during the last few years in sumptuous cabarets in Los Angeles.

After an audition, the manager decided to offer Eve Black a trial appearance. It is difficult to conceive of a person better fitted to step into such a role without preparation. Entirely without self-consciousness, amused by every trifle, she could give even the most banal remark a little twist of novelty. Though her voice was ordinary, the contagious quality of her own excitement set people humming with her involuntarily on almost any tune. Unabashed and unstudied, she approached even the most forbidding figures with the spontaneity of a cordial puppy. When telling a threadbare anecdote she was able, with a flashing sweep of her eyes, to bring in almost any bystander as if by a personal and promising invitation.

Even if she had had sufficient perseverance to work regularly at such a job, it is unlikely that she could have sustained the effect of those few performances. Once accustomed to her antics, audiences would soon have noticed the mediocrity of her voice and tired of her familiar little jokes and pantomimes. There is little doubt, however, that for those three nights the Viennese Petticoat was indeed a club worth visiting.

Eve White, after several days of complete subjugation, finally regained contact and control in Jacksonville. With no clue to the circumstances until Ralph returned to the apartment, she was numb and helpless with fear. After learning from him enough of the story to orient herself, in a despair more complete than any she had yet experienced, she took the first available train out of Jacksonville and returned alone.

Later in the physician's office Eve Black denied as emphatically as ever that Ralph was her husband. Not with regret, but with pride, she said she had found in the physical intimacy with him no pleasure but a good deal of petty annoyance. After the new dress, the hat, the shoes and the handbag had been purchased in Jacksonville, she had taken few pains to conceal this. When the physician tried to make Eve Black consider the ethics of her behavior in this episode, her eyes danced with mischief.

"I got the dress I wanted, didn't I?" she snapped triumphantly.

NOT LONG after the events just mentioned, Eve White made the decision to obtain a divorce from her husband. All doubt and vacillation seemed to have left her. On learning that her husband had taken Eve Black to Jacksonville and spent the week-end with her, she knew that she would never go back to him. Her reactions indicated something even more complex than the hurt of a faithfully conventional wife. They reflected also deep horror in the awareness that her own person had, without her will or knowledge, been used in this peculiarly treacherous affair. Eve Black was delighted with the decision but her reactions showed that she was very little concerned personally.

"If she had good sense, and wasn't so finicky, she'd have got rid of the sorry lout years ago," was one of her comments.

Sometime before this a small business transaction involving Eve White and several members of her family had brought to our attention interesting questions concerning her legal status. On our advice she sought the services of a distinguished attorney. In discussing the case with us her counsel explained that the law of our state does not officially recognize multiple personality, or afford precedent to indicate what should be done if one such identity should object to commitments made by either or both of the others. After being introduced to all three of his clients, our learned consultant suggested that all three of the personalities sign any important legal paper.

Now, without delay, Eve White consulted this attorney in the matter of the divorce. Both Jane and Eve Black in discussions with him agreed to support Eve White and to add their signatures to hers on the legal documents.

A few months after Eve White obtained her divorce, Jane reported on a social experience of her own which seemed now to be growing in importance to her. It had begun when the frivolous Eve had gone to a dance and was for the moment unoccupied. Jane in retrospect thus describes the incident:

"May I have this dance?" a good-looking, well-dressed young man asked. It was then that by mere chance I emerged. And for the first time in my life I danced. I did it very poorly, but nevertheless, I had fun the balance of the evening. The handsome, soft-spoken stranger who called himself Earl Lancaster was to bring much happiness into my lonely life.

I had turned a corner. Dr. Thigpen had told me one afternoon in his office, "Jane, the day will come when you will see things differently. You will want love, a husband, a home and children. You have a lot of feeling somewhere there inside of you."

I thought he was wrong. I was sure I would never need any of the things that two people with the same interests want. I thought I was a woman created to live alone.

I remember when I had to tell Earl about my illness. I knew I must. It would not be fair otherwise. After I had told him, I asked him how he felt about dating me.

"The same as I did before," he said.

That's the kind of person Earl is. We know that if this love of ours has a happy ending it will indeed be a miracle. We are faced by the fact that Eve White or Eve Black may be the remaining personality, but he is willing to wait and see. Can anyone blame me for wanting to live?

Though much of Jane's diary now reflected her interest in this young man and the new aspects of feeling and living that were opening before her, she also described her growing interest in Eve White's daughter, writing:

She is the first person I loved beside my doctor. For this tiny intelligent child I want to do the things that a mother might do, even though I have never been a mother. Where do I fit into the picture? Sometimes I feel I don't belong in it at all. But then how do I get out of it?

Jane now seemed to think more about experiences that were personal to herself. Earlier she had functioned largely as a commentator on the problems of the two Eves and had been more or less content in this role. She now sometimes spoke of Eve White's work as "our" job rather than "her" job.

Eve White had made good improvement since the divorce. She did not show any evidence of regretting this step. However, a note of resignation increasingly pervaded her writings. Sometimes her attitude seemed plainly that of one who has accepted extinction as inevitable. During this period she wrote:

My greatest worries lie in trying to look ahead to the future for my baby daughter. What hurts me is for her to climb on my knee,

touch my face with her tiny hands and ask, "Are you my Mommy
or is it one of the others?"

What answer can I give my child?

I only hope that Jane will learn to love her as I do. If so, I will
not fear. I don't mind dying. About my life, there's always been
something missing. I don't know what it is; but I don't suppose it
matters now.

Though Jane continued to be serene in manner she began to
report strange and disturbing feelings and unpleasant experiences
entirely novel to her. She now complained of severe headaches, of
weird and terrifying nightmares. She repeatedly expressed fear and
emphasized increasingly the horror caused by her dreams. Snakes
continually appeared, often gruesomely, in the bizarre nocturnal
scenes. From the records Jane made, let us quote:

For the last few nights I have dreamed that various parts of my
body were turning into snakes. Each night more of me is consumed
by reptiles. It's getting hard for me even to try to sleep, because I am
afraid. I awaken at night and feel as if all these horrible, unbelievable
things are really happening to me. It has taken as long as an hour
for me to convince myself my hands and feet were not snakes.

In a dream I was looking through the window into an old deserted
hut. In the center of the room was a snake pit. Lots of men were
standing round it. All of them had scaly hands — like snakes. Into
the room from a side door came Earl. They took him and threw
him in the pit. When he emerged his feet and hands were black
and they also looked like snakes. Two nights later I dreamed the
same dream, except this time the man forced into the pit was my
doctor.

A few weeks later, during an interview in the office, Jane was
discussing a recent trip Eve White had made to her parents' home,
where she saw Bonnie. While the mother was playing with her
little girl outside the house, Jane emerged. Bonnie now threw a
small rubber ball and missed her aim. The ball rolled under the
house, which stood relatively high off the ground on pillars. Lattice-

work with thick vines partly screened but did not entirely close off the space between floor and ground. An adult, by stooping, could make his way under the beams with little difficulty. Jane thought she would be able to find the ball.

After taking a few steps in the dim light she became sharply aware of the pungent scent given off by earth underneath the house. She felt surprisingly alone, as if she had unintentionally traversed a great distance. Something about this odor seemed curious. Or meaningful? Not locating the ball at once in the obscurity, Jane felt her way slowly past a broken wheelbarrow, a pile of rotting boards, and several empty barrels. Beyond this it was difficult to see at all.

As she looked intently, the thought came to her that perhaps Eve White had played in this place as a child and knew every nook and corner of its strange dark expanse. She herself, mused Jane, had never before been under a house. Perhaps it was for this reason that these surroundings pressed upon her senses as something obscurely stirring. Suddenly she seemed to be losing her balance; she was swept by a sensation as if she were drifting free of gravity. Her head felt light. It was not just this place that seemed to change, but something in *her* changed that gave to the whole world an indescribable freshness. Yes, Jane said, it was somewhat like the feelings she had when she first came to life, or awareness, almost a year earlier in this office.

She was frightened, but an illogical exhilaration almost drowned her fear. Then it became clear that she was disproportionately large in her surroundings, a gigantic being. Before this reaction could be fully assimilated there was a quick reversal of orientation. As if looking through the other end of a telescope, she now felt overwhelmed by a realization of her smallness. The floor and the beams still prevented her from standing erect. Her sudden sense of diminutiveness fell against a broader background than the immediate environment.

Jane, unlike the two Eves, had often spoken freely about the incommunicable shades of personal emotion. Though she was immeasurably more articulate than the others, her discourse on such subjects had lacked the depth and specificity of what she now seemed to be trying to convey. In a sense this experience under the house was almost like the filling in of a new dimension.

Now she mentioned a peculiar and unrecognizable familiarity that began to permeate the whole scope of her awareness. There was an inexplicable stillness as if time paused — for how long, one would never know. After a few moments the intensity of her un-usual feeling diminished greatly. She found Bonnie's ball and came out into the clear afternoon sunlight. To her surprise, all of what she had experienced so vividly only a minute before had almost vanished. She could remember it, of course; but it seemed much farther away than anything so recent could be.

The doctor asked Jane to seek in her own memory, and in what she knew indirectly of the two Eves, for some event that might suggest a link between her feelings under the house and earlier happenings. She tried, but with no success. Eve White was then summoned to consciousness and questioned, but nothing could be obtained that threw light on what Jane had described.

Later during this interview Eve White was hypnotized and in this state various associations were followed out at length. And then Eve White spoke of a blue cup. She had mentioned this before when she first discussed Flo's china doll. Her voice took on unusual animation and she spontaneously pursued this subject. It was, she felt, in very early childhood that she had been playing with this blue china cup. The cup itself was etched sharp in memory before any surrounding material could be brought into focus. Soon she was absorbed in recalling details of the scene in which she and her cousin Flo had been playing with the blue cup.

She was now showing considerable emotion, speaking very rapidly. Someone else seemed to be with her and Flo. No; it seemed now that the presence of this third child was only a bit of fantasy. She herself (how vivid this was becoming) had on a red dress when she and her cousin as small children were playing with the cup. A red corduroy jumper, it was. Now, as if her eyes had magically opened, Eve White announced that this place where they were playing was under the house. Visibly disturbed, she began now to speak almost chaotically. The doctor made out some-thing about chairs . . . a great crowd of people . . . flowers. . . . She abruptly fell silent, as if the zigzag path of association down which she was racing had suddenly ended.

A moment later she awoke spontaneously from hypnosis. Then, with a quick shudder of her body, she changed. Eve Black had emerged unbidden and without warning. She said at once that she wanted the therapist to explain what was the purpose of this interview. For the first time there was a note in her tone that suggested seriousness. Then, almost wistfully, she asked, "Doc, do you think we're ever going to get well?"

At last her invincible confidence seemed to waver. When the therapist asked her if she could remember anything about the blue cup, or about Eve White as a young child playing under the house with Flo, she shook her head.

"I feel funny," she said slowly. "I don't like this business. I guess . . . I'm scared."

She spoke for a moment about the many good times she had enjoyed, then surprisingly said she "didn't seem to have real fun any more." And she complained again of "feeling funny."

If she was indeed sad or serious, there was nothing about her that suggested it was the sadness or seriousness of Eve White, or that she had acquired any of Jane's feeling. If new attitudes were emerging in this hitherto irrepressible female entity, they seemed specifically her own. Though for the moment deprived of her bounce and sparkle, she was in gesture, expression and idiom, as distinctly as ever before, Eve Black.

She now seemed more of a child than ever. Her eyes no longer sparkled with the familiar challenge; but there was still a hint of robust frolic, an afterglow of the full vitality. She smiled, and instead of the inevitable play of coquetry there seemed to be the trace of an affection as warm and simple as that of a puppy.

"I was just thinking about the first time I was in this office. . . . You know, Doc, I hardly know how to say it . . . but you've treated me right good. . . . Remember my red dress?"

Here her words became unclear. She began to sob. To the doctor the reality of Eve Black softly, pitifully sobbing was almost unimaginable: tears were not a part of her world. He now felt shaken, disoriented. Eve Black, the capricious, invulnerable symbol of mischief, had, it seemed, somehow found at least a hint of sorrow, a glimpse of the suffering those who are not abstainers from life are bound to discover.

The doctor realized that something extraordinary was going on. She spoke in brief, rapid spurts, in fragments, with intervals of silence. She was looking at him intently with large soft eyes. These eyes, though changed, were no more like the eyes of Eve White or of Jane than when they first opened upon him in the office more than two years ago. He distinguished phrases now and then. There was something again about the red dress . . . she smiled.

"Oh, Doc," she said very softly, "I feel so funny . . . I — oh, well. . . . Maybe you'll be able to figure it out about me. I don't know at all. . . . I want you to have it. Please take it and keep it to remember me by. Only you and I know why I wanted it so bad. . . . Yes, Doc . . . the red dress . . ."

There were a few more unclear words. Then in silence all expression left her face. Her eyes closed. When they opened the doctor found that he was talking with Eve White, who knew nothing at all of what had just occurred. For a few minutes her present situation was discussed. Her parents, she said, had been kinder to her than ever before, and more coöperative, during the months that followed her divorce. The presence of Jane was then requested.

Jane brought out nothing of particular importance. Planning to terminate the interview, the therapist asked her permission to speak again with Eve White, who had come for the interview and whom he meant to restore to consciousness before the patient left.

Jane's neck stiffened abruptly and she gazed blankly at the physician. Her features contorted. Staring now in glassy horror past the man who faced her, she suddenly cried out in frantic shattered tones:

"Mother . . . ! Oh, Mother . . . ! Don't make me . . . Don't . . . Don't . . . I can't do it! I can't!"

Seizing her head at the temples with both hands, she began a banshee's scream that did not reach its eerie and piercing crescendo until the amazed physician had reached the office of his colleague across the hall.

CHAPTER 6

IT WAS a remarkable scream. Wordless, primitive, sustained, it scarcely seemed human. Hurrying back across the hall, we were both in the office a moment after it subsided. Still quickened by excitement we looked silently at the patient, then at each other.

"Which one is it?" one of us finally asked.

After further scrutiny the other, in sharp astonishment, replied, "Why . . . it isn't any one of the three. . . . It isn't Jane. It isn't Eve White; and yet, it isn't Eve Black!"

So it seemed to us at that moment, and so it still seems now, more than two years later. We asked her then who she was and she could give no clear reply. Her terror was steadily subsiding but she was still bewildered. After a little while we asked again who she was.

"I'm not sure . . . why, I can't tell," she finally murmured.

We did not press her further at this point for specific information. With her consent we were able to transcribe by tape recorder a verbatim account of what followed. It was soon plain that, in contrast with Jane when she had emerged approximately a year ago, this manifestation was equipped with memory. She knew a great deal about the experiences of Eve White, and also of Jane and Eve Black. This young woman's immediate problem seemed to lie in identifying herself, in discovering and realizing just what and who she was.

It is indeed doubtful if there can be any cornerstone of human consciousness more fundamental than the familiar but inexpressible sense of self. Jane, though without memory of any antecedent life on her initial appearance, had a firm and clear sense of her own identity, unlike the disturbing inner uncertainty now experienced by our patient. As she talked with us, we both felt that this person was like Jane in many respects; still neither of us could quite feel that this *was* Jane. On into the evening many points of great interest to us were discussed.

"When you asked me to let you speak with Eve White," she said, referring to the therapist's last request before the startling scream, "when you asked for her, I suddenly realized, *I am Eve White!*"

It must have been a realization of dismaying intensity. Shaken deep within, there came to her now an opposite realization.

"She isn't there. . . . There isn't an Eve White any more. . . . Why, she's gone . . . gone . . . she's dead . . . no more. . . . They're both gone forever!"

The sense of death had pressed upon her with sudden and fearful immensity. With this sense there flashed before her the incident from long ago, when she and Flo had been playing under the house with the blue cup. It was *there,* and *then,* that her mother had called her, telling her to come into the house and change her dress. Her grandmother's funeral . . . the lost memory stood forth in almost the freshness of immediate perception. The sad and solemn group of adults . . . the uncanny stillness everywhere . . . the flowers, and the specific odor of those flowers. . . .

Her mother was holding her up high off the floor and telling her she must touch her dead grandmother's face. Appalled, the young child shrank from this demanded contact. Fragmentary ideas of death, heard spoken of during the grandmother's illness, fears that had stirred for the moment and then been evaded by the little girl, all now coalesced. Her mother kept insisting that she

must touch this immobile face in the coffin. She burst into tears, squirmed and struggled to pull away. Her mother, embarrassed and unnerved by the conspicuous display, intensified her insistence.

The force upon the young child seemed inexorable. Despite her horror she put her hand against the face of the corpse. When her small warm hand felt the cold flesh of this dead face, recognizable as that of the grandmother she remembered alive, a devastating intimation of mortality shook all her senses. All her old horror of the ditch and of the drowned man who had been dragged from its slimy depths joined her present reaction. The scaly monster which her imagination and that of other children had created as a symbol of death and horror inhabiting those fearful waters became palpably real in the cold touch of her grandmother's corpse.

She had cried out, as her hand moved forward: "No, no . . .! Oh, no, Mother . . . I can't . . . Don't make me do it." As her hand left the clammy cheek, all those fragmentary terrors fused into an unbearable reality. It was then that the child had screamed.

Who was it that had screamed again today in the doctor's office?

It was Jane, despite her lack of ability to recall any early life at all before this, in whom the lost item of experience recurred. Our new patient was unable to tell us whether or not the realization of it was also experienced simultaneously by the dormant ones, Eve White and Eve Black. In the searing intensity of the moment, a new unit had apparently been welded. What was this unit? It was difficult at this point to estimate. In her background was the great cry of anguish and terror that in a sense marked her birth. A few days later our patient said, "It seems to me I can remember hearing someone scream. After I got home I could not be sure whether it was I or not."

She impressed us as having undergone an experience strange and profound and difficult to communicate. After the terror of the moment subsided, however, she seemed to reflect qualities we had not seen before in any of the three manifestations. We felt a dimensional difference.

> *And as I looked a quickening gust*
> *Of wind blew up to me and thrust*

Into my face a miracle
Of orchard-breath, and with the smell —
I know not how such things can be! —
*I breathed my soul back into me.**

Had she, we wondered, really done something of this sort? Had a great and basic change come about? Or were we merely dealing with another peculiar facet of a patient still as disordered as before? Unlike the three other manifestations, our patient now reacted as if she did not regard herself as altogether separate from the previous personalities. She did not find or seem to seek a new name for herself, as Jane had immediately done a year earlier.

As her initial bewilderment lessened during those first hours, she showed an increasing tendency to identify herself with Jane. The identification did not seem to be sure or complete, nor did she simply reject all the past experiences of the two Eves as alien. Some of these experiences she accepted as her own. Others remained as isolated from her sense of self as they had been to the earlier Jane. After considerable discussion she decided to call herself Mrs. Evelyn White, our original patient's full legal name.

Later she reported that she had wept a great part of the day following the dramatic event in the office.

"I felt lonely, empty," she said.

What was she crying about?

"Eve Black chiefly, I believe. Doctor, I missed her so much. I can't describe it. They just weren't there any more. It made me feel awfully sad. At the time I wasn't missing Eve White. I was just missing Eve Black. . . . I wouldn't have thought anyone could miss her in such a way. . . . I knew something had to happen one way or the other. . . . But then, you're going to miss them, too — aren't you?"

When asked about Bonnie, she said, as if quite surprised, "Why, I feel that she is my own little girl. Before, she was Eve White's child. I loved her, but not the way I do now."

*From "Renascence" in *Renascence and Other Poems* by Edna St. Vincent Millay. Harper & Brothers. Copyright 1912, 1940 by Edna St. Vincent Millay.

We asked if it were possible for her to think of Eve White and Eve Black as not really lost but in a sense regained.

"I don't think so," she said, "at least not now. I feel I have really lost something. Suppose a screen had been put up in front of you. Now for a year you have two sisters. You are aware of them working, playing, living, though all the time the screen hides them. You know where they go and in a sense you go with them, though you are then behind the screen. All of a sudden the screen is not there. And they are nowhere. It is amazing how suddenly it came to me that they weren't there any longer. You can't help being lonely for them. . . . Looking back I have the feeling that Eve Black may have known she would never see you again. . . . When she started crying I began to realize something drastic was happening."

Referring to the last motion pictures made of the three personalities about two weeks before, she said:

"Doctor, you almost didn't get your movies. There was a difference in Eve Black even then, wasn't there? She didn't quite have the buoyance. I am awfully sorry she didn't take that red dress [to Atlanta where the sound movies were made]. She seemed very sorry she didn't have it. I told the family it was her request that you have it now. If you want it, I will bring it to you."

"I think you should have it made over," the physician suggested, "so you can wear it."

"No," she replied. "There is no possible way to redesign it. No woman outside of show business could wear it except Eve Black. No other woman would go outside the house with it on."

As SEVERAL weeks passed the new, or different, Evelyn White seemed to become more firmly the new, single personality, solidifying, so to speak, into the specific personal form in which she had found herself after the resolution of the separate entities. The resemblance to Jane persisted but did not increase. Her appearance, her gestures, gait, tone of voice, posture, idiom, tastes and outlook gave the effect of some close relative of Jane's who shared her looks and characteristics. We felt as if this were a more substantial and complete woman than the separate Jane.

She never lapsed into the flagrant manner of Eve Black. Nor did we find in her conduct any indications of capriciousness or irresponsibility. Yet there were moments when her glance sparkled with hints of vitality and mirth more striking than anything of that sort we could remember in Jane alone. She did not lose the earlier determination of Eve White to wait until she was capable of looking after her daughter safely before trying to take the little girl to live with her. In making long-range plans about this she was, however, more active and decisive.

She retained the interest Jane had found in Earl Lancaster. Through Jane this pleasant relation had always impressed us as something with perhaps a bit more of form than of substance. The change in her relations with the young man seemed to us chiefly a conversion of Jane's fanciful attitudes and hopes into something more concrete. There seemed now to be also a more deeply felt appraisal of practical difficulties.

It has been noted that the semantic differential tests run on the three manifestations gave results that suggested Jane as the original personality, which had become dissociated. The interpretation of the tests derives a particular interest from the fact that it was Jane's consciousness, the one that had never before established contact with memory of childhood, through which the incident at the funeral was suddenly recalled. Does this indicate that our patient, as an infant and young child prior to that experience, was Jane? — or chiefly Jane? — or more fundamentally Jane than either of the Eves?

It is interesting to ask ourselves if the child who was terrified by the cold touch of the corpse was actually closer to a small hypothetical Jane than to a small hypothetical Eve White. Could this fright have played a part in such a child's becoming the little girl Eve White remembered herself as being? If the incident alone seems insufficient to account for a personality change, a dissociation, or a deep repression of its memory, might it not have served as a sharp and final stimulus to trigger off the effect of deeper and broader conflicts? Could poorly understood fears of parental rejection, childish dreads of death (and of the dead) have mobilized at the funeral and brought into action a great variety of conflicts that had been accumulating perhaps since birth? Insecurities that she had accumulated during the time she was nursing at the breast, when she was struggling with the difficulties of toilet training may have contributed their part. The twin sisters had been born only five or six months before the grandmother died. Possibly Eve at this time felt herself replaced by them.

It is generally believed that a small child's chief problems arise in its relations with parents and brothers and sisters. Eve White pictured her parents as good. Eve Black always expressed distaste for them, particularly for the mother. It seems likely that prior to her grandmother's funeral Eve enjoyed reasonably good relations with her father, but that a good many conflicts occurred between the little girl and her mother, who usually maintained the discipline.

The adult Eve White thought with affection of her younger twin sisters. Eve Black disliked them, and felt no regret in having bitten their toes and otherwise mistreated them. According to the parents Eve appeared to love the twins, but even before the funeral occasionally showed some indications of jealousy.

In connection with this a point made in the interpretation of the Rorschach and other projective tests is of interest:

> . . . Actually the problem started at a much earlier period of life, with a strong feeling of rejection by her parents, especially after the birth of her twin sisters. Mrs. White loves them dearly; Miss Black despises them. In this connection an episode is related by Miss Black. After quitting school to help support the family, she (that is to say Mrs. White) sent home money to be used for overcoats for her twin sisters, denying herself a badly wanted wrist watch. When the money was used to buy them two wrist watches instead of overcoats, she reacted with strong, but repressed, hostility. Significantly, she removed her wrist watch while examined as Mrs. White, stating that she doesn't like jewelry.

After the memory of attending her grandmother's funeral had been regained, the patient was able to fill in a good deal of detail. Her mother had insisted that she put her hand to the face of the corpse because of a belief that if one touches a dead person one will grieve less painfully. Behind this there was also a religious feeling that children should be taught not to shrink from death but to see in it the passing of the soul to immortality. The mother saw in this act of gently touching the dead face a test of faith, and perhaps lost sight of how seriously frightened the child had become.

The patient's mother herself had already described the incident to us almost two years earlier. The recorded details of the funeral given by the mother coincided well with the memory finally regained by the patient. Both of the parents had realized their little girl was acutely upset. They told us that her strange moods and occasional tantrum spells began shortly afterward. They also remembered that she woke up repeatedly during the night after the funeral, crying out and screaming as if in a wild nightmare.

The parents had told us of so many other happenings that impressed us as deserving careful investigation that the grandmother's funeral seemed only one of numerous major incidents. We found little difficulty in leading our patient to recall through association many of these items. It seemed to us advisable to encourage her to recall all potentially influential material from early life spontaneously rather than to thrust it upon her ourselves. The doctor had frequently tried to lead Eve White, Eve Black and also Jane toward a memory of this experience by bringing up material that might stimulate its recollection.

He had also questioned Eve White about her grandparents and death was, of course, discussed. After inquiries about the maternal grandparents, the therapist had asked, "What was your father's mother like? Was she playful and lively?"

"I'm not sure," Eve White had replied. "I don't seem to remember her well. You see, she died when I was very small."

The incident at the funeral appeared to be deeply forgotten or actively repressed from the awareness of Eve White. No trace of it was ever elicited during similar attempts with Eve Black. Through the bits of the others' memories which Jane continued to accumulate we had searched for some link that might lead to the funeral, but without success.

It is widely believed today that psychiatric illness is often an unsuccessful but purposeful effort toward adaptation, and that it may constitute a sacrifice of the patient's health in order to insure his survival. Did the small child Eve White suddenly find herself confronted by the terror of death in a particularly devastating form, or in a new degree of intensity, at this funeral?

Our patient strongly emphasized the connection she had felt between the cold, clammy feeling of her dead grandmother's flesh and her fears about the monster she had so long believed to exist in the deep ditch where a man had drowned. The threat and horror of this fantasy, perhaps a symbol of her imperfect concepts of death itself, now came down upon her directly. The mystery and threat of death were a vague but terrible focal point toward which all feelings of guilt and fear seemed to lead. Our patient felt that the huge snakes by which Jane was tormented in her nightmares were, at least in part, reflections of this cruel reptiliary phantom of the ditch.

Death to many children seems a form of punishment. In law the ultimate penalty for the wrongdoer is execution. Proverbially, the wages of sin is death. The boy who disobediently scoots out on his bicycle into the swift traffic of the highway may be killed. Many of the rules of conduct that the very young child must first learn are those that will preserve his life. Often physical pain and fright reinforce the verbal warning. As a final and fearful consequence of misbehavior looms the hideous threat of death itself. This may be conceived by a child as the sum of all imaginable pains and at the same time as irreversible banishment. The child, and indeed the adult also, sometimes evades contemplating or even accepting unbearably distressing eventualities.

If the experience at her grandmother's funeral brought upon five-year-old Eve a new and terrifying reaction to death, it is quite possible that this might have motivated her extraordinary efforts to be good and to avoid what she had been taught was bad or evil. This may have been the beginning of a pattern of unusual conformity and restraint. Impulses that are regularly denied and subdued may, it seems, gain indirect expression in common psychiatric symptoms, or if sufficiently powerful may shatter the personality in a schizophrenic psychosis.

It has been said also that the banished and blocked tendencies may unite and organize beneath the level of consciousness, eventually becoming the nucleus of another personality. If these concealed forces become strong enough to challenge the conscious personality and to replace it in command, we are dealing with what is said to be *another* and *different personality*. Since we have assumed that the banished or repressed impulses were unacceptable to the formerly dominant consciousness, it will not be surprising if the new personality differs strikingly from the first.

If little Eve, after her grandmother's funeral, set herself to resist many natural impulses, we have a possible progenitor of the restrained, invariably conforming woman who first came to us as a patient. If the tendencies denied expression did, indeed, remain unconscious but alive and gradually organized into a disparate purposive unit, we have a theoretical explanation of the origin of Eve Black. It is so easy to see in her an outlet for Eve White's suppressed feelings that one might say she might have been born for this purpose.

One may, if he likes, and with some justification, think of Jane as the representative of a broader and more balanced human viewpoint. Was she a manifestation of some mere compromise between the two Eves? Or was she the shadowing forth of still other things, once potential in the little child, which could find no secure habitation in either of the two organized extremes? Was the final Evelyn who emerged a combination of all three manifestations? — or, perhaps, some new creation born through their dramatic coalescence but including also elements never conscious or actively operational in any of them as they had appeared to us?

We do not know. It would be a gross mistake for us to consider this as an explanation derived from evidence, and a grosser folly to present it as a scientifically established analysis of our patient's disorder. We are merely offering some of our thoughts, some of the items about which we wondered while dealing clinically with the manifestations that often astonished us.

AFTER the synthesis took place we found nothing in our patient that suggested the presence of Eve Black as an entity. Nothing has occurred since that would lead us to think she may occasionally have emerged to consciousness or to control. We have mentioned that in the new Evelyn there appears to be an energy, a capacity for vivacity and humor that we never saw in Eve White or even in Jane. Jane was not without the qualities these words indicate, but in Evelyn it has often seemed as if some emotional element of Eve Black might be sparkling through patterns of behavior quite unlike her own.

One may regard this as an indirect expression of a still organized but no longer openly active Eve Black who is, so to speak, imprisoned in the unconscious. On the other hand, one may think of Eve Black as having participated in the synthesis, as having contributed some real elements to the conscious and active personality we now call Evelyn. Perhaps, through a more mature character, the original impulses that we have conceived of as uniting in rebellion long ago against Eve White may find true and appropriate fulfillment. Perhaps, instead of being banished to some lifeless limbo, the charming and childlike vitality of Eve Black may find meaningful consummation, and possibly even make a contribution not unlike a redemption.

ONLY a few days ago we had the pleasure of talking again with Mrs. Evelyn Lancaster. It was a delightful and gratifying experience. We had kept in touch with her by correspondence, but to see her again, almost two years after the integration which had so dramatically occurred, was an experience we had long anticipated.

From the time the manifestations of multiple personality ceased, she had not been seriously troubled by headaches. There had been no blackout spells. The distressing nightmares that had afflicted Jane never recurred. Though we could only hope that further serious dissociations would not occur, she felt all the conviction of certainty that the disparate Eve White and Eve Black and the separate Jane of the past were gone forever. Her problems in the first months of her new life were not, in the ordinary sense, psychiatric symptoms. She had only the wish and the need to orient herself in a world still in many subtle ways strange and unexplored.

Though much of Eve White's past still seemed not quite her own, she never wavered in the sense of motherhood toward Bonnie. Though genuinely devoted, she was less desperately absorbed in her little girl than Eve White had been. At the basis of all her planning was a longing to have the child with her. She had seen the reasonableness of her former husband's wish that Bonnie remain with the grandparents until sufficient time had passed for some more reliable estimate to be made of her future health. There was at first some difficulty in her recognizing Eve White's parents as her own. They did not, however, even at first seem entirely foreign to her in this role, as they had to Eve Black and to the original Jane. Gradually she oriented herself to her status as their daughter. She impressed us as being able to recognize and accept in the mother elements that Eve White had reacted to with emotional withdrawal. None of Eve Black's careless scorn appeared in this daughter's feeling toward her parents. Despite certain disagreements she seemed able to regard them both with warmth and respect, as thoroughly deserving of her love.

After the coalescence, she often discussed with us the problems concerning her steadily increasing wish to marry. Earl Lancaster's profession, chemical engineering, would probably require that he move about the United States through the next fifteen or twenty years. Would it be detrimental to Bonnie's chances for happiness if she had to grow up moving from place to place? Our patient had frankly and fully discussed her strange illness with Earl, and he had assured her it made no difference to him. Yet, was it possible for this extraordinary past not to thrust itself somehow into their relations? Lacking some part of the experience most women at her age had acquired, would she be able to fill the role of a wife adequately? She was convinced Earl wanted Bonnie with them, but would he be able to accept this insecure little girl without reservation? These were questions to which reasoning alone could furnish no certain and satisfactory answers.

Almost a year after her divorce, Earl found that he must leave within a week for a distant city. Evelyn's new existence had grown about him as ivy finds its way about a supporting tree. They decided to marry without delay.

Now after almost a year and a half of marriage she sat talking with us. Her voice, her general appearance, her mannerisms and her posture were clearly those of the Evelyn we had first known after the sudden disappearance of Eve White, Eve Black and Jane. When she stood and walked it was not with quite the stateliness that had so clearly distinguished Jane. She looked in far better health than before, and had in fact gained twelve pounds. This, and her greater animation, lent to her figure and her movements something that recalled a little more definitely than before her marriage Eve Black's exuberant appearance. She was unquestionably a far more attractive woman than we had ever seen her before.

She did not wear stockings when she came back to see us. Neither Eve White nor Jane had complained of any irritation from nylon; but Eve Black, as we have noted, complained that the stockings Eve White put on caused itching. Before the resolution occurred, we had all three personalities tested for allergy to nylon. No objective sensitivity was found in any one of them. But after her marriage Evelyn developed a severe rash, and her local physician found in her a specific allergic sensitivity to nylon.

We had learned from her letters that she and Earl had not immediately reacted according to the old formula by which people are said to marry and, in uncomplicated simplicity, live happily thereafter. Mrs. Lancaster's difficulties seemed to have little or no relation to the old problems of Eve White and Eve Black. They were for the most part reactions to the subtle, scarcely less than magic process through which man and woman either achieve the valid goal of love in marriage or find disillusion in what had seemed so rich and bright a promise.

The emotional closeness that our patient needed to find in her marriage probably cannot ever be obtained ready-made. Apparently it must be developed out of an interaction of lives, out of sorrow, misunderstanding and despair no less than out of pleasure. Perhaps it was necessary that they be suffered in order for the growth of understanding and of love to be possible.

No, Mrs. Lancaster told us, physical love had not been really satisfactory during the first months of the marriage. The change did not occur until a broader change all through their personal relations had come.

"It's something there isn't any way of explaining," Evelyn said. "I suppose I just had to learn something from inside of me that you can't get to know in a hurry. And no matter what anybody might do, there's no way for it to come except by growing."

For a year now things had been exactly right for them both. When Earl Lancaster talked with us at the same time, a few days ago, he said that it made him feel very foolish to remember the attitude he had held about many small matters during the first months after the marriage. He felt confident the happiness they had worked out was secure and would now continue.

Bonnie had come to stay with them a few times when they had been settled for a month or two. After six months she came to remain for two weeks. When the time came for the child to return to her grandparents she seemed more reluctant than before to part with her mother. Earl drove her in the car to the grandparents' home. After her suitcase had been brought into the house and he had visited a while with Evelyn's mother and father, he said good-by and went toward the car.

The little girl now, to his astonishment, broke into a run toward him. "Daddy," she cried, "oh, Daddy, I want to go back with you. Please . . . please, Daddy, take me too."

Her feelings impressed the grandparents. They profoundly moved Earl Lancaster. He swept her up in his arms and held her very close. He had not realized until then that she had been able to accept him as he had hoped. Since then Bonnie has remained with her mother and her new father.

After long discussions with the patient and with her husband, separately and together, we felt that, particularly during the past year, she must have made admirable progress. We felt that the happiness she expressed was genuine. We are convinced that she has been able to make a happy life for her husband and her child. Will all this endure?

Three testings with the semantic differential have been made since only one personality remained for observation. The first of these showed changes in keeping with the responses of a normal and healthy person. But one test administered almost a year after marriage was far from encouraging, showing an increasing degree of emotional disorder. Some of the responses on this occasion showed considerable resemblance to those of Eve Black when she was active. Our co-workers point out, however, that "the *concepts* are still placed in the socially approved regions of the space, unlike Eve Black's." The last test was administered at approximately the time of our recent interview with Evelyn. The changes this time, though not conclusive, indicated improvement. There was nothing, however, that paralleled the encouraging gains reported by Mrs. Lancaster and her husband and which seemed to us so impressive clinically. Is this improvement deep and quite real, or is it more superficial than it seemed to the patient and her husband, and to us? Only time can give us this answer.

Whether or not Evelyn Lancaster will continue to enjoy a happy life we are unable to predict. Whatever may come, there seems to us little doubt that she has already won her way to a remarkable victory against unusual odds. No life lasts forever. If the integration she somehow achieved breaks and she becomes unable to fill her present role, we shall nevertheless remember that she reached a goal of love and fulfillment that many people, even without the strange and formidable handicaps that beset her, never know. Be it win, lose or draw — can we withhold from her our admiration? Though we cannot predict, we can prayerfully wish her well.

Hervey M. Cleckley

Corbett H. Thigpen

BOTH OF Eve White's doctors are natives of Georgia — Dr. Cleckley was born in Augusta in 1903, Dr. Thigpen in Macon in 1919. Both are graduates of the Medical College of Georgia. Dr. Thigpen served two years in the Army Medical Corps, then completed his training under Dr. Cleckley at the University Hospital in Augusta, and joined his distinguished colleague in private practice, research and authorship.

Dr. Cleckley graduated *summa cum laude* from the University of Georgia and spent two years at Oxford as a Rhodes Scholar, taking a degree in physiology. He is a diplomate of the American Board of Psychiatry and Neurology, and a fellow of the American College of Physicians and of the American Psychiatric Association. He is the author of *The Mask of Sanity,* a widely acclaimed, definitive book on the psychopathic personality; his numerous articles and essays have appeared in scientific and medical journals, textbooks and popular magazines. A new book, *The Caricature of Love,* will be published soon.

Illustrations by Howard Willard

Letter
From Peking

A condensation of the book by

PEARL S. BUCK

Surely no American woman has ever been in a like predicament!

The letter from Red China had come to Elizabeth MacLeod by a devious and dangerous route; her husband, Gerald, had risked his life to write it. Though separated from him by barriers of race and of revolution, Elizabeth remained deeply bound to him in love. As she quietly tended her Vermont farm, the mystery of his letter, and the "predicament" into which it plunged her, remained a tormenting secret.

As rhythmically as season follows upon season, this novel of a woman's courage and devotion moves toward a climax that is surprising and yet inevitable.

THE YEAR is 1950, the month is September, and the day the twenty-fifth. The place? It is this valley in the mountains of Vermont, where I was born and where I lived my childhood through. I crossed the seas, I made my love's country my own. Then came war, and I was an alien in spite of love, and I returned again to the valley.

Half an hour ago I walked down our country road, under the arch of maples, red and gold, to meet the postman. He comes only three times a week to this remote spot in the mountains of Vermont, and three mornings a week I wake early and restless. There is always a chance that a letter will come from Peking, a letter from Gerald. For months no letter has come. But this morning there was a letter. The postman singled it out and gave it to me.

"Here's what you're waitin' for," he said.

I would not open it until he was gone. Then, alone under the arching maple trees blazing with autumn fire, I opened the envelope. I knew, as I read, that I had been expecting this letter. No, rather, I knew that it could not surprise me. Nothing that Gerald does can surprise me, or shock me, or even hurt me. I have loved him. I do love him and shall always love him.

I read the letter, over and over again. In the silent autumn air, no wind stirring, the bright leaves floated down. I could hear Gerald's voice speaking the words he had written.

My Dear Wife:

First, before I say what must be said, let me tell you that I love only you. Whatever I do now, remember that it is you I love. If you never receive a letter from me again, know that in my heart I write you every day.

As I read these words I knew what must follow. I read to the end, and then, Gerald's voice echoing in my ears, I walked home. The house is empty after Rennie leaves for school. I am glad for this loneliness. I am now in my room, at my desk, writing. I have locked the letter into a secret drawer of the desk. I will forget it. At least for a while let me forget, until the numbness has gone from my heart. This is my comfort, to write down all I feel, since there is no one to whom I can speak.

This morning dawned like any other day. I rise early nowadays. Our neighbor farmers rise at four and sleep soon after twilight, as the Chinese farmers do. But Gerald likes the quiet while others sleep, and so I have learned to go late to bed. The night hours in our Chinese house were sweet. The street sounds died after dark, and over the low compound walls the voice of a two-stringed violin floated into our courts. It was made by our neighbor, Mr. Hua, who was a merchant in a nearby silk shop. In summer Gerald and I sat under the pine tree by the goldfish pool, and we let Rennie, our son, stay with us past all sensible bedtime for a child. He is our only son.

Our daughter died in babyhood. In the morning she was laughing, and by night she was gone. I do not know why she died. The sorrow was part of the price I paid for loving Gerald and going with him to China.

For a long time, it seemed very long, we were childless. I grieved but I was saved by Gerald's grief. I thought he would never cease mourning for our lost child. For months he could not sleep and he ate so little that his tall frame, always slender, was skeleton. I suppressed my tears to listen to his grieving.

"I should have stayed in your country," he said. "If we had lived in America, our daughter would not have died. I have robbed you of too much."

I leaned my head upon his breast. "Wherever you go, there I go."

He looked at me strangely. "This is the difference between American women and Chinese women. You are more wife than mother."

"When I am with you I am all wife," I said. "And besides, you would never have been happy in America."

I knew it then and I know it now. Though in Peking I was often homesick in fleeting moments for the clean cool mountains of Vermont, I was happy there. It is a jewel of a city, richly set, gilded with time and history, the people courteous and gay, and I saw my life stretching ahead of me in peace and beauty, and there, I supposed, I would be buried by Gerald's side, both of us old and full of years.

Yet here I am, in this Vermont village of Raleigh, in a lonely farmhouse, with Rennie, our son, seventeen years old. And now, I do not think I shall ever see Gerald again.

As I said, the day began as any other does. I rose at six, I helped Matt milk our four cows and I set the can on the barn stoop for the milk truck to pick up, saving out the big pewter pitcher full for Rennie. Then I went into the kitchen and made his breakfast. I have returned to the hours of my childhood upon this land which belonged to my grandfather and then to my father, and now is mine.

My father was an inventor in a minor way, scamping his farm work to build "contraptions," as he called them. Two or three were fairly successful, an egg-washing machine, for example. But we fed from the farm and for cash depended upon a legacy left my father by his father, who was a famous lawyer. When Gerald and I were married, my father was already dead, and my mother lived here alone. She died before Rennie was born and left me the farm, and Matt Greene took care of it while I was in Peking, and he comes every day as he always has. For when we saw that we must part, Gerald and I, it was to this place that I returned.

Rennie came down this morning, his cheeks rosy from the cold air of windows open in his bedroom. "Good morning, Mother," he said, and kissed my cheek.

"Good morning, son," I said.

This ritual his father has always insisted upon.

"When you leave the presence of your parents," Gerald instructed his son, "you must say good-by to them, you must tell them where you go, and upon your return you must show yourself before them and inquire how they are. This is filial piety."

"How are you this morning, Mother?" Rennie inquired.

"Very well, thank you," I said.

"I hope you slept?"

"I did, thank you," I said.

We smiled at each other, Rennie and I, remembering Gerald. Rennie looks like his father. He is tall for his age. Hair and eyes are black, and his skin, smooth as only Chinese ancestors can bequeath, is the color of Guernsey cream. His profile is beautiful, the features subtly subdued and yet strong.

"Sit down, son," I said. "Your breakfast is ready."

Breakfast for Rennie is a monumental meal. He heaps his oatmeal with brown sugar and rich milk. Gerald has forbidden white sugar, and in Peking we used only the dark Chinese sugar. Milk is American, but Rennie is American too, his Chinese blood only one fourth of his ancestral inheritance. His body is not Chinese. He is strong-boned, his hands and feet are well shaped but big, and he has not his father's elegant structure.

"Three eggs, please," he said as usual.

It is a good thing I have hens. My small legacy would not suffice for eggs and meat on the scale my son enjoys. . . . I must not so soon begin to say mine. Rennie is also Gerald's son. But I do not know how much the letter will change my life.

The dining-room window looks on the road, conveniently, and from his seat at the head of the table Rennie can see the school bus coming. At first we left the seat empty, against the time when husband and father might sit there. For when we left Gerald on the wharf at Shanghai, he said he might join us in three months. At the end of three months he said nothing of his coming, and his letters were already weeks apart. So, because he could see the road, Rennie said he would take his father's chair for the present, and I did not say yes or no.

Perhaps I knew already that the letter was on its way.

"There's the bus," Rennie shouted. His eggs and bacon were gone, so were three slices of brown toast and butter, and he drank down his second glass of milk and reached for his windbreaker and cap.

"Good-by, Mother!"

"Good-by, son," I said.

When Rennie learned from American children in Shanghai to say Mom or Ma, Gerald was stern.

"Mother is a beautiful word," he said gravely. "You shall not corrupt it."

He spoke in Chinese as he always does when he wishes to teach his son, and Rennie obeyed.

When I was alone, the house silent about me, I washed the dishes and then went upstairs to make the beds. My room, the one my parents used, stretches across the front of the house. It has five windows and the landscape changes with every day and hour. This morning when I rose at six the golden moon, round and huge, was sinking behind the wooded mountains. The level rays made black shadows from the pointed cedars upon the gray rocks beneath. I loved the safety of our compound walls in Peking, but I love this landscape better. Without Gerald, I choose my own country. With him any land serves and all are beautiful.

I made the big four-poster bed and dusted the bureaus and chests and the white-painted chimney piece. I wonder sometimes that I labor so easily in this house, when in our Chinese house I needed five servants, or thought I did. Gerald did not like to see me work with my hands. It is true that I have nice hands. It was the first thing he said to me.

"You have lovely hands."

"Do I?" I asked stupidly. No, not stupidly, for I wanted to hear him say it again.

"American girls do not usually have good hands. I notice this because my mother, being Chinese, had exquisite hands."

Perhaps he began to love me because my hands made him think of his mother's. How can I know now?

It has been nearly three months since I have had a letter from

Gerald — until today. The letter is mailed from Hongkong, and it is inside an envelope addressed by a strange hand.

"You must not worry if my letters are far apart now," Gerald writes. "I cannot tell you the difficulties, I cannot even tell you how this letter reaches you. When you answer, do not send the letter to me, but to the address on the envelope. It may be months before I can reply."

Until the war with Japan came, we were never apart. Then, when it seemed that the northern provinces would fall easily to the enemy, Gerald said I must take Rennie to Chungking before the railroad to Hankow was cut.

"Without you?" I cried.

"I will follow when I can," he said. "I cannot leave until the college leaves with me."

He was the president of the university, and responsibility was heavy upon him. I knew he was right, and Rennie and I set forth for Chungking. It was not an easy journey. The train was crowded with refugees, who clung even upon the roofs of the cars, and the hotel in Hankow was full of the escaping rich and their retinues. I made the most of the dying prestige of the white man and found

a tiny space for Rennie and me, and by urgency and bribes I bought passage upon the small steamer that makes the perilous journey up the Yangtse gorges to Chungking.

Thither Gerald was to follow, and he did, months later, his students and faculty with him. Meanwhile Rennie and I had found a small house in the hills above the city. Oh, the joy of reunion with the beloved! He came in, so gaunt he seemed to have added inches to his height. But he was content. His students and faculty had stayed with him, he had led them to safety. The city gentry had given him the use of several ancient ancestral halls, and all were housed.

When I put my arms about him that day I felt him tremble and knew how tired he was.

"Here you can rest," I told him.

He looked about the home I had made. I have a passion for big rooms. When I first found the brick farmhouse near Chungking, I told the owner that I would take it only if he allowed me to tear out two partitions in the main building and make three rooms into one. Therefore the room that Gerald saw was large and comfortable. We had brought nothing with us from Peking, but I knew how to find what I needed in the small shops of any Chinese city. Chinese craftsmen are skilled and they love beauty.

"You have the genius of a homemaker," Gerald said. He sat down in a cushioned wicker chair and leaned his head back.

"It is heaven," he said, and closed his eyes.

I cannot write for crying —

It is the first day of February. For weeks our Vermont landscape has been winter-bound, the mountains white and the valley silent under snow. Three days ago a warm wind and sunshine melted the snow, a deceptive thaw, for winter will come back again. We have some of our deepest snows in March, and even in April. Sometimes the spring sugaring is delayed for days because the sap freezes on its way down to the sugarhouse. Today the valley is hidden in mist and the mountains have vanished. I can see no farther than the gate to the dooryard. My father put up the fence for my mother, who, Boston reared, could not bear the frightening distances she saw from the windows of this house, the mountains rolling away.

"I must live behind a gate," she told my father, "else how do I know where I belong?"

He put up the fence, enclosing plenty of lawn and the clump of white birch. My mother was a pretty woman. But she was rigid in mind and body. She demanded fences and gates and she seldom went beyond them. When I told her I wanted to marry Gerald MacLeod she was not pleased. She did not want me to marry.

"There is much in marriage that is distasteful to a nice woman," she said when I asked her why she did not want me to marry. "Although MacLeod is a good name," she added.

I considered whether I would tell her that Gerald was half Chinese. He can pass for a dark Caucasian, for while his eyes are slightly almond-shaped, they are large and his brows are handsome. He is far more beautiful as a man than I am as a woman. I am small and fair and my eyes are gray. I have never been sure I was pretty. Gerald has not told me I was pretty.

"Your skin is exquisite."

"Your mouth is very sweet."

Such words he has said, but never declaring beauty.

But if I considered concealing Gerald's Chinese blood, it was only for a moment. My mother was exceedingly acute. She could surmise what she did not know. I said, carefully casual,

"Gerald's father lives in Peking. He is American but he married a Chinese lady and so Gerald is half Chinese."

My mother's little mouth opened with horror.

"Oh, Elizabeth — no!"

Only my mother called me Elizabeth. Gerald calls me Eve. It is his love name for me. By others I am called by every possible variation.

"Eve," he said, that day when we were newly betrothed, "you are my first love."

"Shall I call you Adam?" I asked half playfully.

He looked half amused, half cynical. "I doubt that Christians would concede the name to a Chinese," he remarked.

"You insist upon being Chinese, but you aren't — not by half," I retorted. "And please, Gerald, when you meet my mother, be the American half."

He became very Chinese at this, and made a show of being inscrutable and polite and evasive, all with humor, and I did not know how he would behave to my mother. I sorrowed that my father was dead, for he would have enjoyed Gerald. The windows of my father's mind were open to the world.

I should have trusted Gerald, for when he met my mother, he appeared before her as an extremely handsome young American, his Chinese ancestry escaping only in his natural grace, and in the straightness of his sleekly brushed, very black hair. Even his eyes were alert and frank. Sometimes they were Chinese in their look, revealing the self-contained and sometimes distant person who lives within the soul of my beloved. He won her cool little heart, so far as it could be won.

This is not to say that she had no misgivings. More than once after that she summoned me to her room late at night, and there she sat in her Windsor chair, wrapped in her gray flannelette dressing gown and her hair in black kid curlers.

"Elizabeth, I have a dread fear that when you have a child it will look Chinese."

"He might look like the MacLeods," I suggested.

"There's no guarantee," she retorted, "and how I could bear to have a Chinese grandchild I do not know. I could not explain it in Boston."

For my mother was never a true Vermonter but always a citizen of Boston, spiritually and mentally.

"Don't worry, Mother," I said. "Gerald and I will live in Peking."

This startled her. "You'll never go and live in China!" she remonstrated.

"Didn't you come and live in Vermont?" I parried.

"But China," she persisted. "I never knew anyone to go to Peking."

"Grandmother MacLeod went," I told her. "When Gerald was small she visited his parents in Peking and she liked it so well that she stayed until she died. What's more, she's buried there."

"She couldn't help dying, wherever she was," my mother declared grimly.

"She wanted to be buried there — Gerald says so."

My mother could only sigh. "I'll never go to Peking."

"You might," I said gaily. I was too happy to be anything but gay in those days.

She was right. She never went to Peking. Within a year after Gerald and I were married, she died of pneumonia and I remembered what she had said every winter, drawing her gray shawl about her.

"These Vermont winters will be the death of me," she always said, and, in the end, it was true. She was winter-killed, but part of it was the winter she carried in her own soul, wherever she was.

TODAY the valley lies under a scintillating sun and the warmth of it draws the mists from the melting snow. I dread the spring this year. It is useless now to watch and wait for the postman. I shall never get another letter from Gerald. When Matt brought in the mail this morning, I said, "Put it on the desk in the office." But I went to look, just the same.

I was busy, for we have the orchard to prune before the sap begins to run in the sugarbush. We raise good apples, old-fashioned and sound. My favorites are the pound apples, each weighing a pound, or very nearly, red-skinned and crisp and a nice balance between sour and sweet. When I bite into one I remember that Gerald does not like apples. Chinese apples are pithy and tasteless, but even our good American apples could not tempt him. And once when I brought him a plate of Bartlett pears he did not finish even one.

"They are soft," he said. "The pears in Peking are as crisp as celery and full of clear juice."

"Then they are not pears," I said to tease him.

"Wait and see," he said.

For by then we knew we would be married. And when I did eat Peking pears they were delicious and they held their freshness all through the winter.

We have pruned all day, Matt and I. He is a silent fellow, a Vermonter, lank and lean, his teeth gone too early from a wretched diet. He looks upon my brown breads and green salads with distaste and, though I press him to share my luncheon, he sits apart and munches what he calls lunch meat between two huge slabs of white bread. Matt knows of my years in China and doubtless he wonders about Gerald but he never asks me a question that does not pertain to the farm. Save for this, his conversation consists of bits of bad news from the valley. Today we did not talk long. "I want to finish the orchard before Rennie comes home from school," I said. And we went back to work.

And so I prune my apple trees, remembering that fruit is borne on the small and twiggy branches, and never on the bold young growth. Saw and shears I can use well enough, and I take the large branches first, cutting upward for an inch or two, lest the wood split. When the saw is sharp, my neighbors say, it is time to prune the fruit trees, a saying true enough, for during the winter I oil the tools and sharpen the saws and the scythe. I have an old-fashioned wheel of sandstone that does well for the larger tools, but the small ones I sharpen by hand against a strip of flint.

Rennie asks me every few days, "Mother, no letter?"

I shake my head. "I am afraid it is getting difficult for your father," I say. "The anti-American feeling in China is growing under the skillful Communist propaganda."

Rennie muses, "What is Communism, really?"

And I tell him of Karl Marx, the strange little man who lived his narrow little life, and somehow managed, by the power of his wayward brain, to lay hold upon millions of human lives.

"Even our lives, Rennie," I said. "Because of him we are separated, you from your father and I from my husband."

"And can my father not free himself?" he asked.

How could I answer this? "I suppose," I said, "that if our country, here, went Communist we'd stay, believing in our past and in our future."

"I don't know even if this is my country," he said.

"It is yours because it is mine," I said. "And let that be the end of it."

It is not the end, as I well know. Rennie will have to choose his own country.

Sooner or later I shall have to tell him that I have his father's last letter upstairs, locked into the secret drawer of my mother's desk. But I put off the day. Rennie went on talking this evening after our supper, which we ate by the kitchen fireplace. A crane is built into it and a great pot hangs from the crane, in which I heat water when electricity fails in a summer thunderstorm.

"I should think my father could get a letter to us somehow," Rennie continued.

"We do not know what rigors are imposed upon him," I replied. "It is dangerous for him that his father is American."

"Where is my grandfather MacLeod?" Rennie asked.

I keep a wooden bowl of apples on the kitchen table and while Rennie talked he was biting deeply into the white flesh of a red Baldwin.

"He's in Kansas. We shall have to go and find him one of these days," I said. "And do you forget that you used to call him Baba?"

I had planned long ago to visit Gerald's father. It was one of my beloved's last requests to me that day when we stood on the dock in Shanghai.

"Go and see my father and take Rennie with you," Gerald bade me. "It will comfort him to see his grandson."

"Is that why you are sending us to America?" I demanded.

"One reason among others," he replied.

"In that case I will stay here," I retorted.

"You must go," Gerald said, "and Rennie must go with you."

And then reluctantly he said what we both knew and had never spoken aloud. "Your lives will not be safe if you stay here."

I saw him glance about him as he spoke the words. For the first time Gerald was afraid. He had gone through war and bombing without a qualm.

"What of you?" I asked and certainly I was afraid.

"Half of me is Chinese," he said. "I shall make that serve."

"But will They?" I muttered. We were already calling the Communists "They."

"I shall become indispensable," he replied.

I wished with all my heart that this conversation had taken place when we were at home in Peking, in our bedroom, the doors locked, the windows closed. Then I could have thrown myself on his breast and forced the truth from him. But I was standing beside him on the dock, the wind blowing my hair, and I could only ask in a stupid low voice that conveyed no passion, "And why, Gerald, do you wish to make yourself indispensable here?"

"One has to choose," he said.

There was no time for more. The tug was waiting to take us to the ship, and in the silent crowd upon the small vessel it would not have been safe to talk. I kept thinking, when had it become dangerous to talk? At what moment had the people, and among them ourselves, ceased to be gay and communicative? When had they become silent and afraid? The change was gradual, but when it came it was absolute. And it had culminated in the silence between Gerald and me when we parted.

I CANNOT sleep the nights through. I get up and prowl about the house, careful not to wake Rennie. He guesses that something is wrong, but he thinks I grieve because I have not heard from his father for so many months.

He says to me, "Mother, I am sure there are many letters waiting in some forgotten place. You know how the postmen are over there.

They sit down to eat a bowl of hot rice, or they lie under a tree to sleep."

Actually this is not true. The postal service to and from Peking was always excellent, and I suppose it is no worse now. It was organized by the English, who are always thorough. I smile and say, "Of course you are right, and I will not worry. No news is good news."

It is a true old proverb. How much better it would be now if I had not this letter lying like a live thing in the secret drawer of my desk! I have sealed it with red sealing wax, lest by some impossible chance Rennie might be rummaging one day and find it.

Last night I was too lonely. I am still a wife, but without my husband. When a man dies, his widow dies by so much, too, perhaps. If her love has been great, a part of her dies and it can never be reborn with another man. But I am not a widow. In the night I lie in my solitary bed and all my dreams fly across the sea. I walk the well-known street to our gate. It is barred but, bodiless, I go through and cross the courtyard and enter the locked door. The gateman does not wake. He cannot hear me, nor could he prevent me if he did. There is my home. It is as I left it, believing that surely I would come back. Gerald and I cannot be parted. That is what I believed.

I said to the servants, "Keep everything as I have it."

"We will," they promised.

"Do not forget," I said. "Our master must have hot food when he comes in at night, however late the hour."

"Never, never can we forget," they promised.

"I shall return," I said.

"Our mistress will return," they said.

Now, remembering, my soul passes swiftly through the rooms to the bedroom where Gerald lies asleep. Is he alone? Is he still alone? My soul stands fearful at the door.

I get out of bed and I open the secret drawer of the desk. I break the seal I set. I read the opening words again.

"Let me tell you that I love only you."

I bend my head and weep. Is it not enough that he has written these words? My heart unanswered, I seal the letter once more and I put it away in the secret drawer. I cannot return to my bed. When a woman is widowed by death, does passion die? But Gerald is not dead. He is there, in our house. He comes home at night, he eats and sleeps and wakes to rise again. He looks upon this same moon which shines outside my window now. Surely, surely he knows. He knows that I stand here by the window, that I look out at the moon, rising above the mists of a spring night. I remember, I remember —

Gerald, always too sensitive, was obsessed with a strange terror in those first days when he had barely spoken to me of love. He feared that I might be offended.

I cried out against him. "Oh darling, how silly you are!"

I was saying "darling" long before he could bring himself to speak the word. When he began to call me by endearing names, it was not easily and, in the presence of others, never.

I remember the look in his grave dark eyes.

"I can live without your love," he said, "but I could not live if, having had it, I should lose it. This is why I dare not ask you to marry me."

"I shall always love you," I cried.

It was on such a night as this, a moonlight night, that we spoke. The spring was late that year and we had lingered under the birch trees to be alone and away from my mother, and I was cold and he opened his coat and put it about my shoulders and I walked in his shelter.

In June he had his degree from Harvard. My mother came to Commencement and I was singing proud to hear the honors he received. *"Summa cum laude"* — the words were spoken again and yet again. My mother was warmer than I had ever seen her toward him when he came striding toward us, still in his cap and gown. There was no man there to equal him in beauty. For the moment his reserve was gone. He was triumphant and happy and he caught our hands, my mother's and mine.

"Thank you for coming," he said. "Without you, I should have had no family. I'd have been lonely."

"Congratulations," my mother said.

She pressed his hand in both hers, but I stood tiptoe and kissed his cheek. It was the first time I had kissed him before my mother and he blushed and glanced at her and smiled when she did not reprove me.

We had dinner together that night, the three of us, at a Chinese restaurant in Boston, where he had already ordered our meal, and my mother condescended to taste one strange dish after another. I ate everything, liking all, and Gerald laughed at me and loved me and I knew it, in spite of his careful reserve.

He came home with us the next day, and by evening we were in the house. It was a clear night, the air cool and sweet as only the air of the mountains can be, and my mother said she was tired, and she went to bed. Gerald and I sat late on the stone terrace my father had built the summer before he died, and somehow I fell to talking about him.

"I wish he could know about you," I said.

"What about me?" Gerald asked. He held my hand now, his hand cool and firm.

"I wish, I wish my father could know the man who is to be my husband," I said.

A bold thing I was, but I knew that Gerald loved me.

He sat silent for a time, holding my hand. Then he rose from the bench where we were sitting and he drew me up to him and kissed me as never before had he kissed me.

It was I who broke away from that long kiss. "Now we are engaged," I whispered.

We sat down again and he talked to me of Peking, and for the first time he spoke of his mother. She had not been a beautiful woman, he said, but she had extraordinary grace. Her hands were delicate and always fragrant. He remembered their scent when she smoothed his cheeks.

"Chinese women do not kiss their children as Western women do," he said. "They nuzzle them and smell them when they are babies. When I grew out of babyhood she smoothed my cheeks with both her hands. Her palms were soft and sweet."

"Who was she," I asked, "and how did she come to marry your father?"

"I think," he said, "that my father was disappointed in love. The

American woman he wanted to marry would not go to China with him, or was forbidden to go by her parents. She was not strong enough to disobey them, I suppose. He went to China alone and he lived alone for ten years. And then, you know how the Chinese are — " He caught himself. "No, how can you know how the Chinese are? Well, they think every man and woman must marry for it is what Heaven ordains, and there can be no health in a people unless there is health in the individual man and woman. So Chinese friends besought my father to marry, and his best friend, who is my uncle Han Yu-ren, offered him his sister. She was not young. She was, in a way, a widow. The man to whom she had been betrothed as a child, by her parents, died a week before the wedding. Had she been less independent, I suppose she would have followed tradition and never married. She might even have become a nun."

"She was willing to marry an American?" I asked.

"That is what drew my father to her," Gerald said. "Most young Chinese women would not have accepted a foreign man."

"Had she seen your father?" I asked.

"Once," he said, "when my father visited his friend's house, she was in the main hall. He did not notice her."

"Your father is very handsome," I reminded him. He had once shown me his father's picture. "Were they happy?" I persisted.

He considered the question. "They had a measured happiness. It was impossible to be altogether unhappy with my mother. She was never gay but never sad, and she created order wherever she was."

"Is order so important?" I cried. For I am not orderly by nature.

"There is no dignity to life except with order," Gerald said.

We talked thus slowly and thoughtfully, our hands clasped. The moon was high and the mountains were clear against the sky.

We heard the grandfather clock in the hall strike twelve and we rose together and went into the house and up the stairs. At the head of the stairs we paused. He took me in his arms and kissed me again, not passionately but gently and with deep tenderness.

Then he went into the guest room and shut the door. And I

went to my own room and closed the door behind me. A calm happiness pervaded me.

I FIND I must not dwell upon memory or it becomes unbearable. I am thankful that the sap has begun to run in the sugarbush for I have no choice now but to be busy. Rennie has permission to stay out of school for a few days. His grades are high. Matt, Rennie and I work from dawn to dark and at night I am too tired to dream. I think of cutting off my long hair because today it fell down my back, the hairpins failing to hold in the wind.

"I shall certainly cut this off," I cried, seizing the long tail of hair and twisting it against my head.

The wind carried my words to Rennie and he cupped his hands and called to me. "You shall not, either!"

Later when we were eating our luncheon I asked him why he would not let me cut my hair and he said because he did not like a short-haired woman.

"I am only your mother," I said.

"Short-haired mother, then," he retorted and laughed at me.

I wonder if Gerald laughed as easily when he was a boy. There is no one to tell me. I had no sooner written those words than I thought, there is Gerald's father. He will remember. As soon as this sugaring is finished, Rennie and I will go and find Gerald's father. I want him here so I can talk about his son.

Gerald's father left Peking before the Japanese entered. He said that he could not bear to see it. He went to a small town in Kansas, Little Springs. I have no idea how he lives now. He has written to us once, soon after we came to Vermont, and wanted news of Gerald, which I gave. He has not replied.

I said to Rennie the next day, "Rennie, how would you like to have your grandfather MacLeod come and live with us?"

"I shall have to think about it," Rennie said. He is prudent, this boy, cautious and careful.

The days passed while he thought and we had no time to talk. Sugaring is hard work but we are fortunate because my father tapped the trees and laid pipes throughout the bush, and those pipes run into three main pipes through which, by force of gravity, the sap is conveyed to a small sugarhouse in the valley. Now Rennie and I, with Matt's help, make sugar with twice the ease that our neighbors do. They see and wonder and sometimes give spare praise to my father, but none of them do likewise. They continue to carry buckets as they have always done and as their ancestors did.

In the warm sunlit days sap runs fast into the sugarhouse. When that begins, Rennie and Matt do the outside work and I stay in the sugarhouse. We eat then from our stores of food, heating what was put up earlier in the glass jars of summertime and harvest. We drop into sleep immediately after supper, Rennie's cheeks burned with wind and snow and mine with fire.

Today, however, winter has returned. The sap is frozen and the roads are drifting with deepening snow. We can rest, Rennie and I, and Matt has taken over the sugarhouse for the time being. We dallied over our breakfast and Rennie picked up a book. I interrupted him.

"Rennie, have you thought about your grandfather coming to live with us?"

He looked up from the window seat where he was lying, the book propped on his breast.

"I have thought," he said. "I'd like it." And he went back to his book.

Son of Gerald! He has thought, in silence he has decided, and it is as good as done. When the dishes were washed I went upstairs to consider the room the grandfather would have. The house is too big for us, it could house a dozen children. Half stone, half timber, it stands facing the south and the valley. Every summer someone from New York or Chicago wants to buy it from me. I am offered a fortune large enough so that we need never sugar again. And I always refuse.

So now I walk the wide upstairs hall and reflect upon the rooms. I choose the corner at south and east. Rennie has the southwest room, because he likes to sleep on holidays and does not want the wakening sun. But an old man will not sleep late and this is the room. It is square, it has four windows, and a fireplace stands between the two to the east. Deep window sills and seats beneath them, a floor of wide pine planks, walls papered a faded pink. My mother chose this room when she was old and her furniture is here, Victorian walnut, and the white ruffled curtains that she made and hung. The bed is absurdly large, the headboard high and scrolled and the footboard solid. It is a good room for an old gentleman.

WE COULD not go until the sugaring was over. It was interrupted by an ice storm. In March, midseason, a warm rain poured upon us from a low gray sky. We were frightened lest the sap cease to flow, the trees deceived by seeming spring. Then sudden winds blew gusts of cold southward from Canada, and the rain froze upon the trees. Sap was assured, but alas, winds crashed the big trees. Sleepless in the night I heard the crack of breaking branches, sharp as gun shots, and almost as dreadful. In the morning the sun shone again and Rennie and I walked through the sugarbush to see what we had lost. Icicles of frozen sap hung from the ends of the broken branches and melting in the sun they dripped their sweetness upon the earth below. I detest waste and here was waste, but then Rennie reminded me that a tree is prudent and never gives up all its sugar.

"At least we can enjoy the beauty," I said. So we stood on top of the mountain behind our house and surveyed the glittering landscape.

For six weeks of hard work, we had a hundred gallons of amber-clear maple syrup, to be boiled later into sugar. When the buds began to swell in April, the season was over, and I told Matt that he must tend the spring plowing alone, for Rennie and I were going to Kansas. We would be back, I told him, before the seeds he planted could sprout.

Rennie and I set forth on our journey. I tried to create an image of his grandfather for Rennie as plains and mountains flew across the windows of the train, but it was dim even in my own mind. I saw everyone through the bright mists of my love for Gerald. I am one of the fortunate women who marries her first love.

The first run of maple syrup, John Burroughs says, is like first love, "always the best, always the fullest, always the sweetest, while there is a purity and delicacy of flavor about the sugar that far surpasses any subsequent yield."

"Your grandfather," I told Rennie, "is tall and very thin and aristocratic in his appearance. He comes from Virginia, where his forebears emigrated early from Scotland. It is a wonder that he ever married a Chinese lady."

Rennie withdrew by the slightest movement. He does not wish to talk about his Chinese grandmother. I suspect the prejudices of his schoolfellows may be creeping into his soul. If so, then Gerald's father will help me.

"Your grandfather had dark hair and dark eyes, like your father," I went on. "His hair is probably silver-white by now. Can you remember him at all?"

"I don't remember," Rennie said stubbornly. Whenever we

speak of the life we lived in Peking he does not remember. He wants to be American.

The landscape passes too quickly by the window. Someday I shall travel slowly over the miles we whirl over now. I would like to stop at every village and town and walk on the country roads that wind away from us in an instant. Last night in my berth I pulled the curtain aside and gazed out into the moonlight. I did not know where we were. My nation is so vast that within its endless borders even I can be a stranger. I ought not to blame Gerald that he does not come here, lest he be exiled.

I wept on his bosom that last night in the Shanghai hotel. "Why won't you come with me?" I sobbed. "What is it here that you love better than your wife?"

"No one and nothing," he said. "Consider, my Eve, that if I leave China now it would be forever. And I'd be a stranger in America."

"I'd be there," I cried.

"Though you were there," he said gravely.

At midnight, in the vastness of the land over which we sped, I felt myself a stranger, and I remembered what he said.

WE FOUND Gerald's father. He was living alone in a shack at the edge of a cluster of one-story houses in western Kansas. Little Springs is a small town, less than a town. It is on the high plains, halfway to the mountains. It was easy to find him, for when we asked at the station everybody knew him in a strange, respectful, doubtful sort of way.

The shirt-sleeved man at the ticket window, talking around the cud of tobacco in his mouth, directed us to the far end of the one street, and a mile beyond it in a one-room unpainted house we found Gerald's father. The door was open, although the air is chill here in April, and he was sitting inside at a rough table, wearing, of all things, his old padded Chinese robe and reading a Chinese book.

When he saw us he got to his feet in his formal fashion and stood there smiling. He has let his beard grow and his hair is too long. Both are silver-white. He is terribly thin and his eyes are huge. I never knew before how much he looks like Gerald. I flew to him and put my arms around him.

"Baba — why on earth are you here?"

He lifted his bent head, he recognized me, strangely without surprise, as though he did not know where he was. He did not embrace me but he did not push my arms away. He said in a mild distant voice, "I was taken ill on the train and they put me off here, and here perforce I stopped. There is no reason for me to live one place rather than another."

How selfishly Gerald and I lived on in the house in Peking in those perilous prewar days! We knew we were selfish, and yet we clutched every doomed hour of happiness. Yet it is also true that we believed anyone who reached America had reached Heaven. We had a few letters from Baba, saying that he was comfortable and we were not to worry about him. And beset with our own worries, in wars and dangers, we simply let it go at that.

Baba was looking at Rennie and I stepped back.

"You remember your grandson," I said.

He put out his hand, a frail big hand, and I nodded to Rennie to bid him come forward.

"Gerald's son?" the old man inquired.

"Of course," I said. How much does he remember and how much is forgotten?

"Yes, yes," the grandfather murmured. "Sit down, sit down."

There were not two other seats and Rennie sat on the edge of the table and I upon a stool.

"Baba, how do you live?" I asked.

"They bring me food," he said vaguely. "A woman cleans my house and washes my clothes. I don't need money. People are kind here."

He does not know where he is. I suppose he simply got off the train ill and bewildered and somebody let him have this house.

"I have money," he was saying. He opened the drawer in the table and took out a small parcel wrapped in a piece of yellow Chinese silk and opening it he showed me five one-dollar bills. Then he wrapped it up again and put it in the drawer.

Rennie and I looked at each other. We agreed, without words.

We must take Baba home with us, and without delay. There was one train east and one train west each day.

"Have you had your luncheon, Baba?" I asked. If we made haste we could still catch the eastward train.

"I think so," he replied.

"What did you eat?"

He got up slowly and went to an old-fashioned icebox in the corner and opened it. I looked inside and saw a half-empty bottle of milk, a pat of butter, three eggs and a small meat pie, a wedge of which had been cut out.

Rennie was standing in the door, looking over the plains.

"Let's get going," he said.

I turned to Baba. "Will you come and live with us?"

He was sitting by the table again and he carefully closed the clothbound Chinese book.

"Do you wish me to come and live with you?" he inquired.

"More than anything," I said.

"Where is Gerald?" he asked.

"He is still in Peking."

"Will he return?"

"I — hope so."

"Someone is coming," Rennie said.

A man was walking toward us in long strides and in a moment was at the door, a man past youth and not yet middle-aged, tall and square-shouldered, sandy-haired, his skin the color of his hair, a wind-blown Western face.

"I came down to see what was going on," he said in a hearty voice. "I keep an eye on my old neighbor."

"Are you the owner of this shack?" I asked.

"Yes — it's on my farm."

"It was good of you to take my father-in-law into shelter," I said.

"I don't know what to think of folks who let an old man wander around alone," he said severely.

"We had no idea — " I began and stopped.

How could I explain Peking, or even China? As well try to explain a distant planet!

"Now that we have found him," I said, "we will take him home."

Then I remembered. "I am Mrs. Gerald MacLeod. This is my son, Rennie."

"I'm Sam Blaine," he said. But he was looking at Rennie. He was thinking that Rennie looked "different." Who, he was thinking, are these people?

"Where do you come from?" he asked.

"We live in Vermont," I said.

"Where's your husband?"

I hesitated. To say that Gerald wanted to stay in Communist China would be to bring down suspicion upon us all.

"He is abroad," I said.

Sam Blaine leaned against the door and looked us over thoughtfully. Then he spoke to Baba.

"Old friend, you recognize this lady and the boy?"

Baba nodded peacefully. "She is my son's wife. The boy is Gerald's son."

"You want to go with them?"

"I'll go with them."

"Not unless you want to — I'll look after you if you want to stay."

"I will go," Baba said.

"Well — " The tall man was doubtful. "If you say so — "

"If we hurry we can still catch the afternoon train," I said.

"I'll fetch my car. I'll be back in fifteen minutes." Sam Blaine strode off.

I saw now that Rennie was in distress. He was looking at his grandfather and making up his mind whether to speak.

"Well?" I inquired.

"Are you going to take him on the train wearing that Chinese gown?" my son demanded.

Baba surveyed himself. "It's a very nice gown," he observed. "I bought it in Peking. The silk is still good. It is warm and soft."

"Mother!" Rennie cried.

"Baba, we will take the gown with us," I said. "But perhaps it will be best if we find your coat. Americans are not used to people who look different."

The gentle old man said nothing. Rennie was already reaching behind a curtain which hung against the wall and served as a closet. He produced the dark-gray suit in which Baba had left Peking, and the dark overcoat Gerald had bought him at the English tailor shop in the old Legation Quarter. They looked very little worn. Baba let Rennie help him into the gray suit and we put on his overcoat and found his black Homburg hat and he stood quite patient under our appraisal. I was not sure he knew what was happening to him. He simply gave himself into our hands.

Dust and noise outside the door announced that Sam Blaine had returned. I had packed the suitcase and Rennie led his grandfather to the car. Sam Blaine leaped out, and in a half minute we were in the car, red and chrome and monstrous, and comfortable as a bed.

"I have never seen such a car," I said. I was in the front seat, and Rennie and Baba were behind.

"Made to order," Sam Blaine said. "My order."

He drove fast and I stopped talking. I shall never grow used to speed. Years of riding in rickshaws and mule carts have reduced my tempo permanently, perhaps. We reached the station in time for the train, and Baba, supported by Rennie and Sam Blaine, was lifted up the steps.

"Good-by, ma'am," Sam Blaine said, and wrenched my hand. "You might write me, and tell me how the old man makes it."

"I will," I promised.

We settled ourselves into a compartment, Baba, Rennie and I. Then I was conscious of pain in my hand, the one Sam Blaine had held in his crushing grip.

Matt has dug the garden and plowed our fields. I am experimenting this year by putting the land into permanent hay. Grass farming, I believe, is the only answer to our short season in these mountains. A hundred years ago men made fields among the rocks and tried to grow grain, and their fields have returned to wilderness. Eighteen thousand folk, the old records say, once gathered on the side of Mount Stratton to hear Daniel Webster speak. I doubt eighteen hundred could gather now were Daniel Webster to rise from the grave. They have gone away, those folk, and their children and children's children are living their lives in distant places. They went away in search of home, even as I have returned to find my home.

For I am beginning to know that I shall never return to the house in Peking. It must cease to exist for me, though it stands as it has stood for centuries, a house encompassed by walls, and the gate in those walls is of heavy cedar, bound in solid brass. In and out of the gate the beloved comes and goes, but my roots there must die. I have returned to the land of my fathers. I ask myself if I should read Gerald's letter to Baba, and then cannot bear the thought of sharing my secret, not today. For this is our wedding day, Gerald's and mine, the fifteenth day of May, and I have spent it in the fields, seeding grass for permanent cover, leaving Matt to clean the barn and milk the cows.

Twenty years ago today Gerald and I were married quietly in the big living room. Then I went to China with him and I was drawn into its vast slumberous life. I felt at home there as everyone does. I do not know why it is so, but people came to visit Peking and stayed to live out their lives.

I tell myself that now all is changed, even in that eternal city. The long slumber is over. A terrible new energy possesses the people. I tell myself that they do not want me there. But I cannot believe that my friend Sumei does not love me any more, not when I remember how we nursed our babies together and talked and laughed and told each other what we had paid at the markets that day for eggs and fish and fruits. I cannot believe that old Madame Li does not love me any more, she who often drew me down to sit beside her so that she could smooth my hands with hers. These were my friends, I love them still and surely they love me. They would say as Gerald says to me in the letter, "I love you and will always love you, but — "

How can there be buts if love continues? That is the question I cannot answer. And silence lies between us.

When I came in to make supper Baba was enjoying the late sun on the kitchen terrace. He wears his Chinese gown every day, and he sits and reads his few old Chinese books and seldom speaks.

The doctor in our valley, Dr. Bruce Spaulden, tells me he must have had a mild stroke when he was alone there in Little Springs.

Bruce Spaulden is a good man and a good doctor, very tall, an honest face, strong features. I have not had time to know him well. "There's nothing to do," he said. "Simply take care of him as you are doing." Bruce is never in a hurry, but not communicative. He had come to examine Baba at my request, because Baba is not the man I remember as Gerald's father. In Peking his mind was keen, cultivated, witty, the mind of a scholar. I was afraid of him and charmed by him when I went to live in his house with Gerald. He knew everything and information flowed from him with pure naturalness, never with condescension. The subtle mellowing which China seems to leave upon all who give themselves to her had reached perfection in him.

"Gerald, how can I ever please your father?" I cried on the first night we spent in the Peking house.

"My darling," Gerald said, "you need not try to please him. He is delighted with you because you don't pretend. Neither does he. You can take each other as you are."

Baba has still that naturalness and he has his old-fashioned courtesy. Without one word to Rennie he teaches his grandson the manners he is losing since he became an American schoolboy. Baba will not sit down at the table until I am seated. He is careful to tell me when he goes for one of his short walks into the sugarbush and to tell me when he returns. He loves to walk slowly among the ferns now unrolling their fronds in a carpet of jade green beneath the trees.

Rennie comes home late because of baseball at school, and Baba sits in the kitchen with me and we talk. Oh, but it is different talk now. He is not childish but something has gone from him. The old scintillating wit is silent, the mind rests. He is sweet and gentle and easy to live with. He accepts his daily bread. I am not sure he knows where he is. I think he forgets at times who I am. He looks at Rennie now and then with strange thoughtfulness. I feel he is inquiring of himself whether this is Gerald or Gerald's son, or even, sometimes, whether he knows him. . . . No, it would be cruel to show him Gerald's letter.

Tonight, when we had eaten our supper, Rennie was off again to go with his friends to a motion picture. It is Saturday. So Baba and I were alone and I lit the lamp. I took up my knitting and sat down by the table and Baba remained in his armchair. And while I knitted a sweater for Rennie, I could not but think of Gerald. Never before, in the years since we parted, had our anniversary passed without a letter from him. Somehow or other he has managed to get a letter out to reach me in time for this night, and so to renew his love. I have the letters upstairs, in my sandalwood box. On other years I have read them all again, in full faith that someday our separation would end. I do not know whether I shall have the courage to read them tonight.

Baba sat quietly and watched me with patient eyes. I could not bear this and so I began to talk.

"Baba, tell me, can you remember when you married Gerald's mother?"

"I do remember her," he said. "Her name was Ai-lan. Her surname was Han. She was a good woman and a good wife."

"How did you come to marry her?"

He pondered this, his eyes vague.

"I cannot remember," he said. "I was advisor then to the Young Emperor. My friend, Han Yu-ren, suggested her to me. He thought I was lonely, and he had a sister younger than I. She was Ai-lan."

"Were you in love, Baba?" I asked.

Again the pause. He sat there in my father's old brown leather armchair, the light of the lamp falling upon his Chinese robe of crimson silk, his hands folded upon his lap, and his white hair and beard shining, his eyes dark and troubled. He was trying to think.

"Never mind, Baba," I said. "It was all so long ago."

"It is not that I do not wish to tell you," he said. "I am trying to remember. I think I was in love, but not with Ai-lan. I was in love with someone else. I am trying to remember."

"Was she a Chinese lady?" I asked, knowing she was not.

"Not Chinese," he said. "I cannot remember her name."

Oh, what a thing to say! My knitting fell from my hands. To be in love and then to pass beyond even the memory of the beloved's name! Could Gerald one day, in Peking, years hence, forget even my name?

Baba began to talk again. "I was lonely because that one whose name I cannot remember did not return my love. And when Yu-ren said to me that he had a sister, I thought it might be a good thing to be married to a Chinese lady. She could help me, I thought, in my work with the Chinese."

I took up my knitting again. "Strange, was it not, that a Chinese lady should be unmarried?"

He said quite easily now, "She had been betrothed and her fiancé had died. I think Yu-ren said he had died when she was quite young. She was twenty-five when we were married and I was thirty."

"Wasn't it extraordinary that she was willing to marry a foreigner?" I had somehow opened a door into Baba's mind and I pressed my advantage. I wanted to know Gerald's mother. There was not even a picture of her in the Peking house. I knew that Gerald loved her painfully well, but I did not know why it was with pain.

The Vermont night was quiet about us, a lovely May night, moonless and soft. The house was silent. I felt no barrier between Baba and me as he spoke with the simple words of a child, sometimes in English and sometimes in Chinese. It was strange and beautiful to hear the liquid tones of the ancient Peking language in this room.

Here is the story Baba told me, sitting in the brown armchair, his long pale hands folded one upon the other, his eyes fixed on my face sometimes, and sometimes moving away to the darkening window, an old man reliving a handful of vivid years in his youth.

They had been married, he and Gerald's mother, according to the ancient Buddhist rites. Her parents were dead, and her elder brother, Han Yu-ren, was the head of the family. She had lived in the Han household, pursuing her studies.

"Was she beautiful, Baba?"

He considered this. "She was not," he said at last, "although there were times when she very nearly approached beauty. She was beautiful when she read aloud to me the ancient poetry she enjoyed. And also she played quite well upon her lute and she had a sweet melancholy voice. When she played in the evenings, she always wiped tears from her eyes. I do not know why she wept."

"After Gerald was born, was she happy?"

A vague trouble passed over Baba's face. "I do not know whether it can be called happiness. She was changed. She read no more poetry and she never again played her lute. Instead she became interested in the revolution. Until then she had paid no heed to political affairs. I do not remember that she ever read a newspaper before Gerald was born. But afterward, she began to read new books and magazines. She became friendly with Sun Yat-sen. I remember we quarreled over it."

"I cannot imagine you quarreling, Baba," I said.

"I did not like Sun Yat-sen. I distrusted him. I was then the advisor to the Throne, you understand. I believed that the old form of government was the best. Besides, Sun was not educated in the classics. He had been only to missionary schools."

I was astonished to hear Baba speak so well. Something of the man I had known appeared before me. I put down my knitting to watch and to listen while he went on.

"She, who had been reared in every ancient tradition, was suddenly another woman than the one I had married. As a Chinese lady she had never left our house. Now, as the child grew out of babyhood, she began to go here and there to meetings. I knew she went to hear Sun Yat-sen. He was an upstart, the son of a Southern peasant, and I told her so. And then she accused me."

His voice trembled and he could not go on.

"Of what did she accuse you, Baba?"

He looked at me piteously, his lower lip trembling. "She said that I wished to keep the Emperor on the throne for the sake of my salary. She said that I was a foreigner and our two races could never mingle. She said I was loyal to my own. She had been sweet and gentle, and now suddenly she was cruel and angry. She said I never loved her."

Ah, that was the reason for the change! She loved and knew she was not loved, and so she left her home and wandered where she could find shelter. I had not the heart to tell Baba what he did not know. Her heart had woken when she saw her son. This child, half white, she had borne in ignorance of his fate. Where was his place? She knew that if he went to the land of his father, she would be left without love. His place must be in her country and, that she might keep him, she would make a new country for him. Oh, I do not doubt that I am putting it very crudely. Doubtless she imagined she did all for the sake of her people. She listened to the old arguments, that her people were insulted, the land threatened by foreigners. But I know that we do what we do for secret reasons of our own. She wanted to keep her son.

"How old was Gerald when his mother died?" I asked.

Baba spoke with sudden promptness, surprising me.

"She did not die. She was killed."

"What!"

We sat staring at each other. I saw something terrible now in Baba's eyes, not sorrow, not vagueness. No, I saw fright.

"I warned her," he said. He was trembling under the thin silk of his robe. "I told her that I could not save her if she persisted. For she became a violent revolutionist — you understand? Not merely a patriot. She became one of Them."

"Baba — no!"

"Yes, yes! First she became a friend of the wife of Sun Yat-sen. The two women spent hours together, sometimes in my house. I forbade it at last. I was afraid for myself and for Gerald. I said, 'If you must meet with those traitors, it shall not be in my house, or in the presence of my son.' And she took those two words and threw them back at me as one flings a dagger.

" 'Your son!' "

I heard the Chinese voice as clearly as though she stood in this room. Thousands of miles and years away I heard the words.

"Oh Baba, go on!"

"She went out of my house and I never saw her again."

"She was not dead?"

"No — not then. I went to her brother and we searched for her. It was he who found her at last. But he would not tell me where she was. He said, 'It is better for you not to know.' I knew she was with Them in the South, where they were making the revolution."

"Did Gerald never see her again either?"

For all the time Baba was talking, I saw Gerald growing up in that great house, alone with his father, but dreaming, I suppose, of his mother. What child does not dream of his mother? When I had first finished college I taught for a year in an orphanage in New York, a foundling home for girls. Bed and crib lay side by side, rooms full of children who had been deserted and betrayed. By day they played and sometimes even laughed, but again and again at night I was waked by the dreadful sound of their weeping. For when a child moaned in her sleep she murmured "Mother," and the word waked every child of the twenty or thirty in the room, one and then another, and they wailed the word aloud. "Mother — Mother —" Who can assuage such grief? I gave up my job and went away, but I have never forgotten the weeping children, dreaming of their unknown mothers. The child Gerald, lonely in the house with his foreign father, takes his place with the weeping children.

"He did see his mother," Baba said, his answer to my question. "She was very correct about that. She would not see him secretly, but she asked whether Gerald might come to her."

"And were you willing?"

"Not at first. I did not wish his mind to be contaminated. She said that she would not teach him anything. I allowed him therefore to meet her. She came to Peking in order that she might see him in her ancestral home."

"Was it for hours or days?" I asked.

"Sometimes for hours, sometimes for days, depending upon what she considered her duties to Them. They always came first."

Ah, the child must have felt that. Gerald is oversensitive to people.

"What I did not like," Baba was saying, "was that the child longed to live in his mother's ancestral house. He did not return willingly to me. I suppose that he was given sweets and made much of by servants and lesser relatives. You know how it is."

I did know. Those old Chinese families adore their men children. In the men children is their hope of eternal life. The boys are guarded and pampered and loved. They are absorbed into the mighty ocean of love, centuries old. Only the strongest and the most self-sufficient can emerge from such love into independent beings.

I think my dead child could have been such a one had she been a boy. But she was a girl. Her name was Ru-an. I try not to think of her. I have seen many children but never one like her. My first-born she was, and Gerald was Chinese enough so that I saw disappointment in his eyes when he came into the hospital room. She lay in the crook of my arm.

"Your daughter, sir," I said to Gerald. I was very happy, in love with my life, my husband, my house, the city of Peking, the country of China.

He sat down beside the bed and he gravely inspected the child. I saw he was doing his best to hide his disappointment.

"She is quite small," he said.

I was angry. "On the contrary, Gerald. She weighs eight pounds. Also she is intelligent."

"Intelligent," he murmured, staring at the round sleeping face.

"Yes." I yielded to him nearly always but I knew I would never yield to him about my daughter. She was to be beautiful, strong and intelligent. And so she was and so she continued to be, until she died.

Oh, let me not think of her death!

"Baba, you are tired," I said and I rolled up my knitting. "You must go to bed. We will talk another time."

"I have not finished. I have not told you how Gerald's mother was killed."

It was a dread death, that I could see. I saw it in his widened eyes staring at the dark window, the pinched whiteness about his nostrils, his tightened lips.

"She was shot," he said. He was trembling again.

"Baba — don't tell me! Don't think of it."

He went on as though I had not spoken. "In 1930, in Nanking, she was seized by order of the secret police of the Nationalist government. She was living alone. She had not accompanied her friend, Madame Sun. She had not left with the others on the Long March. For reasons I never knew she had been told to remain in the city. Perhaps she was a spy. She was taken from her bed one cold morning in early spring, before dawn, and she was forced to walk, just as she was, in her night robes, to the Drum Tower, and there, with her back to the wall, and her eyes not blindfolded, she was shot."

"Baba — how did you know?"

"She had a servant, an old woman. That woman came to me — " His voice faded to silence. His whole frame seemed to shrink. His eyelids dropped over his staring eyes.

"Come, Baba," I said. "You are too weary."

And I led him to his room and stayed near until he was in bed and at last asleep.

I wish I had asked Baba if Gerald was ever told the manner of his mother's death. I think he was. The Chinese tell each other everything. Who can keep a secret there? Someone would have told. Gerald knows.

YESTERDAY the answer came to the question I did not ask. The postman brought a magazine under Chinese stamps. There are three of them on the magazine. I had not seen these new Communist stamps before. Each carries the face of a young man. One is a soldier, one is a machinist, one is a peasant. There is no name on the wrapper. It merely says P.O.B. No. 305, Peking, China. But I know Gerald sent it. For when I opened the magazine, I found it was dedicated to a martyr of the revolution. She was shot in Nanking on May the fifteenth, 1930. Her name was Han Ai-lan. She was Gerald's mother.

There is a picture of her on the cover. The face is calm and austere, a narrow face, the eyes large and lustrous, the hair drawn back from the high forehead, the lips, tenderly cut in youth, perhaps, are stern. I can see Gerald's face emerging from this face. The lines are the same.

So Gerald knows. I do not doubt now that the old servant woman bore a message to him from his mother. The mother would have told the son how she died and for what cause.

He did know, he did remember. For it was he who set our

wedding day, May the fifteenth. He did not tell me why, but I know now. He cannot write me a letter, but he has sent me his mother's picture and the story of her life as a revolutionist. He wants me to understand.

Oh, beloved, I try, I try.

It GROWS no easier to live alone, woman without man. I feel a certain hardness in me. I am not as tenderhearted as I was. The daily exercise of love is gone and I fear an atrophy. I wonder how other women live, who have had husbands and have them no more.

But Gerald still lives. He is not dead, but liveth. I do not read the Scriptures regularly, but now I crave spiritual food. This morning, a summer's day in early June, full of life and burgeoning, the garden forcing itself, the late apple trees in full blossom, the grass new green, I felt my blood running through me, too swift and strong, and my soul cried out for succor. Then I took the small worn leatherbound New Testament which had been my father's, and it opened to these words. "He is not dead, but liveth." It is enough. I closed the book and went to my work.

Oh, good hard work that a farm has ever ready — I bless it. I went to the barn and there discovered that my prize cow, Cecily, had in the night presented me with a fine heifer calf. Mother and child were doing well, and Cecily looked at me smugly through the bars of the maternity stall. She is a pink-nosed Guernsey and she is slightly dish-faced, which lends her a saucy air. Her figure is impeccable, by Guernsey standards. She did not rise when she saw me, excusing herself doubtless by her achievement. The calf is exquisite, with a dainty head and good lines of back and rump. She stared at me with faint alarm, and her mother licked her cheek for reassurance. Cecily was complacent. I offered her the mash that Matt concocts for such occasions and she ate it without greed, delicately and as a favor to me.

I came away cheered. Life flows on, whatever the need of the heart. I turned to the garden and attacked the young weeds, though of all tasks I hate weeding. The seeds are up, however, and the race is on. I worked hard all day, stopping only to make luncheon for Baba and me at noon. Rennie is in the last lap of his school year. He goes to college in the autumn and I fear my loneliness but I must not feed upon him. Baba and I will live here together like two old folk. . . .

Ah, but I am not old. Tonight when the young moon rose, I could not go to bed. Rennie is away this evening. He is in love, I think. He put on his best dark-blue suit, a white shirt and a crimson tie. He had even polished his Sunday shoes. I do not know who she is. I must wait.

Baba went to bed early. He likes to be under cover, as he puts it, by half past eight. But it is only the beginning of the night then, and I came to the narrow terrace that faces the moon, and lay down on the long chair. The air is chill, though it is June, and I wrapped myself in my white shawl and let myself dream of the beloved.

My mind floats over land and sea to the city which is his, and like a ghost I creep through the streets, and in the gate where he lives. This I have done again and again in the five years we have been parted. There is nothing eternal about our separation. At any moment he may decide to come here to me. If he does, I will not ask a question, I will not ask why did you, or how could you? I will open my arms and receive him. It is enough that he returns.

There hangs the moon! Upon a summer night in Peking we sit in the east courtyard. Our house belonged once to a Manchu prince, a lowly one, a younger brother. It is not large enough for a palace, but those who lived in it loved it well enough to add beauty here and there. The gates between the courts are moon-shaped, framed in tiles set in lacelike patterns. A lotus pool lies in the east court, and a cluster of bamboos hides the wall. The street is on the other side of the house, and the court is quiet. Moreover, the east court leads into our bedroom, Gerald's and mine. The huge Chinese bed stands against the inner wall.

At first, as a bride, I complained about the bed. It is too hard, I said, a wooden frame and a bottom of woven rattan to sleep upon. Gerald laughed at me and said that I wanted the beauty and not the hardness of Chinese life. And I said why should we sleep on wood and rattan when we could have a spring mattress, and is that a sin? Not sin, he said, but inconsistency. We should be one thing or the other. Why not have the best of both, I said, and so when he went to Tientsin to order supplies for the college year, he brought back an American spring mattress. And it was a game between us that I should pretend to force him to admit its comfort while he pretended to like the old hard Chinese bed bottom. We laughed a great deal in those days. I do not remember that he laughed with anyone else. He was to that degree not like his Chinese friends, for Chinese laugh easily and gaily. But Gerald is grave. He can be somber and at such times he is silent. Nothing I could say would make him speak. Only love could bring him back to me, warm physical love, informed by heart and mind. Sitting there alone on the terrace, I stretched out my arms to him across the sea.

RENNIE came home at midnight and found me still on the terrace. "You haven't been waiting for me, I hope, Mom?" he said.

Yes, he is getting to be an American. The stately name of Mother, upon which his father always insisted, has become Mom.

"No," I said. "I was just thinking about your father and wondering what he is doing tonight — working, probably."

Rennie did not answer. Instead, rather ostentatiously, he lit a cigarette. I know that he smokes, and he knows that I know, but it is the first time he has done so before me.

"Give me one, will you?" I said.

He looked surprised and held out the pack. "I didn't know you smoked," he said and lit my cigarette.

"I don't," I retorted. "But you seem to enjoy it, and why not I?"

He was embarrassed and I fear the pleasure went out of his cigarette. Perhaps it is necessary for the young to have something to defy. I suspect they hate this modern permissiveness. There is nothing in it to set their teeth against. At any rate, Rennie soon put out his cigarette. He stretched himself in the other long chair and locked his hands behind his head. I heard him sigh.

"How old were you when you were married, Mom?"

"I was twenty-three."

"Gee, that was old."

"It didn't seem so," I said. "Your father and I were engaged for a year."

"Why didn't you get married before?"

How much does one reveal to a child? Rennie's profile in the moonlight was not a child's. He has grown three and a half inches this year. He is already as tall as Gerald. The bones of his face are hardening and the lines are strengthening. If these are outward signs of manhood, there must be inward changes, too.

"Your father was afraid I might not like China. More than that, he wanted to be sure that I could love what was Chinese in him. Until he was sure, he would not marry me."

Our son pondered this. "What is Chinese in him?" he asked at last. "I can't even remember him clearly."

"Why, Rennie, you were twelve when we left."

"I know — I should remember. I don't know why I can't."

He does not want to remember his father — that is why. But I must not accuse him. Let me seize this opportunity to help him remember.

"You know how he looks."

"He really looks Chinese," Rennie said unwillingly.

"Yes, he looks Chinese until he is with Chinese and then he looks American."

"If he were here he'd look Chinese all right."

"What of it? The Chinese are very handsome, especially those in the North, where your grandparents lived."

"Is my father more Chinese inside or more American?" Rennie asked.

"I think that when he is Chinese he is very Chinese. There are other times when he is very American."

"For example?"

Rennie has the precise mind of a scientist. How can I answer him? For it was when we were alone, husband and wife, that Gerald was American. That surely was his true self.

"He is very Chinese when it comes to family," I said. "He treats you as a Chinese father does his son, with an inexorable loving firmness. He never lets you forget that you are not only his son but you are the grandson, the great-grandson, a thousand times over, of many men before you."

"But I have other ancestors — yours, Mom — and maybe I'm more like them."

"It may be that you are."

I knew that he had not reached the real meaning of all this talk. What can one do with the young except wait? Soon he began again.

"Mom, do you think my being part Chinese will keep an American girl from liking me?"

"Certainly not," I said. "It would be much more likely that a Chinese girl wouldn't like the American in you."

"I couldn't fall for a Chinese girl."

"You might. They're very beautiful, many of them."

"I shan't go back to China," he told me.

"You might go back someday to see your father, if he doesn't come here to us."

"Will he come here, do you think?"

This, this was the moment to tell him about the letter locked in my desk. I am afraid to tell him. He is too young to understand, too ignorant to have mercy.

"I hope he will come. Let's both hope. And who's the girl, Rennie?"

For of course there is a girl. All the talk has simply been leading up to it.

He sat up surprised. "Mom, how did you know?"

"Oh, I know," I said, trying to laugh. "I really know more than you think I do."

He lay back to stare again at the moon.

"She's the girl in that white house down the road. Summer people."

I knew people had moved into the house, but I have been too busy to call on them. Now of course I must go.

"What's her name?"

"Allegra Woods."

"What does the father do?"

"Business of some sort in New Jersey."

"How did you happen to meet?"

"She was walking down the road one day, toward Moore's Falls, and I happened along and she asked where she was."

"You must bring her to see me," I said. All the warnings were quivering inside me. My son is in danger. The hour I had foreseen since the day he was laid in my arms, newborn, has now come. A girl has looked at him. He has looked at the girl. What girl is this?

"It's getting cold," I said. "We must go inside."

I hope the friendship will not move too quickly into something else. Rennie brought Allegra here today. They have been meeting every day, I think.

"Mother," he said, now very formal, "this is Allegra Woods."

I was doing the mending in the living room and the lamp was lit, and Baba was sitting in peaceful silence in the brown leather armchair, his feet, in velvet Chinese shoes, on the hassock. He was wearing his crimson silk Chinese robe. I had helped him wash his hair and his beard today and they were snow white.

"How do you do, Allegra," I said. I took my spectacles off by habit, since it is not good Chinese manners to greet a stranger, or a friend, in spectacles.

The young girl made a graceful movement toward me, not quite a bow, nor yet a curtsy. Then she put out a slim hand.

"How do you do, Mrs. MacLeod."

"This is Rennie's grandfather," I said, looking toward Baba.

For some reason Baba decided to be difficult. He said in Chinese, very clearly, "Who is this female?"

Rennie flushed. He pretends he has forgotten all his Chinese but when he wishes he remembers it perfectly. He spoke in sharp English. "Grandfather, this is my friend Allegra Woods."

Baba nodded his head like an old mandarin.

"She should be at home with her parents," he said in Chinese.

I laughed. "Allegra, you mustn't mind him. He lived in China for so many years he has forgotten he is an American."

Her blue eyes grew wide. "In China? Rennie didn't tell me."

Then Rennie has not told her everything. I must be careful not to tell too much.

"Yes," I said cheerfully. "We all lived there. Rennie's father is still there. As a matter of fact, Rennie was born in Peking."

"Really? But I thought China was Communist?"

"Just now, yes."

"Then how can his father — "

"He is the president of a great college and he feels it his duty to stay with his students."

"I see."

But she didn't see, that I knew. She looked thoughtfully at Rennie, her eyes big and blue.

"Get some ice cream, Rennie," I said. "There's plenty in the freezer."

"Come along, Allegra." He seized her hand.

"Did you have to tell her everything at once?" Rennie groaned that night when he came home.

"I did not tell her everything," I said.

"She said now she knew why I seemed queer." Rennie choked.

I longed to put my arms about him but he would have hated it. Better to speak the truth.

"You will have to accept yourself," I said. "You are partly Chinese, one fourth by blood. You will never be happy until you are proud of all that you are — not just of a part."

I kissed his cheek and went away. The Allegras of this world are not for him, but he will have to find it out for himself. Then when the pain is over he will discover a woman who is his, and whose he can be.

What, I wonder, made me know Gerald was mine? I remember that spring day in my senior year at Radcliffe. I was hurrying to my class in philosophy, my arm full of books. I was late to class and much distracted by the beauty of the season when I saw Gerald run with his striking grace down the steps of the hall I was about to enter. I shall remember forever the glint of the sun on his black hair, the lively glance of his black eyes, and the clear smoothness of his cream skin.

We did not speak that day on the steps, but we looked full into one another's eyes, and I made up my mind forever. I would learn what his name was and tell him he was mine.

It did not happen in a day or a week but it did in a month. For I kept looking at him because he was handsome, the most beautiful man I had ever seen. Soon I was speaking to him, managing to walk out the door of a classroom when he did. And he was shy but he could not shake me off. And then I asked him one day to meet my mother. I was in love.

He let me know at last — oh what a long time it was before he let me know, three months, four months — I thought he would never tell me.

"I don't know whether you can consider me as a friend — " He wet his dry lips.

"I can and I do," I said, laughing with joy.

After we were married, I asked him why he stammered so much that day. He said, stammering again, though by then we were in our bedroom by the east court of the Peking house, "The — the fact is, I never thought I'd be — be in love, you know — with an American girl."

"Didn't you, now," I teased. "And whom would you be marrying please, if not me?"

He said soberly, "I always supposed I would marry a Chinese. It was my mother's wish."

That is what he said, long ago. Now, I keep looking at the picture of Gerald's mother. It is not cold. Behind the steadfast eyes of a Chinese woman I feel a powerful warmth. We might have been friends, she and I, unless she had decided first that I was her enemy. She would have decided, not I. I was never deceived by Chinese women, not even by the flowerlike lovely girls. They are the strongest women in the world. Seeming always to yield, they never yield. Theirs is the strength that centuries have given them, the strength of the unwanted. It was always the sons who were welcomed at birth, who were given privilege and pampering love. And the daughters, accepting this, generation after generation, had to learn to think first of themselves.

I have put the picture back into the drawer and locked it fast. But it haunts me. Today, which is Saturday, Baba and I being at lunch together alone, since Rennie is off fishing, I could not refrain from speaking again of her.

"Baba, you remember we were speaking of Gerald's mother? I want to talk more about her."

He was eating neatly with chopsticks, a habit which he assumes whenever I cook rice.

He put them down. "What is it you wish to know?"

"I have a picture of her upstairs."

He turned quite pale. "How is it you have it?"

"It is in a magazine."

I could not tell him Gerald had sent it.

"Fetch it," he said.

I ran upstairs and brought it down and placed it before him. He put on his spectacles and looked at it carefully.

"Ye-es," he said slowly, "ye-es, I can recognize her. But it is not as she used to look."

"How did she look?"

"When I lifted her wedding veil, I thought her nearly beautiful."

"Yes, Baba?" This was because he paused so long.

"Afterward I was not sure. She could make her face quite strange to me."

"Why did she?"

"I did not ask. We were never close enough for questions."

He took up his chopsticks again and began to eat. I wonder if that Chinese woman did love him long ago, and because he did not love her, she took what she had, the child, and made the child her own. Who can tell me now?

Tonight the moon is full upon the mountains and the shadows in the valley are black. The graveled road is silvered and I see two figures walking slowly at the far end into the trees, their arms entwined. I know they are Rennie and Allegra. They have walked out of the moonlight now into the shadows beneath the maple trees.

A change began with the new moon this month. Rennie was silent and hurried, not by work but because of haste and urgency in himself. He came and went without speaking and if he saw me looking at him he turned his head away.

Last night I stayed until long past midnight upon the terrace, so late that the wind was cool, and I wrapped my red wool scarf about me. Then I saw Rennie springing up the hill. He looked like a man in the night, so tall and strong and powerful. He saw me and he did not come to the terrace, but went instead to the door of the kitchen. I could bear it no longer.

"Rennie!"

He paused, his hand on the latch.

"Yes?"

"Come here, please."

He came quietly and calmly.

"You're up late," he said.

"I have waited for you."

His voice is a man's voice now. "You mustn't wait for me — not any more."

"I cannot sleep when I do not know where you are," I said.

"You will have to learn to sleep, not knowing."

I was suddenly angry because I knew he was right. And I could not keep from speaking the truth.

"I know you are with Allegra every evening and I don't like her."

It is the first time I have spoken my growing dislike for this girl whom Rennie is beginning to love. If Gerald were here, I could talk with him and heed his advice.

"Sit down, Rennie," I said. "It is late, but not too late for what I want to say."

He sat down on the low wall of the terrace, his back to the moon so that his face was in shadow and mine in the light. And I went on:

"It is not that I disapprove of Allegra for her own sake. She is like many other girls, pretty and sweet and shallow. She will make some man quite happy, a man who does not need much. He will be happy with Allegra and she with him for the heart of each has the measure of a cup and no more, and so they fulfill one another. But you, Rennie, need a fountain of love, living and eternal. You must find a deep woman, my son, a woman with an overflowing heart. When you find her, believe me, I shall never lie awake again, however late you come home."

"Allegra says you are jealous," Rennie retorted.

"That is because she knows she is not the one you should love, and she knows that I know it, too."

We were on the edge of a great bitterness, my son and I, and I drew back from the abyss.

I tried to speak calmly. "I suppose the reason I long so much for you to love one who can truly love you is because your father and I have been utterly happy together. I have never loved another man, nor had he loved another woman before me. It is old-fashioned, I know. It is quite the thing now, I hear, to say that one must experiment in love. Perhaps that is true for the shallow-hearted. But it is not true for the deep in heart. Your father and I are among those few. It made our love complete when we knew that what we gave each to the other was new and never given before. I assure you it did."

How glad I am that I have never shown Rennie the letter I have locked in my desk upstairs! For whatever the letter means I know that Gerald still loves only me. But Rennie could not know and he will never know if he does not find his mate.

"It's strange then that my father does not even write to you," he said cruelly.

"Not strange," I replied. "There is some reason why he cannot write, a reason that has nothing to do with you and me. There are many such reasons that separate people now. We must not allow them to destroy love. We must wait, still loving."

I was teaching myself as well as Rennie.

Rennie got up and kissed my cheek. "You needn't worry, Mom," he said. "And you're mistaken about Allegra. She's all right. Anyway, I'm not my father and she is not you, and we have to live our own lives."

To this there could be no reply.

"Good night, Mom."

"Good night, my son," I said.

I heard him clatter up the back stairs from the kitchen to his room. This summer he moved from the room next to mine, where he has lived since we came home, announcing that he would take the room over the kitchen. I know, of course, that he wants that room so he can come and go without passing my door. He has the right to come and go without telling me. And if Allegra were the girl I dream of for him, I would not care. Yet no mother can save her son. She can only watch and wait and wring her hands. I am sure he did not understand when I spoke of deephearted love. I am sorry for Allegra, too, for if this goes on he will make demands on her far beyond what she is able to give. His passion will mightily exceed hers, and she will be made miserable because she knows she is not enough for him. It is Allegra I pity and I see that she must be protected from Rennie. I must save Rennie, but I must save Allegra too.

TODAY Rennie is full of joy. He thinks he has clarified his relationship to me. He is free, he thinks, and he came downstairs this morning all life and cheer, his beautiful face aglow, his eyes shining with love. He kissed me briskly on the cheek, and sat down at the table to eat breakfast.

"I must begin cleaning the brush from the high sugarbush," he said, his voice loud and clear. "Matt can help me when he has done the barn."

"I suppose so," I said.

He was off then, very busy — and I washed the dishes and tended the house. Rennie thinks I should have a dishwasher but I will not. I like the quiet reflective moments after a meal, my hands in the hot soapy water and the view from the kitchen window before my eyes. Then, too, I love my dishes. Some I brought with me from the house in Peking, and the rest are my mother's and ones that I used as a child. I do not understand women who complain about their houses and their children and their husbands. This is our dear daily work. And I do not like new things. It takes time to become acquainted with possessions, and they should not change. Whenever a dish is lost or broken, something of life goes with it.

This morning I used for porringers the blue Chinese bowls lined with yellow porcelain. Alas, when I washed mine, it slipped from my fingers and fell against the sink and broke to pieces. I could not keep the tears from rushing to my eyes. I carried the bits of lovely pottery outside and buried them under the old apple tree by the front door.

When I came back into the kitchen Baba was there, waiting to be fed. He is growing very old now, and childish. I tucked the napkin in his collar but he would not lift his hand to his spoon, and I fed him. He ate then quite patiently, in silence, his eyes fixed vaguely on the window.

"I go back to my bed," he said when the dish was empty.

"Sit on the terrace a while in the sun," I suggested.

He shook his head and I had to coax him. "Do you not remember how the grandfathers in Peking always sit against the walls of the houses where the sun shines? They do not get out of bed and eat and go back to bed again. They like the sun, and the air is warm today and without wind."

He rose obediently and I wrapped a scarf about his neck and led him to the terrace and sat him down on the bench against the wall. He sat there, his eyes closed as though he slept, and I forgot him. At noon, ashamed, I hurried out to find him panting somewhat with the heat, his cheeks flushed and his dark eyes open in reproach.

"Shall I go to bed now?" he inquired.

"Indeed you shall," I said, "after you have had some tea and a boiled egg with your rice."

He ate without demur, relishing the Chinese tea, and I took him up to bed, and pulled the shades and left him fast asleep. The sun and air did him good, but how could I forget him? How selfish to let my mind dwell only upon my son!

Yet the hours of thought while I tended my house have cleared my mind. There is no better time for a woman to think than in the hours when she sweeps and dusts and makes beds. The physical activity sends blood coursing through her frame and the brain awakes. Yes, I shall go to see Allegra's mother.

Mrs. Woods was sitting on the porch of her house when I opened the gate. The house is a pleasant one, white-painted and the shutters green, a conventional house even to the flower beds and the walk between them. She was sewing needlepoint.

She rose when I came to the steps. She is a plump, middle-aged woman, a round friendly face, the sort of woman to be seen on any porch anywhere, a good woman, somewhat timid.

"Come in," Mrs. Woods said, seeming flustered.

"I am Mrs. Gerald MacLeod," I said, "and I live up the road."

"I know your boy Rennie," she said. "We'd best sit inside, because the mites are bad today. I was just about to move."

We went inside a narrow hall with a red carpet, the straight stairs leading to the second floor. To the right was a dining room and to the left a largish living room. It was pleasant and comfortable. There were a few magazines on the table beside the couch but no books. How could Rennie live in a house without books?

"Take that chair," Mrs. Woods said. "It's my husband's, and so it's the most comfortable."

There was suddenly a mild twinkle in her gray eyes that I liked. I sat down and came to the point at once.

"I'm sure you know that Rennie and Allegra are seeing each other. I want to know what you think about it. They're so young. . . ."

Her round face grew concerned. It is a sweet childish face.

Allegra is much prettier. The father, perhaps, has straightened the lines of her face. But she has her mother's curved figure.

"They are young," she agreed. "Mr. Woods and I have been worried. Of course we want Allegra to feel free. But she's only a senior in high school next year. We wouldn't want her to think she shouldn't finish high school."

"Heavens, no," I said. "And Rennie will have to go to college — and after that he will have still more years somewhere, perhaps in Europe, or perhaps in China, where his father is."

Real horror broke over my neighbor's face. "China? Nobody can go there, can they?"

"Not now," I said, "but Rennie may join his father there someday, when the world is better."

"Is his father — a Chinese?" Mrs. Woods spoke the word apologetically.

"No," I said, "at least, not altogether. His father, Rennie's grandfather, is American. He lives with us. My husband is president of a great university in China. He feels it his duty to stay by his work."

"Isn't China Communist?" Her voice was vaguely reproachful.

"Yes," I said, "and my husband is not Communist, I can assure you. But he still feels he must stay." Then the truth forced itself from me. "You see, his mother was Chinese."

"She was?" Mrs. Woods' voice was an exclamation. "Then that's why Rennie — we thought maybe he had Indian blood."

"Didn't Rennie tell Allegra?"

"No, no, I'm sure he didn't."

"Then I am glad I told. It is better for you to know before they fall too much in love."

"I should say so."

Her face was flushed with thought, her plump hands clenched together on her lap. Suddenly she looked up and her eyes met mine. "You poor thing," she said, "it's dreadful for you, isn't it?"

"What — Rennie?"

"The whole business — marrying somebody way off — a Chinese!"

"My husband is American," I said. "His father registered his birth at the American Embassy in Peking. Rennie was registered there, too."

"Still and all — it's different, somehow."

"I've been completely happy," I said. "So happy that I must make sure Rennie will be happy, too. I couldn't let him marry a girl who merely tolerated his being partly Chinese. She must be proud of it. She must understand that he is the richer for it, as a man and — yes, even as an American."

She could not follow me, though she tried, bless her, and I could not keep from liking her more and more. She is simple and honest. I hope she will continue as my friend, so that we can talk as woman to woman. I miss a good friend. Matt's wife is good, but she is ignorant and besides she and Matt quarrel constantly. They live alone on the mountainside opposite ours, their children gone now. Matt groans sometimes on a gray morning, "Oh, that woman has been the death of me these forty years!" And when I take a lettuce to Mrs. Matt she tells me of Matt's wickedness and how he won't shave but once a week, and she declares that he's been torture these forty years. But Mrs. Woods is a happy wife and mother. I can see that.

Mr. Woods came in then, a thin, bald man, his eyes very blue. This is his vacation, he told me. He works in an accountant's office in Passaic, New Jersey.

"I am your neighbor, Mr. Woods, and frankly I came to see you and Mrs. Woods about my son and your daughter," I said.

"Mrs. MacLeod tells me her husband is Chinese," Mrs. Woods said significantly.

"No, no," I cried. "I said that he is American, although his mother was Chinese. She was a lady of high birth. She is dead now."

"No kidding," Mr. Woods exclaimed in a low voice. "Well, now! I don't know as I ever knew of anyone mixed like that."

It was obvious that he was shocked, and at the same time he did not want to hurt me. He was sorry for me, and couldn't put it into words.

I got up. "Thank you both," I said as cheerfully as I could. "Please don't worry. Rennie will be going off to college soon, and young people forget easily. Allegra is so pretty that she must have a lot of boy friends."

They grasped at the suggestion. "She is very popular," Mrs. Woods said proudly.

Allegra came in at this moment. Her cheeks were rose pink. She had on a white sleeveless frock, short and tight, and only a young pretty girl could have suffered its severity.

"Hello, Mrs. MacLeod," she said with a quick smile.

"I'm afraid Rennie kept you up too late, last night," I said. "I scolded him for it."

"Oh, I can always sleep," Allegra said. She sat on the couch beside her father and he put his arm around her shoulders and squeezed her against him.

"How's my honey?"

"Just fine," Allegra said and leaned her fair head against his shoulder.

Mrs. Woods watched them tenderly. "They're such chums," she murmured. It was touching to see how the parents adored this child, their only one.

They were anxious for me to be gone. They would not talk to the child before me. I got up and bade them good-by as if nothing had happened, as though we had not rearranged two lives. We lingered on the porch, we admired the sweet Williams along the path. And so I went home.

When Rennie came in to supper I had no chance to tell him what I had done. He ate in a hurry and in his work clothes, and then rushed to his room to bathe and change. In a few minutes he raced through the kitchen in clean blue jeans and a fresh shirt.

"Good night, Mom," he called as he went.

"Good night, son," I said.

When I had washed the dishes and had settled Baba for the night, I went to my room. Tonight I could sleep. Whatever I had to meet, I would face it in the morning.

I WAKED early and got up immediately, knowing what awaited me. When I came downstairs Rennie was there at the kitchen table. He had made a pot of coffee and was drinking it, black and strong.

"You haven't been to bed," I said.

He blazed at me. "How could I sleep? She has gone."

I sat down and poured myself a cup of coffee. "Go on. Say whatever you want to say. Let's have it out."

My son was terrible to see. His face was pale and his eyes were burning black. His lips were parched and bitten.

"You went to her parents. You told them."

"Nothing but the truth," I said quietly.

"You wouldn't wait until they knew me!"

Oh, what bitterness in his voice!

"It is better for them to know the truth first," I said. "If she loves you enough to defy her parents, I will say nothing — I swear I will not."

"At least you might have warned me," he cried.

I would not yield to him. "I had to see how they felt, and see it with my own eyes. What they feel cannot be overcome unless your love and hers are equal. I know — I know!"

"She does love me," he muttered. "She told me so."

"She loves you all she can, but it is not enough. It will never be enough, because she is small — small, I tell you! I do not blame her. She cannot help what she is born. But you are born big — as big as the world."

"Damn you," he whispered.

I looked at him. "Now I am glad your father is not here."

We stared at each other. I kept looking at my son's face and his gaze broke, he so young, so proud in such grief.

"Why did you ever give me birth?" he muttered, and then he sobbed once and leaped from the room.

THE HOUSE is too still. I knew when I opened my eyes this morning that Rennie was gone. It was a gray morning, a soft rain drifting over the trees and misting into my open window. The curtains hung limp. It was well past dawn and time for milking. By now I should hear Rennie stirring. I got up and closed the window and stood looking down the valley half hidden by rain, summoning my courage to go to his room. I tried to think of Gerald but my heart did not call and his did not answer. I could not see his face and when I forced the eyes of my mind toward him, I saw only the stretching miles of land and the terrible gray sea between us.

I opened the door of Rennie's room and looked in. The bed was empty, neatly made. All the room was neat and I was frightened by such order. On any other morning his clothes would have been piled on the armchair, his shoes scattered, his books open on the table. I ran across the room to his closet lest it be empty. Oh, what joy to see his clothes still hanging there! I counted his suits, the brown second best, his work clothes, the jackets and slacks. No, his best dark-blue suit was gone.

Then I saw the envelope on his desk, addressed to me.

I sat down to read it because I was too weak to stand. "Dear Mother," Rennie said. *Mother.* Not Mom. "I have gone to find Allegra. I have to see for myself why she has changed — if she has. Don't get in touch with me — don't telephone, don't write. See you when I get home. Rennie."

Now there is nothing to do but wait. Blessings on old Baba, who is all I have left! I went back to my room and bathed and dressed and descended to the kitchen.

And then I was disturbed by plaintive sounds and I heard Baba's voice. I went upstairs. He lay in his bed, the covers drawn tight about his neck, his dark eyes bewildered.

"I can't get up," he murmured.

"Are you in pain, Baba?" I asked.

"No pain," he said indistinctly.

"Lie still," I said. "I will send for the doctor."

So I went to the telephone. It was early and Bruce Spaulden had not left home.

"Yes?" His voice was crisp.

"Bruce, I think Baba has had another stroke."

"I'll be over. Just keep him covered and quiet."

I went back to Baba and told him that Bruce was coming and then I made the room tidy. Baba lay there, quiet and good, and watched me, and I saw his face beginning to draw toward the left.

Now I heard Bruce's footsteps in the hall downstairs and he came upstairs and into the room. "Good morning, Elizabeth," he said.

It was the first time he had called me by my name and I was startled.

"Good morning," I said. "Here is my poor Baba, waiting."

Baba turned piteous eyes toward the doctor.

Bruce sat down by the bed and made his examination. There is something wonderful in the way a good doctor examines his patient, his mind concentrated, his hands sure in exploration. I stood respectful, admiring Bruce. He is lean, as most Vermonters are, tall and serious. His hair is an ordinary brown and straight, his nose is straight and his mouth firm. When he smiles his face changes altogether. It is mischievous and almost gay. He is even-tempered, inclined to silence and meditation. I have absorbed a Chinese curiosity into my being and I wanted to ask him why he was not married. To a Chinese anything can be asked between friends.

He covered Baba carefully. "Not too serious," he said. "There will be more of these little strokes. He'll sleep a lot. Let him sleep."

Indeed Baba was already sleeping, breathing softly aloud. We left him and went downstairs into the living room.

"Have you had breakfast?" I asked.

"No," Bruce said.

"Let us breakfast together. I'm lonely because Rennie has gone — "

"Gone?"

"For only a few days, I hope, but I don't know."

And I told him about Allegra. Bruce smiled rather grimly. "He'll be back. We always come back to our mothers."

I was busy getting the breakfast on the table, eggs, coffee, toast and fruit. When we were seated I asked my question.

"Because I am so happily married, Bruce, I ask why you have never married."

"Too busy," he said, buttering toast.

"It's not my business — but — "

"Go on," he said. "I lead a simple life. No secrets."

"Are you happy as you are?"

"I don't know. I suppose so. I haven't asked myself."

I poured his second cup of coffee. What he did not wish to tell he would not tell. That is a Vermonter, too.

When he was gone, suddenly and to my own surprise I gave myself over to weeping for Gerald. I knew that the doors of the house in Peking were shut against me.

LAST WEEK, coming home from my Saturday shopping, I was charmed by the sight of a black mother ewe and her twin white lambs, cropping grass in a roadside pasture, and I stopped the car and got out to watch the mother and her children. The sunlight was bright, mild, Vermont sunshine, never hot as the Chinese sun was hot. I sat down on a round gray rock. At this the mother ewe was gently alarmed and bleated softly. Immediately the baby lambs came to her side and stood trembling on their slender legs, and peered at me. I thought that I would like to own the black ewe and her white lambs. They can crop the short grass on the hillside about my house and keep the semblance of a lawn.

I went to find the farmer who owns the ewe and after some search I found one of the wry individuals who cling to this soil, a man who farms a little and tinkers at whatever job comes his way. He was mending a table when I came from behind his small frame house. "Well?" he inquired without good morning.

"I'd like to know if your black ewe and white lambs are for sale," I said.

"Might be," he said.

"How much will you take for them?" I asked.

"Don't know as I want to sell," he said, and measured his ruler against a strip of wood. "I'll think it over."

"Do," I said. "I'll be at home this afternoon."

He came this morning, two days later, leading the ewe and the lambs on a rope. "Ten dollars in cash and the rest in maple syrup," he announced.

We argued for a half hour or so over the quantity of syrup but I yielded, since, being a Vermonter, he would not, and now the ewe and the lambs are cropping the grass on my hillside. She, with the lambs, provides me with a comfort I cannot fathom. It is a small comfort, but deep, another tie to this earth. I own something more, something alive.

SOMETIMES, wandering the Chinese roads outside our city, Gerald and I came upon a peasant standing in quiet reverence before a small wayside shrine. Inside the shrine two gods sat, male and female, a married pair, for so the peasants conceive their gods to be. They cannot imagine a solitary god. That, they believe, would be against the law of life. So before the divine pair the peasant stood to light a stick of incense. It was a sight simple and good. I said to Gerald, "Would that we could pray in this fashion and believe!"

"It is not that we cannot believe," he replied. "It is that we do not want anything enough. Faith rises from necessity. We have no necessity."

Out of my necessity now, I find that I must pray. Out of my intense anxiety for my son I have gone each night to his room and standing in the empty silence I pray for him. How far the prayer rises I cannot guess. Whether there is a listening ear I do not know. But at least the prayer crowding my heart to agony is released and I am relieved. Some of the burden is lifted.

RENNIE has come home. He came last night, late. I was asleep but I wake at the slightest sound. I heard a door open, the kitchen door.

No one except Rennie has a key. The next sound would be the refrigerator, opened and shut. . . . Yes, that sound, too, I heard. I longed to spring from my bed and run downstairs and enfold him. But I had grown cautious. It was no longer what I wished to give but what he would accept. He had learned to live without me and without his home. I would not go downstairs. The days of childhood communion were over.

In my bed I lay, the faint moonlight streaming across the counterpane, and I listened. He ate at the kitchen table. I heard the clink of a dish and the scrape of a chair. He ate well, for it was a full half hour before I heard the door to the stair open, the little winding back stair that goes only to his room. I heard the sound of water running into the bathtub cautiously and at half cock, so as not to wake me. Oh, how thankful was I that he had come home! Thank God, thank God!

Then I heard the door handle turn softly. When I saw him standing in the doorway, wrapped in his old red wool bathrobe, I spoke as easily as if he had never been away.

"Is that you, Rennie?"

In such foolish words great moments are encompassed. He answered as easily. "How are you, Mother?"

"I am well. Did you just get back?"

"I had something to eat downstairs."

He came toward the bed and sat down on the edge of it, and we gazed at each other in the moonlight.

"Shall I put on the light?" I asked.

"No," he said. "Did I wake you?"

"It doesn't matter," I said, pretending to be sleepy. "I don't get up as early as I used to. Matt milks the cows."

"Is everything all right?" he asked.

"I've bought a black ewe and twin white lambs so that I need not cut the grass."

"I saw them in the moonlight."

Then it seemed we had nothing more to say. I would not let a question escape from the prison of my heart.

"You haven't asked me where I have been, Mother."

"You might have written me," I said.

"I couldn't," he said. "And it doesn't matter where I've been. . . . Mother, why did you let me be born? I asked you before."

"You didn't wait for my answer," I reminded him.

"I will wait now," he said.

"Your father and I love each other with all our hearts and when there is such love between two young and healthy human beings, one a man, the other a woman, a child is their hope."

"You might have thought what it would mean to me."

Oh, what a bitter cry this was!

"Your father thought of it. I said that our child would be so strong, so beautiful, so self-sufficient, that he would meet any situation and be the conqueror."

His eyes were as black as dead coals.

"When I was in China," he said, "they called me a foreigner. I did not care then, for I thought I had another country, America."

"People have been kind to you here," I said.

"It is not kindness I want — it is love."

"You have much love," I said. "Your father loves you and I love you. And love will come to you someday from a woman."

"Allegra is not allowed to love me. Her parents forbid it."

"Can she not be disobedient?" I inquired. "My mother forbade me to love your father, too, but I disobeyed. And I have never been sorry."

No, I am not sorry, though Gerald's last letter lies upstairs in my desk, a thing alive with sorrow.

"Not all women are strong," Rennie said and he looked at me with something like distaste. "And because a woman is not strong, it does not mean that her love is the less valuable."

"What is Allegra afraid of?" I tried to hide my scorn.

"She is afraid of what I carry in my veins, the ancestry."

"You mean the Chinese part of you," I said.

He nodded, and he knotted his hands together.

"The very part of you that I love most and am most proud of because I love your father, you wish you did not have. Shame on you, Rennie!"

"You don't understand," he cried. "You are American, your ancestry is pure — "

"Oh, pure," I cried, "the rebels of half a dozen nations in Europe —"

"You are all white," he said stubbornly.

It was not the moment for argument.

"I am going to Kansas," he went on. "I'll work on Sam's ranch this summer, and go to college in the autumn."

No "if you don't mind, Mother," no "unless you need my help here." But I am proud and I do not ask my son's help.

"When will you go?" I asked.

"I suppose I ought to stop long enough to see Baba," he replied.

Perhaps it is time for me to tell him of Baba's wife. Some of this rebel blood in him comes from her. She suffered, too, because she was not loved. Perhaps she can help him now as I cannot.

"Stay a day, at least, Rennie. There are things I want to say to you before you go — things I have never told you."

He looked at me quickly with those dark, dark eyes.

"All right," he said, "if that's the way you want it —"

When Baba woke the next morning we went upstairs. There he was, lying upon his pillows exactly as he had gone to sleep, his white hair scarcely ruffled, his dark eyes vague and only half open. I spoke to him.

"Baba, good morning. See who has come to you."

He opened his eyes and stared at me. "Who is that? Is it Gerald?"

"No — no — no. It is Rennie."

He had forgotten his own grandson. "Should I know him?" he inquired.

"Yes, you should," I said. "He is Gerald's son — and mine."

"Gerald's son," he mused. "Had Gerald a son?"

I turned to implore. "Rennie, forgive him. He is so old. He has forgotten everything."

Oh, what a look of sadness was on the young face!

"It doesn't matter," Rennie said. "Nothing matters."

"Go to sleep again, Baba," I said. "I will come back soon." We tiptoed out again, and I knew that I had lost. Baba has withdrawn from us into the distances of old age.

I was frantic to reclaim my son. "Rennie, come into my room now. I have pictures to show you."

In my room he sat down as formally as a guest and waited. And I took out the picture of Gerald's mother.

"This is the Chinese lady Baba married," I told him. "This is your grandmother. She is quite beautiful, in her own dignified way. She is someone to be proud of, the daughter of an ancient family."

Rennie took the picture and gazed at the calm Chinese face. "Why did Baba marry her?"

"He wanted to become part of the country to which he had dedicated his life. He thought he could get near to the people he loved."

"Now he has forgotten everything," Rennie said. "He does not know even me. I suppose he never loved her."

Rennie gave me back the picture. He got to his feet and leaned down from his height and kissed my cheek.

"Good-by, Mother," he said. He went away immediately. I heard his old car whirl down the road in a cloud of summer dust. This time he may never come back. What I remember is that he spoke again as his father taught him, his English classic and pure. The slang, the American boy talk, he had wiped from tongue and lips.

I CANNOT follow Rennie even if I would, for here is Baba, who has no one but me. I am held on this quiet farm, remote from everyone except Matt and his wife, and they know only the language of a hate-filled love. They quarrel and enjoy themselves in combat by day and I do not doubt also by night. Seven children they have bred together. They have needed no other companionship, no other excitement, I do believe. Matt is insanely jealous and Mrs. Matt is proud of his jealousy, boasting of its oppression.

"If Matt so much as sees a man's hat in the house, he takes conniptions," she boasts, and her little round wrinkled face glows with pleasure.

She said that this morning when I crossed the dusty road to

praise her flower beds. Before I could reply, as I always do, that she is lucky Matt still cares enough about her to be jealous, the postman handed me a few letters at the gate, none of any importance except a thin gray envelope sent from Singapore. The handwriting was strange.

"Your husband?" the postman asked.

"No," I said. I left him and went to the rock beside the spring, and sat there in the shade of a leaning apple tree and tore open the envelope.

"Dear Elder Sister," the letter began.

It was from her.

All these months I have not answered Gerald's letter. He asked my permission and I have not given it. Underneath all that I do has been the knowledge of this delay, a secret as hidden as a sin.

She writes in English, but not well. She wants me to understand that she will not enter my house to take my place until I give permission.

You have lived in Peking very long [she writes]. I think you understand something very much about us Chinese people. Here now it is hard for living. It is also hard for MacLeod, your husband, and he is wishing so much for some woman to take care of house and mending and cooking, and so forth. At my former request, he wrote to you asking your agreement to my coming to his house as wife-in-absence. You know this is quite common, no more second wife or concubine, as before, which is too old-fashioned, but wife-in-absence. Of course if you come back, I will go away if you wish. To you I have respect as younger to elder. Please permit me, and tell me how everything should be in caring for our husband. I wish to do what you tell me and make him so happy. This is my duty. But first your permission, please, to save his life. I send this letter to a secret friend in Singapore and please return to same.

Your humble younger sister,

MEI-LAN

The address in Singapore is to a silk shop. Someone there, I suppose, is her secret friend, someone in touch with this strange new China, by which I am rejected. Shall I give my permission for another woman to take my place? Surely no American woman has ever been in a like predicament. I cannot answer this letter today. I do not know what to say, until I am in communion with Gerald again.

I take his letter from the locked drawer of my desk and though I have sworn that I will not look at it again, I do so. I set it down here. This is the letter from Peking, Gerald's last letter.

My Dear Wife:

First, before I say what must be said, let me tell you that I love only you. Whatever I do now, remember that it is you I love. If you never receive a letter from me again, know that in my heart I write you every day. I say this because of what I must next tell you. It is imperative for me to take into my home a Chinese woman. It is not only that I need someone to look after the house, to wash my clothes, mend and so on. You know how helpless I am in these matters. But it is necessary now for me to prove myself. It is not enough, it seems, for me to swear loyalty to those in present power. I must forswear my past, I must curse my non-Chinese blood. I have been ordered to choose another woman. I tell you because you and I have always been honest, one with the other. If I were to be less than honest with you now, it would mean that I had indeed forgotten our life together. I shall never forget.

I cannot write again. It would be too dangerous for me and for our son. You think him safe in your country, but he is not safe anywhere unless I repudiate him and you. Do not believe I have done so in reality. I wish to stay alive, if possible, until these days are past. If I meet death in spite of all my efforts to avoid it, remember that my only thought is of you, my Eve.

GERALD

I do not know why I have delayed all these months to do what I knew had to be done. Now that this letter has come from the woman, I see that I must give permission at once. Perhaps I shall cable. No, to receive a cable from America might make trouble for a Chinese even in Singapore. I will write and send the letter air mail. I am writing for Gerald. Yes, dear and beloved, I am writing this for you.

DEAR YOUNGER SISTER:

Your letter has come to my hand. I have read it. I give my permission. You may not take my place, for each woman has her own place in a man's life, but you may enter my house and make your own place there. It is true, as you say, that I understand. Nevertheless, my heart breaks. Care for him well, for I love him.

ELIZABETH

I stamped the envelope and took it to the post office and slipped it into the box under the window. I had done what I must and I went home. Baba was not yet out of bed, his day beginning at noon and ending at twilight. He seemed drowsy, vague. But when he was dressed and sitting in his armchair, when he had eaten his bowl of oatmeal and drunk a cup of tea, he suddenly seemed awake and knowing. Perhaps Rennie had left a dart of memory in him, by which he was pricked.

"Did someone come here yesterday?" he inquired.

"Yes, Baba. It was Rennie, your grandson."

He reflected upon this information. A half hour later, while I was straightening his room, he spoke with sudden clarity.

"But I thought it was Ai-lan."

"How could it be, when she was a woman?"

"She looked like a man," he said. "She put on a uniform. It was of dark-blue cotton, the jacket buttoned, and trousers like a man. It startled me."

So Rennie looks like his Chinese grandmother! He looks like Gerald, certainly. Then Gerald looks like his mother.

"Ai-lan was killed," Baba said painfully. His old face wrinkled and tears dripped from his eyes. He wept for his dead wife. But why now, after all the years?

"Did you love her, Baba?" I asked.

"I couldn't love her," he said. "I tried, for the Scriptures say a man must cleave to his wife. They do not say how it is to be done. And she knows I could not."

"You gave her a son," I reminded him for comfort.

"Ah, but she knew," he retorted. "She knew very well. On the morning he was born, a fine spring morning, I went into her room. She lay with the child sleeping on her arm. 'I have given you a son.' That was what she said. And I couldn't speak. The child had long black hair. It was a shock to think my son was Chinese. I wasn't prepared."

He shook his head in vague distress.

What he meant was that he had not thought of a child. He married Gerald's mother for reasons of his own. He did not want a son. And that not being wanted had remained deep in Gerald's being, a dagger never withdrawn, a wound never healed. It was the wound that kept Gerald from coming with me to my country. I feel it. But Rennie carries the mark and he is here. Oh, how deep is the wound of not being loved! From generation to generation the newborn heart is wounded afresh and cannot be healed until love is found, in someone, somewhere.

Baba had begun to weep again and I asked, to divert him,

"Baba, do you remember Sam Blaine? You lived in his little house, in Kansas."

"Did I?"

"Yes. Rennie has gone there to work on the ranch. Sam Blaine was kind to you when you were taken ill on the train and they put you off. He became your friend. Now he is Rennie's friend."

He remembered none of it, but at least he forgot to weep. I pushed his chair to the window, and he gazed peacefully out upon the rising hills and the valleys. He likes to watch the sheep. I went away to do my day's work.

Tonight when Baba was in bed he suddenly remembered about Sam Blaine. I had said good night, when Baba spoke.

"Sam Blaine is forty-two years old. He has never married. His father owned two thousand acres of good black earth. He was a cattleman, and he owned mines in Nevada, too. Sam was his only child."

"Baba," I cried, "how well you remember!" So I sat down and Baba said he had been taken from the train, ill and feverish, and told to wait in the station until a doctor could be summoned. Sam

Blaine, who had come to the depot to fetch some freight, took Baba home with him and put him to bed.

"I had typhoid fever," Baba said. "I was very ill."

And bit by bit he told me the story. When he woke in the night, not knowing where he was, Sam sat by the bed and talked about China. He had been there during the war. As Baba told me this, he was suddenly bewildered, and looked at me with troubled eyes. "Where is that land where we once lived?"

"It is across the sea. And Gerald is there."

He was puzzled. "Then why are we here?"

Why, indeed? My heart broke and I leaned my head on his bony old breast.

"Now it is you who are weeping," he said and he lay patient and still, waiting for me to lift my head. There was no warmth in him, only a final patience, and my tears dried.

"It is time for you to sleep," I told him.

I drew the blanket about his shoulders and went away.

TONIGHT, when loneliness became intolerable, I went upstairs and took down the box of Gerald's letters and I laid them out upon my desk in order of time. There are only twelve, not including the final one. The first one was written soon after we left him in Shanghai. He was cheerful, believing that nothing could be worse than the years of war through which we had already passed. He was hopeful about the new government. We had no presentiments, in spite of old Mr. Pilowski, the White Russian who managed the hotel where we stayed.

"Not to be trusted," Mr. Pilowski declared, and brushed up his stiff mustaches. "Never are revolutionaries to be trusted — no, not in the world. So they came into my Russia, promising all and seizing everything. So did they in France before, killing the kings and the queens and themselves behaving worsely."

Gerald argued with him. "We can scarcely go on as we are, Mr. Pilowski. The people are wretched after the war. Inflation is crushing. Nothing is being done."

"Someday, you will know that nothing being done is better

than wickedness being done," Mr. Pilowski declared. Gerald smiled, refusing further argument, still believing himself right. It is the arrogance of the Chinese to believe they are more reasonable, more sane, than all other peoples. In some ways it is true.

"Everything goes well," he writes in his first letter. "I am beginning to think you should have stayed in China. Rennie could have taken his college work here in Peking. I believe that a new day is coming in this old, old country of mine."

Not "our" old, old country, but "mine." He was already choosing his country, alone, if need be.

The hopefulness continues through to the fifth letter. Then I see the first hint of doubt.

"My Eve," he writes, "perhaps it is better that you are away for a year or so. In order to succeed the new government must clear away all obstacles. Do you remember Liu Chin, the silk merchant? It seems he was a traitor. He was so mild, so gentle. Today he was shot at the Marco Polo Bridge with eleven others, two of them women. Some do not like the new order, but we must live with it and through it. The Minister of Education unfortunately is not a man of wide education. I am having to replace — " He scratches that out. It appears that already it is not safe to be frank. Thereafter Gerald writes no more of anything of importance. He tells me when the yellow Shantung rose in the east court blooms.

"Dear Eve, the rose is late this year. We have had dust storms, the most severe I have ever known. The goldfish are dying in the pool. The gardener went home to his parents in Shansi a month ago. I have had difficulty in finding another. People do not want to work — " The words are scratched out again. People do not want to work? Why not?

The eighth letter is very short. "Dear Wife: I am engaging the professors for next semester. The new dean is a clever young man with many ideas. The dean of women is a former student of mine. Tell Rennie to study engineering. It will be better for him than teaching. Tonight is hot and still. I face a long lonely summer."

The ninth letter is listless. Commencement is over and he is tired. I know the mood. We used to take a journey, go perhaps to the sea at Peitaiho, or travel to the Diamond Mountains in

Korea. One year we went to Tai Shan and lived in a Buddhist temple for a month. I wonder if Rennie remembers. The old abbot taught him how to play cat's cradle with a strip of silk.

Three months passed before the tenth letter reached me. I wept when I read it and it makes me weep now. For I see that my beloved has resigned himself to that which he does not understand. "I wonder if I chose wisely in not going with you and our son to America. It is too late now. In case I never see you — " Here he scratches words again.

The eleventh letter is all but final. "Dearly Loved, it is better for us not to plan the day of meeting. It is better to live life as we find it, you on your side of the world, I on mine. Let Rennie be an American. If he forgets me let it be so."

It is easy to see the story now. He is a prisoner. The city he chose has become his cell. He is no longer free. And I am not free because I love him. As long as he lives I shall not be free. . . . Let me be glad that at least a woman is at his side. Though she be not I, he has someone with him. So why do I weep?

And I continue to weep.

This morning Baba frightened me by a fainting fit. He got up as usual and I gave him his slight breakfast in his room. Then, in the midst of thanking me, he crumpled in his chair. I called to Matt to telephone Bruce Spaulden. Meanwhile I stood beside Baba's chair, not daring to move him, and frightened lest Bruce be already started on his rounds.

Luckily he was not. He came running up the gravel walk from the gate, hatless and without his coat, his bag swinging from his hand. The door was open and he entered, and leaped upstairs and into the room, his thin Vermont face without a smile, and his eyes seeing nothing but his patient. I stood silent, waiting his command.

"Pull up his sleeve."

I pulled up Baba's sleeve. Into the slack old flesh of his upper arm Bruce drove the needle quickly and with skill. Then he lifted Baba in his arms and laid him on his bed.

"Cover him and keep him warm," he told me. "He will pull

out of it, likely, but one of these days he won't. You aren't to be scared. Even if I were sitting right beside him when it happens I couldn't do anything."

"I'll stay by him until he wakes," I said.

"Not necessary," Bruce said. "Go about your business. Come in every now and then and see how he is."

He was packing his bag while I covered Baba and tucked the quilt about him. The morning was warm, but Baba's flesh was cool.

I looked up to see Bruce watching me.

"Come downstairs," he said.

I followed him. He sat down in the hall on the ladder-back chair near the big clock.

"This is no time to ask," he said in his abrupt way. "But I don't know as one time is better than another when a man has something on his mind. . . . Elizabeth, will you marry me?"

He was not joking. For a second I thought he was, but his intense eyes told me better.

"I am married already," I said. "My husband is in Peking."

"Might as well be dead," he muttered.

I said, "For me he lives."

Bruce got up, snatched his bag and made for the door. There he turned to look at me.

"All the same, Elizabeth," he said, "things being what they are in this uncertain world, my offer holds."

"I wish you hadn't made it," I said. "Now I'll think of it every time I see you."

"Which is exactly as I wish it," he said.

He grinned suddenly, then he was gone. And I stood there with an odd sort of feeling — not love, only a pleasant sort of female warmth. For the second time in my life a man had proposed to me.

Stupefied, I went back to Baba. He was still unconscious.

TODAY the postman brought me a letter bearing the stamp of the People's Republic of China.

"It must be from your husband," he said, and handed me the

letter as proudly as though he had fetched it himself from across the westward sea.

"Thank you," I said. I knew the moment that I looked at the handwriting that it was not from Gerald. It was from — what shall I call her? I cannot use the word concubine. Yet I suppose that is what she is. I suppose the Chinese on our street in Peking call her his Chinese wife and me his American wife. But the dagger piercing me is this question — if she can write, why cannot he? Is it that he cannot bring himself to acknowledge that he desecrates our love?

I opened the letter.

DEAR ELDER SISTER:

Your letter has come. I thank you for such answer. Now it is my duty to tell you of our husband. I send this letter in the secret way. If it is found by the wrong person, then you will never see it. But I try. Now I tell you our husband is well but he is sad. He does not talk to me. He goes every day to his office, and at night he comes home. The house is as you left it. Only I cannot keep it so clean. Sometimes he complains. I tell him I cannot do all as well as you do. But I cook what he likes to eat. He does not mention your name but he keeps you in his mind as secret joy. In the night when the moon shines he walks into the courts and stares at the moon. Is it the same moon in your country? To the moon he gives his thinking of you.

His health is good except that he does not sleep much. We have no children. He told me he does not want a child. I said what of me? He said, it is better for you not to have my child because the blood is mixed. But I hope for a child. I go to temple and pray before the Goddess of Childbirth. I go in secret because they tell us not to believe in gods now. Please take care of yourself. If you were here the house would not be lonely as now. We could be friends.

YOUR YOUNGER SISTER

I feel strangely better for the letter. It is sweet and simple and I am surprised that I am not jealous. When the moon rises over these mountains in Vermont, I shall go out and stand in its light, knowing that a few hours before he has so stood. Thank you, my younger sister.

I live this strange inner life. No one in the valley could possibly understand it even if I could speak of it. And I cannot speak. But now I do most earnestly wish to leave that world in which I lived with Gerald and enter this world to which I am compelled by circumstances.

If only I could stop remembering, for I can feel Gerald cutting one cord after another between us. It is not only that he no longer writes me. He is also denying himself the thought of me. When there was hope of our meeting again, I could feel his communion with me. On those rough hills of Szechuan, when I was at Chungking and he struggling across country, on foot, leading his students and professors westward, I could feel, especially at sunset and at moonrise, the outreaching of his heart and mind, and we were united. But now, though I send myself across land and sea in search of him, I do not find him. He has withdrawn from me. This means one thing — he has no hope of ever seeing me again. I do not believe he has ceased to love me. It is simply that for us the earthly life is ended. And yet, I am not freed of the past.

When Bruce asked me to marry him, the words reached my ears but not my heart. They echoed in me, reverberating and empty. It is only when I enter Baba's room that meaning comes back to me, not strong and alive as it was in the house in Peking, but quiescent. I feel as one feels in the presence of ruined palaces and silent gardens, no longer used and alive. I return to Baba's room often for no other purpose than to see his ancient figure, wrapped in the Chinese robe of blue brocaded silk, sitting by the window. The few things brought with me from China, a pair of scrolls, a small jade vase, some porcelain bowls from Kiangsi, a rug as blue as the northern Chinese sky, have somehow sorted themselves out of the house and into Baba's room.

"Are you all right, Baba?" I ask.

"Quite all right," he says peaceably.

There he sits, Gerald's father, a beautiful old man, straight and tall, thin as an ascetic, his hair whiter than snow upon the mountain, his white beard uncut. He does not think. He simply is. And it is this elemental existence, pure and childlike, that compels me to remember Peking.

Oh, that dreamlike city! Everything in life was there, the palaces under their roofs of blue and gold, containing a history crowded with imperial men and women. In the wide streets the common folk took on princely airs because the city in which they lived with their ancestors was a kingly city. Even the beggars were not craven. They came out from their corners, hands outstretched but heads held high. I see the streets at night, gay with festivals, or quiet with the good plainness of daily life, lamps burning, candles lit, families gathered about the supper table, men gossiping over water pipes, a woman nursing her little child. I see the city in the glorious fragments of sunlight piercing the yellow dust of a spring storm. I see it a vast summer garden, blue porcelain roofs and golden ornaments gleaming between the dark cedar trees. I see it under snow heavy on the roofs and in the streets, the men and children picking their way as carefully as cats, but cheerfully, their cheeks red with cold and fur caps pulled over their ears.

Winter is for married love in firelit evenings and a house enclosed in snow. The snow fell deep in Peking and the drifts against the gate were as good as any lock. The Chinese admire the beauty of snow, their painters love the white of late snow against the pink of peach blossoms or the red of berries on the Indian bamboo, but they do not like to go out in snow, their shoes being of cloth or velvet, and so Gerald and I had no visitors on snowy nights. Even the old watchman stayed prudently in his little room by the gate, and we were safely alone. We heaped the brazier with coals and we put out the candles and sat by the glow of the fire. That was the time for love, the long night stretching ahead in hours of endless happiness. . . .

How still the Vermont mountains are, how empty of human life! It is autumn again, and the leaves are turning. What life is there in the scanty soil on these mountains that sends the sap running in the maple trees in spring and whose withdrawing in the autumn creates colors so bright and naked? The trees bleed with color now as they bleed in March with sap.

The leaves drift down and the mountains emerge in great sweeping outlines against a sky of royal blue. The work on the farm is done for the year, except for the milking twice a day, the feeding and watering of the cows and hens and gathering of eggs. Matt put up the storm windows and doors yesterday and today the weather turned warm with the same perversity that it used to do in China. But I do not go out as the Chinese farmers did and shake my fist at the Old Man in the Sky. There was a friendly critical relationship between the Chinese gods and the farming folk. The people expected their gods to look after them and to send rain and sunshine in season. Warm weather after the first festival of winter made the winter wheat grow high and so risk being frozen when the bitter days came. A farmer spoke his mind thus to his gods:

"You old Head up yonder! What reason have you for sending down heat instead of cold? Are you drunk up there in Heaven? Is your brain muddled? Consider yourself! I warn you — no more incense, no more gifts to the temple!"

How can I explain that within two days a blizzard came down from the north? How we laughed, Gerald and I! Oh, we had so much good laughter in our marriage. I wonder if his Chinese wife can make him laugh. It is her letters I take out now and read, not his. I try to see him through these letters, but I see only his shadow.

TONIGHT, as I open my window, a flurry of snow rushes in. I feel the flakes cold upon my face and the wind blows through my nightgown. Hurry into bed, let me draw the warm blankets about my shoulders. I will not remember how lonely I must lie. I will think of the comfort of my blankets. They are made of the wool sheared in July from my sheep. My sheep keep me warm and my cows give me milk and butter and cheese. My land gives me food and beauty to look upon. As for the blankets, when I sent in the bags of wool to the factory, I asked that they be dyed a deep pink, and they came back to me the color of crushed roses. I comfort myself with their warmth and color. My comfort and my pleasure are in such small things. It is the small things that are eternal.

Today, while the ground lies white under the snow and the mountains look twice their height, Rennie's first letter has come to me. I sat down in the kitchen, I let my broom fall and tore open the envelope.

"Dear Mother — "

I kissed the words and went on. He writes as if he had left home only yesterday instead of being months away. The letter is sent from a midwestern college. He does not want to go to Harvard, where his father went. He wants to be only himself, he says. So that is what he is, working his way. He is studying hard, he likes physics very much. He is rooming with a boy named George Bowen. George Bowen has a sister. Very intelligent and rather good-looking. Tall.

"Now, Mother, you are not to get ideas. I am through with women."

At eighteen my son is through with women! Oh Allegra, you have hurt him very much. But every man and every woman is hurt by first love, except the rare ones, like Gerald and me, whose first love deepens into the only love.

"I shall be home for Christmas," Rennie writes. Now that is blessed news. It would be too melancholy for Baba and me to think of Christmas alone. If Rennie had not sent me this letter I would have let the day slip past, pretending that it was a day like any other. Now I shall make a plum pudding and dress a turkey. I shall make walnut candies for Rennie and begin at once to knit him a red sweater. And his clothes not mended all these months! He must bring everything home and let me see what has happened. The house is suddenly full of light and life. I dash upstairs to Baba, who is sitting placidly by the window.

"My knees are cold," he says to me in Chinese.

"You have let the rug slip to the floor, careless Baba!"

I pretend to scold him. I tell him the heavenly news.

"Rennie is coming home for Christmas, Baba. Do you understand? Say it after me, 'Rennie is my grandson.'"

He lifts patient old eyes to my face. He repeats in a quavering half-frightened voice, "Rennie is my grandson."

"He is coming home for Christmas."

"Coming home for Christmas," Baba repeats.

I kiss the top of Baba's head and fly off to inspect Rennie's room. I wonder if Matt can help me paint the walls? A pale yellow, I think —

IT is four days before Christmas and Rennie comes home tonight. Meanwhile I have had two letters written in the Peking house but mailed elsewhere, one in Manila, one in Bangkok. This little Chinese woman is resourceful. Gerald's letters are watched and read, doubtless, but hers she can slip into her sleeve and take with her to friends who will mail them in widely separate places. I wonder what she looks like. I have wanted, and not wanted, to ask her for a photograph. But she would send it if she could. She is a chatterbox of a woman, cheerful and loving, who sets store by photographs and keepsakes. She writes of Gerald without mentioning his name, and of the house and what they do.

"He has a cold today. The sand settles in his throat while he talks in the classroom. I have made hot ginger tea and mixed it with honey. He sips it and is better."

Yes, the sands of autumn storms used to make Gerald cough. We used to think of going to some other part of China far from the distant desert of the northwest, but Gerald, when it came to the decision, could never leave Peking.

"One belongs to this city as to a country," he said. "There is no other like it. I should be an alien anywhere else."

And why did I never think of hot ginger tea mixed with honey? She takes better care of him than I did. But does she love him as much? She prattles on:

"The chrysanthemums are bright and healthy this autumn. They bloom against the northern wall of the big courtyard."

That is where they always bloomed. And I planted pink ones and white ones against the wall of the small courtyard outside our bedroom.

"He is working very hard just now. There are new classes and many new students. At night he cannot sleep. If he sleeps he mutters words I cannot understand."

Does he ever speak my name? He is far away from me now. If we met I think he would still be far away. There are all these days between us in which I have no share. He would not be able to speak of them and I could not ask him about them.

I fold the letters away. Rennie comes home tonight. I have his room ready, the walls are pale yellow, the furniture is polished, his bed is made fresh, there are red berries in a bowl on the chimney piece and wood is piled in the wide old-fashioned fireplace. Snow fell again in the night and he will want to ski and so I have waxed his skis and put them in the kitchen entry. Of course I finished everything too early and time plodded, the clock did not move. I toyed with the thought of putting up the Christmas tree and then knew I must not, for he and I have kept to the custom of my childhood when my father and I went up the hill beyond the sugarbush and cut the tree on Christmas Eve. It is important now to cling to family customs. They link the present with the past and reach into the future. If Gerald's mother had been able to draw her family into Baba's house and so given Gerald a place in the clan he would not have grown up solitary. But Baba perhaps would not allow it; or she perhaps felt herself cut off by her strange marriage and so she became a revolutionist. Revolutions are made by those who are desolate and desperate. Now that is what I must prevent Rennie from becoming. He must somehow belong to my country, or he will become a rebel wherever he goes.

So the evening draws near. The mountains cut off the sunset but the sky is red above the snow. Baba feels the excitement in the house and he asked for his best Chinese gown, a dark maroon satin with gold buttons, and he sits in his chair by the window of his bedroom, his dragon-headed cane in his hand. He uses a smooth Malacca every day, but tonight he remembered the dragon-headed one. His white hair and long white beard make him look like an ancient Chinese patriarch, for his skin, always dark, is now leather-hued and wrinkled. Only his proud old aquiline profile declares him Scottish and not Chinese.

I have tied a branch of mountain pine and a clump of scarlet wintergreen berries to the brass knocker. I station myself by the front door.

Through the twilight I see at last the twin glow of automobile lights. He did not tell me when he was coming and so I could not meet him. The car is here. I am suddenly faint and must lean my head against the door. Then I hear the knocker thunder against the brass plate beneath it. I tug at the door and suddenly it is pushed in and there stand two tall men. One of them is Rennie, and the other is Sam, and it is Sam who speaks first.

"Hello, Mrs. MacLeod! I thought I'd come along with Rennie and see how my old gentleman is. You can throw me out if you don't want me for Christmas."

His blue eyes twinkle and glow and he throws his arm around my shoulders and kisses me soundly on my cheek. While I am stammering a welcome, I see only Rennie, standing there waiting, a slight tall dark young man, smiling. It occurs to Sam that he has been boisterous. He steps back, and Rennie comes forward and takes my hand in both of his, and kisses me lightly on the other cheek.

"Hello, Mother — "

He looks down at me, I look up at him. I hasten to speak.

"Come in — come in where it's warm. Good skiing weather tomorrow, Rennie!"

They come in and Rennie stands looking around. I have lit all the lamps and I have lit the candles on the dining-room table. It is set with my best linen and my mother's old silver and a bowl of holly.

"Does it look the same to you?" I ask Rennie.

He shakes his head and does not reply. No, it does not look the same to him because he is not the same. And I discern in him a heartbreaking fear of me, his mother. He is afraid that I will try to make him what he was before, a boy and not a man. He is not willing to be my son if he has to be a boy again. I understand this in a flash of pain.

"Would you like to go to your rooms?" I asked. "Rennie, your room is ready, and I have only to put some towels in the guest room for you, Sam. I'm glad you came."

Yes, I am glad. When I first saw him I was almost angry that a stranger had come with my son. But I know that Rennie wanted him to come so that he would not be alone with me. I must make no demands on this tall silent young man.

"How is the old gentleman?" Sam asked briskly.

"He'll be delighted to see you," I said, and hoped that Baba would remember him.

Upstairs, I opened the door of Baba's room and Sam went in. Rennie had gone to his own room.

"Well, well," Sam shouted. He descended upon Baba and shook his hand while Baba stared at him helplessly.

"Sitting here looking like an old Emperor of China," Sam bellowed amiably. "How are you, Doctor MacLeod?" He drew up a wooden chair in front of Baba.

"I am well," Baba said cautiously. He looked at me, appealing, and then at Sam. "Are you my grandson?" he inquired gently.

Sam roared. "Not quite — not quite! Don't you remember me, sir? I fetched you to the shack on my ranch. Why, we were wonderful friends!"

Baba nodded his head. He tapped his dragon-headed cane softly on the carpet.

"Sam," he said cautiously. "It's Sam."

"Right," Sam cried with delight. "Why, you're in fine shape!"

I longed to slip away to Rennie's room. If I were alone with my son surely there would be one good moment of embrace, and I would ask no more. But when I stole toward the door Sam stopped me.

"Ma'am," he said, "you won't misunderstand me when I say it's better to leave Rennie to himself for a while. He'll come back to you in good time but it'll have to be his time."

"I feel it," I said, and sat down and waited.

At last Rennie came in. He had changed to brown slacks and a tweed jacket that I had never seen before. His black hair was brushed smooth and he wore a red tie. I saw him as a man, a very handsome man. . . .

"How are you, Grandfather?" he said and he came to Baba and knelt at his side as a Chinese grandson might have done and took Baba's hand.

Baba stared at him reflectively.

"Are you my son Gerald?" he asked.

"Only your grandson," Rennie said.

They looked at each other face to face, and I saw the resemblance between them for the first time. Rennie's profile, changing with manhood, takes on the Scottish lines and not the Chinese.

"My grandson," Baba repeated, and suddenly he leaned forward and kissed Rennie on the forehead. Rennie was moved, and put Baba's hand to his cheek.

"I'm glad I came home," he said and I saw tears in his eyes.

We had a merry evening after that. Those two young men made a chair of their crossed hands and they carried Baba downstairs and he sat at the table with us. Then, for gaiety, I ran upstairs and put on my wine velvet dinner gown, which I had not worn since Gerald and I parted. The last night in Shanghai we went to dance at the Astor Hotel, and I put on this one festive gown that I had saved through all the war. We danced cheek to cheek, forgetting the crowded streets outside, and determined for a few hours to mingle with the Europeans gathered in the hotel, most of them ready to sail away forever from the country they loved but to which they could never belong. And we knew, Gerald and I, that he would stay and I must go.

So I went downstairs, and the two young men stood up and looked at me with surprise. I was suddenly a woman, and they had not realized it before. I was glad that Rennie saw me as someone else than mother, for perhaps he will not fear me so much.

I put Rennie at the head of the table, and I sat at the foot, with

Baba at my right so that I could cut his meat for him. And Rennie was suddenly gay, and began to talk, and Sam was as suddenly silent and almost shy.

They were hungry and they ate heartily. It was good to have guests at the table. I took pride in the roast lamb and the peas and the small browned potatoes. And I had remembered the apple pie that Rennie loves, served with cheese and hot coffee.

When dinner was over Baba was lifted into the living room and put in a chair by the fire, and I sat opposite him, and Rennie and Sam pulled up the yellow satin sofa facing the chimney piece. We heard the door knocker.

Rennie turned to me. "Do you expect someone?"

"No," I said. "I cannot imagine who would come at this hour."

I went into the hall and opened the door and Bruce Spaulden stood there, holding out a bunch of pink roses wrapped in cellophane. I took them and thanked him.

"Come in," I said. "We are sitting around the fire."

He came in and I put the roses in an old gray pottery bowl. I saw that Baba had fallen asleep.

"Ought we to take him upstairs?" I asked Bruce.

"He looks comfortable," Bruce said, "and he couldn't be more soundly asleep."

We sat down and Rennie was silent between the two men and I caught him looking at me strangely now and again. I felt suddenly happy as I had not been for a long time and soon we were all talking, and Bruce got up and went to the pantry and made coffee, for he will not drink anything else, but Rennie fetched wine and poured out glasses for himself and Sam, and the talk flowed about us.

I really belong here, I kept thinking. If I were not so lonely, I could forget Peking and at last perhaps I could even forget Gerald. I have not laughed for a long time but I found myself laughing at the three men. Each in his way was playing for my attention, Sam very brusque and Western and masculine and Bruce dark and caustic and wary, and Rennie watchful and tending the fire.

"Revolution," Sam declared, "is an inevitable process. We burst our skins, like snakes, we cast off the old encasements, and emerge afresh."

I was amazed to hear him speak without a trace of his harsh Western idiom. The ranchman's drawl was a shield. I had never seen the real man before.

Bruce drew upon his pipe, slowly and deeply. "There never was a revolution in man's history that paid its way. The end is always lost in the conflict and confusion out of which evil men rise to power."

"You can't hold back revolution for all of that," Sam insisted. "Endurance has its limit. Look at China — "

The winds of Asia rushed into the warm closed room. I was swept across the sea again. By force of will I refused to go.

"Let us not talk of China," I said. "Let us never talk of China. Who knows what is happening there?"

Rennie looked up from the fire and his eyes met mine. I knew I should have to tell him. The life went out of the evening.

When Bruce was leaving he held my hand for a minute at the front door, but I could not be warm. "Thank you again for the pink roses," I said stupidly.

"When I think of roses I think of you," he said under his breath. That was much for him to say, but I could not muster a smile in reply. My heart was hammering in my breast. How can I tell Rennie so that he will not hate his father?

"COME into my room, Rennie," I said when we had said good night to Sam at the head of the stairs. "You and I have had no chance to talk. Let's light the fire and settle ourselves."

I sat in the old red velvet armchair that had once belonged to my Boston grandmother. He sat down in the wooden Windsor opposite me. He had lit the fire and the logs were blazing.

"I can't get used to the way you look," I said. His face has lost its boyish roundness. The cheekbones are defined, the jaw is firm. I should be hard put to it to say where Rennie came from, were he a stranger to me. Spain? Italy? Brazil?

"Tell me what you like best at college," I said.

"Math. Math and music."

Rennie has always loved music. This perhaps is my gift to him. Many hours of my own youth I spent at the old square piano downstairs in the parlor, but since I came home, living on the brink of final separation from Gerald, I have not been able to play.

"It's a good combination, Rennie — the combination Confucius required for the civilized man. He must know the disciplines of mathematics and music."

"They are allied," Rennie said. "They demand the same precision and abstraction. I want to be a scientist."

"Your father will be pleased."

To this Rennie did not reply. He never replies when I mention his father.

"And what about George Bowen's sister?" I inquired, half playfully.

Rennie did not look at me. His eyes were fixed upon the fire. "What about her?"

"Well, is she pretty?"

"She is not pretty — she's beautiful."

"Dark or fair?"

"Fair and calm."

"Do you like her very much, Rennie?"

"I don't know. I don't want to know, I suppose. I'd rather not be hurt again."

Here fell a silence.

"Rennie, I want to talk about your father."

He lifted his head at this, reluctantly interested.

"Have you had a letter?"

"Not recently — not from him. But I did have a — a special letter. I must explain."

And so I began at the beginning. I told him how we met, Gerald and I. I told him how we fell in love. I told him of Peking and how in those years our love deepened and widened into a life complete in companionship.

"There are few such marriages, Rennie," I said.

Rennie is too quick for me. "What is it that you really want to say?"

"I want to tell you that what has happened is not the fault of your father nor is it mine. If the world had not split apart under our feet, we would still be living in the house in Peking."

"And why aren't we?" he demanded.

"You know," I said. "It is because of me. I am American, and your father is half American. It is the split in the world that has driven us apart, exactly as though a tidal wave had rushed between us on a beach and swept us in opposite directions."

"He could have left China," Rennie said.

"He could not."

"And why not?" Rennie insisted. His face was bitter.

"I defend your father," I said. "He is not here to speak for himself. If you must blame anyone, blame Baba. He married your Chinese grandmother without loving her, and that was the primary sin. She who knew she was not loved by her husband gave her life to her country and to what she thought was her duty. And her son ate the sour fruit, and your teeth, Rennie, are set on edge."

"Did she love Baba?" Rennie's voice was low.

"I am sure she did. She loved him, and was rejected by him. There is nothing so explosive in this world as love rejected."

"My father has rejected you," Rennie said brutally.

I denied this passionately. "He has not rejected me. He cannot reject me as long as we love each other. Love still works in us its mercies. It is time for me to show you the letter." I rose and I opened the locked drawer of my desk and took out the letter and gave it to him. He opened the letter and read it twice, thoughtfully. Then he put it back into the envelope and placed it on the small table beside him.

"Thank you, Mother," he said.

"I have given permission to the Chinese woman," I said. "So I will also show you her letters."

Now I gave him the letters from Mei-lan. He read them quickly, his face impassive, and handed them back to me.

"I cannot understand why he has let her come into our house," he said.

His voice was so hard that I could not bear it. "We do not know how much he was compelled."

"I still ask," Rennie said, "why did he stay in Peking if he loved us?"

"You do not love your father enough to forgive him," I said.

"Perhaps that is true," Rennie agreed.

He got up and walked to the window and stood there looking out into the night. The light of the lamp shone through the glass upon the falling snow. The fire burned suddenly blue and a log fell into the ash.

He turned to face me. "Mother, I have something to tell you, too. All that business of Allegra — it very nearly drove me back to Peking. If I am to be rejected because my grandmother was Chinese, I thought, I'd better go back to China. But I'll never go back now. I'll stay with you. This shall be my country."

I cried out, "Oh Rennie, Rennie, don't. . . . Don't decide so quickly against your father!"

"I am not deciding against him. I am deciding for you," Rennie said. And he stooped and kissed my cheek and went away.

I know my son. The decision has *not* come quickly. He has been torn between his two countries, between his father and me. And he has chosen me and mine. Oh Gerald, forgive me! I pray that you will have other sons. If I have robbed you of our son, can I help myself? It is Rennie who decides his own life. And he has as much right to decide as I had when I followed you to Peking and as you had when you would not come home with me. Yes, this is home at last, this Vermont valley.

I sat a long time before the dying fire, a weight gone from me. I am no longer alone in my own country. My son is with me. I shall be happy again, someday.

MONTHS have passed. Rennie is nearing the end of his college year. Sam has been twice to see me. He urges me to divorce Gerald, and today he flew from New York for only an hour, he said, not knowing how this day would end. We have telegraphed for Rennie to come at once, because of what has happened. It happened this morning, when Sam was arguing with me, angry, insistent.

"You must divorce that fellow in Peking — he's no husband to you, Elizabeth!"

"I shall never divorce Gerald," I said. "He loves me."

"If you call desertion love," Sam bellowed.

"He has not deserted me," I was shouting, too, "nor I him. We are divided by history, past and present."

"He could have come home with you," Sam said stubbornly.

"Ah, but you see this is not home to him! Home is a matter of the heart and the spirit. His would have died here."

"You're still in love with him," Sam said, and he turned on me so fierce a stare that I could not defend myself.

"Can't you see that I am determined to marry you?" he cried.

"Oh, no, Sam — no — no!"

We were both breathless, both glaring at each other. Sam bent over me and I pushed him away.

"Don't — "

"Do you hate me?"

"No — not hate — "

At this moment we heard Baba fall in the room above. We heard the clatter of his cane and then so light a fall, his old bones all but fleshless, that we might scarcely have heard except for the terrible wrenching groan. I ran upstairs, Sam following me, and there Baba lay. His head had struck the stone hearth. He was dead.

WE HAD come home from Baba's funeral. Sam stayed; he and Bruce Spaulden took care of every detail for me.

Rennie arrived barely in time for the funeral. He brought with him a tall fair girl, a calm quiet girl whose every movement is slow grace.

"This is Mary Bowen," Rennie said.

"Strange, I have never heard your name," I said, and suddenly I wanted to kiss her. I leaned forward and put my lips to her smooth young cheek.

"You look like a Mary," I said.

"I'm a pretty good Martha, too," she said and smiled.

"Then Rennie is in luck," I said, "for it is not every woman who is both."

They were in love. I know the signs, how well, and I was comforted. I took their hands and between them I went upstairs to where Baba lay in his blue Chinese robe. He lay on top of the white counterpane, and I had put on his feet his black velvet Chinese shoes. Under his hands crossed upon his breast I had put his little worn copy of *The Book of Changes*.

Mary stood looking at him. "How beautiful he is," she whispered. "I wish I could have heard his voice speaking."

And she lifted Rennie's hand and held it against her cheek. From that moment I loved her as my own daughter.

This afternoon a few neighbors gathered with us under the pine tree on the mountain behind the house, and there we buried Baba. Matt helped to dig the grave this morning and we lined it with pine branches, while Mrs. Matt made the collation for the funeral feast. She boiled a ham, for she thinks a baked ham is not worth eating, and set out sandwiches and cake and tea and coffee, ready for the return from the grave.

The day was quiet and the sky mildly overcast, and the minister ead certain passages from the New Testament, which I had narked because Baba had once declared to me that they were taken riginally from the wisdom of Asia and perhaps from Confucius imself. "For," said Baba, "it is not accident that Jesus uttered the ery words long ago spoken by Confucius and Buddha. He was in Nepal in his youth, if we are to believe folk rumors."

Now the good words fell gently and with deep mercy upon the uiet air.

After the ceremony was over, and we did not weep, neither ennie nor I, for death is not sad at the end of a long life, we came ome again. Mrs. Matt was bustling about in a black silk dress and huge white apron and we sat in the living room with the guests. Ve ate and drank and spoke quietly. In a little while they were ll gone.

Bruce stopped a moment with me to search my face and tell me nat I looked pale and must rest.

"You won't mourn?" he said.

"Not for Baba," I said.

"You must not mourn for anyone," he said urgently.

I could not tell him, not yet, that with Baba's death died also the mbol of the past. Baba was a link with other years and with a loved city, with a house which I had believed my home. But ruce's concern was comforting and, when I smiled, I saw that he nged to kiss me. Longing smoldered in his gray eyes. I was not ady. I could not bear the touch of another man's lips — not yet.

So the day ended. As Sam was leaving, he shook my hand hard. et me know if you want anything," he said. "I'm on call."

Suddenly he bent and kissed me on the lips and I stepped back d nearly fell.

"You don't like it," he muttered.

"No," I said honestly.

"I won't do it again," he said and went away. I am sorry he was rt but I do not like to be kissed when I am not ready. The days my youth are past and to a woman full grown a kiss means erything — or nothing.

In the evening Rennie and Mary and I were quietly together on

the terrace, and the air was unusually mild for May. These tw
must go away again tomorrow. It worried them that I was to b
alone, and I did not know how to make them believe that I di
not mind, for indeed I do not know whether I shall mind bein
alone in this old house. I have no near neighbors and the fore
in the valley changes strangely with the night. When the afte
noon sun slants through the near trees to lie upon the beds of fer
and brake, the forest is lively with light and color. But the darkne
falls swiftly, and the forest loses its kindliness. Staring into shadow
growing sinister with night, I remember that for thirty mil
and more forest mingles with swamp and quicksands, wherei
hunters have been lost and never found. Once a woman, a botanis
was lost in the forest that surrounds my home. I do not kno
whether I can live here alone.

"I wish I were finished with college," Rennie said. "I wish th
Mary and I were married and living here with you."

It is the first word that he had spoken to me of marriage.

"If you two are to be married, then I shall be so happy that I sha
have no time to be afraid," I replied.

"We shall certainly be married," Mary said.

"The question is when," Rennie added.

"Why should there be any question?" I inquired. "If you wa
to be married, then marry."

Here I remembered Allegra. "Unless Mary's family has son
reason of their own for delay."

"I have no family except my twin brother, George," Mary sai
"Our parents died when we were children and we lived with n
grandmother. Now she is dead, too."

It is interesting to discover how secretly wicked one can be. F
the sake of my son I rejoiced that three innocent people were
their graves.

"You may marry when you like then," I said. "The weddi
can be in this house where I was married to Rennie's father an
that will make me happy."

"Thank you, Mother," Rennie said. He was lying full leng
upon the long terrace chair, and he got up and went to Mary's si
and took her hand.

"Will you marry me on the eighteenth of June, when I shall be nineteen years old?"

"I will," she said, and smiled up at him.

The moonlight shone on her long fair hair and on Rennie's face. I thought them the most beautiful pair in the world, and my heart yearned for Gerald who could not see them. I used once to be able to reach him with my concentrated thought, but for a long time I had not done so. Now I gathered my whole energy and will upon him, far away in Peking. I tried to reach him and let him share what I saw, this beautiful cream-skinned man who is our son, and Mary, tall and fair and calm.... I could not reach him. Again my heart, my mind were stopped by a barrier I do not understand.

"On the eighteenth day of June this house will be ready for you," I promised Rennie and Mary.

When I went upstairs to bed an hour later, leaving them alone together on the terrace, I could almost imagine that Gerald was gone, or that he had never been, except that he had given me my son.

I AM NOT what is called psychic. I am far too earthy a woman for that. Gerald said once that I am incurably domestic. I can be absorbed in the everyday happenings in house and garden and easily diverted at any time by the talk and antics of human beings. I am not an intellectual, nor am I a dreamer of dreams and I have never seen visions.

I make this statement because I swear that last night, at a quarter past two, I saw Gerald. I am alone in the house and have been alone for five weeks, ever since Rennie and Mary left me the morning after Baba's funeral. I have had, however, an unusual number of valley visitors.

Matt comes early and stays late, and Mrs. Matt makes the pretext of bringing his lunch the occasion for "running in," to see how I am doing. She stays and talks about Matt and his cantankerous ways. Mrs. Matt will not learn that life and man do not change, and that it is the woman who must bend if she is not to break. I know all of Matt's faults by now, that he snores, and that he will not put his false teeth in a glass of water at night but leaves them to grin at her from the bedside table.

The minister comes to see me, and so does Mrs. Monroe, the teacher in our valley's one-room school. And Bruce Spaulden has been here twice, merely to drop in at breakfast time before he makes his calls, to observe me, he says, and make sure that I am not what he describes as "moping."

"Are you happy?" he asked me yesterday. I was weeding the strawberry beds in the warm corner between the main house and the ell.

"I am neither happy nor unhappy," I told him. "I am in a state of blessed calm."

"Permanently so?" he asked, tilting his eyebrows at me.

"Probably not," I said. "Probably it is a transition state between past and future."

"Not too lonely?"

"How can I be with a wedding in the house soon?"

Last night I was tired and went immediately to sleep. When I woke, as I usually do in the night, the radiant face of the bedside clock showed quarter past two. Ever since I was parted from Gerald I resolutely turn on the light and take up my book, whatever it is. I had only opened it when I knew that I was not alone. I was not frightened, only filled with wonder. I looked up and I saw Gerald, standing just inside the closed door. He was sad and thin and much older. He had a short beard, his hair was cropped very short, and he wore Chinese clothes, not the robes of a gentleman but a uniform of the sort that students used to wear, made of dark stuff and the jacket buttoned to the throat. He smiled at me, his grave dark eyes suddenly bright. I think he put out his hand to me, but of this I am not sure for I leaped from my bed and I cried out to him.

"Gerald, Gerald, oh darling — "

I was stopped by a frightful agony in his face. Then I ran to hold him in my arms, but he was gone. I stood where I had seen him stand. There was no one here and the floor was cold beneath my bare feet. I crept back into bed shivering and afraid. I have seen Gerald. I have no doubt of it. And I have seen him as he is now. It could not be a dream nor a trick of memory, else I would have seen his face as it looked when he stood on the dock at Shanghai, when we gazed at each other until the river mists crept between us and my ship sailed out to sea.

"I feel as though my very flesh was torn from yours," he had written me.

Now he was bearded, his hair was cut short, he wore the uniform he had always hated, even when his students put it on proudly. A prisoner's uniform, he had called it. I had never seen him as I saw him now. Therefore it was no dream.

It was impossible to sleep after that. I dressed and went down stairs and walked about the house until the pale dawn gleamed behind the mountains. I do not know what a vision means. Does it signify life or death? And why was his last look an agony? How shall I ever know?

I AM NOT in the least frightened because I have seen Gerald. I am overcome with sadness but not with fear. I cannot be afraid of Gerald in whatever form he comes to me. I have always laughed at tales of dead people who appear to their loved ones. I have never believed in ghosts and spirits. I say to myself that there is some trick of sight and subconscious which betrays my common sense. Then I find myself leading a conversation to the subject of distant persons who suddenly appear before those who think of them, although I tell no one that I have seen Gerald.

Mrs. Matt, for example, declares that she has seen the face of her mother, who lived and died in Ireland. "It was on a bright Easter morning," Mrs. Matt said solemnly. "I'd had a grand fight with Matt the night before and I was in no mood for church. I put on my old clothes and scrubbed the kitchen floor. Matt yelled at me to come to church with him and the children — six of them we had by then. But I wouldn't go and he marched off, leaving me on my knees in a swirl of soap and water. When the house was quietlike, I got up and put away my rag and pail and I washed myself and put on a clean nightygown and laid myself in a clean bed to sleep back my strength. It was then I saw my mother in resurrection. She was in white, like an angel, but her hair was down her back in a little gray pigtail as she always had it for the night. And she said to me, 'Poor soul, ye're only a woman, and ye must tak' it as best ye can.'

" 'True, Mother mine,' I said, and went off to sleep like a babe, and when I woke, Matt was back and he'd fed the children and himself and I got up restored."

A foolish story, but Mrs. Matt believes what she saw.

This afternoon I went to the small library in our nearest town and found half a dozen books on dreams and visions. I am half ashamed of wanting to read them, for I have no faith in second sight. But I ask myself, if a log of wood, a length of pure matter, can be transmuted into energy before my eyes, into ash and flame and heat, cannot a living body, a brilliant mind, a deep and spiritual soul be transmuted into its own likeness but a different stuff? I have embarked upon a quest. I go in search of the one I love. Is Gerald living or is he dead?

THE QUEST ended today in a way so simple, so tragic, that I have no need of further search. A letter from Mei-lan, posted this time from Calcutta, tells me of Gerald's death. She is still in Peking, awaiting, she tells me, the birth of Gerald's child. By some means she smuggled the letter out of China and into India. Perhaps a visiting delegation of Indian diplomats contained one who was Gerald's friend.

The letter is short and written in haste. There are blots on the paper — tears perhaps. Its message is simply this: Gerald was shot while trying to escape from Peking. She did not know that he had planned to escape.

"I think he longed to see you," she writes. "I think he dreamed to go somehow to India."

He was always watched, of course. They never trusted him. I do not know whether among the servants there was one who betrayed him. He was not good at packing clothes or making practical arrangements.

"He told me nothing," she writes. "I think he wished no blame to fall on me. I can always say I do not know."

Gerald was shot just outside his own gate. He got no farther than that. It was midafternoon, the sun was shining, he appeared to be returning to his classes at the university. The gateman saw a man in a hateful uniform step from behind the corner. When Gerald came near the man shot him with a pistol at close range. Then he disappeared. The gateman dared not shout. He lifted Gerald in his arms and brought him inside and laid him on the stones of the main court. Then he locked the gate.

"We buried him secretly in the small court outside his bedroom," Mei-lan writes.

Midafternoon in Peking would perhaps be quarter past two here in our valley, quarter past two in the night. Dare I believe?

I shall never know. All that I do know is that my beloved is no more. In this world, I shall not see his face again.

THERE IS no way to answer the letter, and so I have destroyed it. I wrote to Rennie that his father was dead.

"He made up his mind, it seems, to come to us. That is what she believes — his Chinese wife. He tried to live without us and he could not. Love was stronger in the end than country, stronger than history. This is our comfort. This is the message he sends us, by means of his death. It is enough for us to know. It is enough to make you forgive him, Rennie. Please forgive him! It will make life so much easier for me, so much more happy, if I know you have forgiven your father."

Here I paused to consider whether I should tell Rennie that

I had seen Gerald at the moment after he had died. His spirit escaping his body came home to me, to be remembered forever. Then I decided that I would not tell Rennie. He would not believe, and perhaps I do not wish to test my own faith.

Rennie's reply was swift. "I do forgive him, Mother. I forgive my father freely and with love. I do this for my own sake. If it makes you happy, so much the better. And I have told Mary."

TONIGHT is the eve before the wedding day. It occurs to me that this small book will not be complete unless I tell the story of the wedding, the story which really began that day, long past, upon which I, a gay and heedless girl brimming with ready love, let my heart concentrate upon a tall slender young man, intent upon his books, a studious reserved young man in whom I divined a profound and faithful lover. I suppose, to be honest, that what I saw first in Gerald was a man so beautiful to look at that I was startled into love.

I said to Mary this evening when we were washing the supper dishes together and Rennie was smoking his pipe on the terrace, "Mary, my dear, I hope that Rennie will be a good lover and husband to you. I had such a good lover and husband in his father, and I hope the capacities are inherited."

The tall lovely girl smiled her calm smile. "I am sure Rennie has inherited his father's graces," she said.

"I had sometimes just to suggest a thing or two to his father," I said.

"I will remember that, Mother," she said.

It was the first time she had called me "Mother," and I was overcome with a new joy and stood, dish in one hand and towel in the other. She laughed then and put her arms around me and kissed the top of my head. She is that much taller than I. And I smelled the sweet scent of her bosom and was glad for my son's sake that she is a sweet-smelling woman, her breath as fresh as flowers.

THE WEDDING day has dawned mild and bright. Early in the morning George Bowen drove up to the gate in an old and dusty gray convertible, and I saw him for the first time, a tall fair young man, with the same air of calm that his sister, Mary, has. He stepped over the door of the car and sauntered into the house. I liked him at first sight. He cuffed Rennie amiably, pulled Mary's ear affectionately, and spoke to me as though he loved me.

"I know you very well," he said. "I've wanted to meet you ever since I first saw Rennie."

"Sit down to breakfast with us, George," I said.

George is studying nuclear physics. I had been a little afraid of him when Rennie talked about him. I saw a young man, brilliant, hard, perhaps unloving, as I suppose scientists must be nowadays. Instead here he was, kindly, affectionate, a fine friend for any woman's son. Between these two for wife and brother, Rennie has his world to grow in.

"Eggs, George?" I asked.

"Please, fried on one side," he said, and folded his legs under the table in the breakfast alcove in the kitchen. I try not to be the sentimental mother female we women are supposed to be, but I confess my heart was won when I saw how George Bowen enjoyed his food.

And all through this day he has made himself useful. He persuaded the vacuum cleaner to work again, he carried chairs and cleaned the garage and was approved by Matt. And best of all was his tender understanding of Rennie and Mary.

These two wanted no big wedding, and so about four o'clock in the afternoon they came into the house from wandering in the forest, and they went to their rooms to bathe and change to their wedding garments. Mrs. Matt was in the kitchen with a couple of neighbor women to help with the simple refreshments and she gave me a push.

"Get upstairs and dress yourself," she ordered me.

"It won't take fifteen minutes for that," I said.

"Then see if the bride don't need a pin or two," she said. "I remember very well myself that I needed a pin to the front of my corset cover, I was breathin' that hard."

I went upstairs then, and when I had put on my pale-gray silk frock I knocked on Mary's door and she called to me to come in.

She was dressed and was standing by the window, looking out over the hills. Her wedding gown was white organdy, with fine hand embroidery at the hem and the neck. She had made it herself, and it was exactly right for her. Around her neck was a little gold chain and a locket with Rennie's picture inside.

"Your bouquet is downstairs," I said. "Shall I fetch it now?"

The guests were already coming up the walk, and the minister was in the living room. In the morning we had cut flowers from the fields and put them into bouquets with delicate fronds of brake. But I had a few of my precious roses for Mary's bouquet. We cannot grow roses outdoors here in our cold valley, but I lift my rosebushes in the autumn and bring them into the cellar to sleep, where it is cool and dry and dark, and in the spring I set them out. This year I forced a half dozen to make roses for Mary. They are pale pink and pale yellow, and I cut six half-opened buds this morning and made them into a cluster and set their stems into ice water to keep them from opening too wide.

"Please, Mother," she said.

I went away at once for I heard Rennie leave his room. When I came back with the roses he was standing in front of her, holding her hands in his. I knew very well the look in my son's eyes as he stood looking at his bride. I saw it long ago in his father's eyes for me.

The wedding was perfect in simplicity. The valley people gathered in our living room, only twenty or so for we invited no summer folk. When they were all there, Rennie and Mary clasped hands and went to the minister and stood before him. He rose from his chair, and took his little book from his pocket and spoke the few words that made them husband and wife. After the ceremony was over, the guests surrounded the young bride and groom, and I stood aside and wept quietly because they were so beautiful, until Bruce Spaulden fetched me a cup of fruit punch.

"Occupy yourself with this, my dear," he said, and would not leave my side.

Mrs. Matt set forth the wedding cake she had made, a noble three-tiered confection. Mary cut the slices with Rennie's help, and they exchanged silver goblets, each half full of the sweet wine I make every summer from wild blackberries, while the guests enjoyed the sight of them.

Then, quietly, in the midst of the eating and drinking, the two went upstairs and changed to their traveling clothes and came down again, and waving good-by they ran through the room, but waited for me at the car. There my son swept me into his arms and kissed my cheeks and Mary put her arms about us both, and so I let them go. One by one the guests went away. George Bowen stayed to put away chairs and carry dishes to Mrs. Matt in the kitchen.

When he left he stooped to kiss my cheek.

"Good-by, dear George," I said, "and come back often."

"I will," he said and then without the slightest sentimentality he said, "Shall I call you Mother, too, since now you are Mary's mother?"

"Do," I said gladly.

He winked his left eye at me. "Except you're too young to be a mother to three great gawks."

"Nonsense," I said.

He laughed and cantered down the front steps and stepped into his gray wreck of a car, without opening the door, and went off in a gust of smoke and gravel.

Now only Bruce was left and he stayed the evening with me. He knows that Rennie's father is dead. Rennie told him.

"How did you say it?" I had asked Rennie, half wishing he had not told.

"I said, 'My father is dead in Peking. My mother will live here in the valley. But Mary and I cannot live here where there are no laboratories.'"

"A man must go where his work is," Bruce agreed.

"Well, your work is here," Rennie said bluntly, "and you must be my mother's friend."

"I want to be that and whatever more she will accept me for," Bruce said.

Telling me this a few days ago, Rennie looked straight into my eyes. "Mother, you will please me very much if you decide to marry Bruce."

"Oh, Rennie, no," I whispered. "Don't — don't ask it."

"I don't ask it," he said. "I merely say that I shall be happy if you do."

To this I said nothing. It is still too soon, and perhaps it will always be too soon.

It was comforting, nevertheless, to have Bruce spend the evening with me, when everyone else was gone. I lay on the long chair, and he sat near me and smoked his old brier pipe and said very little. The silence was comforting. I was very near telling him about Gerald, and the house in Peking, and all that has happened to me. I thought of it while the evening wind made gentle music in the pines and the mountains subsided into shadows. I thought of Rennie, too, and of how he had been born, and this led me to Mei-lan, whose child was being born perhaps upon this very day. But in the end I said nothing and silence remained sweeter than speech. When Bruce rose to say good night, my life and love were still hidden within me.

"Thank you, dear Bruce," I said. "You are my best friend now."

He held my hand a long moment. "I'll let it go at that, but only for the present," he said. He put my hand to his cheek and I felt his flesh, smooth-shaven and cool. He said no more, and he went away. After that I was suddenly very tired, but sweetly so and without pain, and I went upstairs and to my bed.

DAYS HAVE passed again and I am already expecting Rennie and Mary to come home for the summer. I have had one more letter from Peking.

"It is my duty," Mei-lan insists, "to tell you that I have borne a son. He is like his father. His skin is white, his hair is dark but soft and fine. His frame is large and strong. My mother says he will be tall. I am astonished to have such a child. We two women, my mother and I, we will devote ourselves to rear him well, for his father's sake and for yours."

Mine? Have I aught to do with her child? Then I remember that this child is Rennie's half brother. It is possible that someday they will meet.

The ways of nature and of life are strange and deep. They are not to be understood. In the midst of angers and of wars love's secret work goes on, and binds us all by blood, and this whether love is denied or love is bestowed.

For you began it, Baba, you know you did. When the young pure American girl you loved would not love you enough to come to Peking for your sake, you flouted love, you said it did not matter and you took a woman whom you could not love. But she loved you, she bore your son, and one day I saw him and loved him utterly, and I went to Peking and made his city mine, until I was sent forth again, alone and forever parted from my love. Yet here are two grandsons, both yours, a globe between them. And because they are yours, they belong together somehow, and they will know it someday.

What do you say to that, Baba? What do you say to that, old Baba, you lying up there on the mountain under the big pine tree?

Pearl S. Buck

PEARL BUCK, world-famous American novelist and Nobel Prize winner, was born in West Virginia when her missionary parents were home on leave from China; they took her back with them when she was a few months old. Eventually she married an American in China, raised a daughter, and began to write the short stories and novels that were to make her one of the most celebrated literary figures of our time. Much of her work, like her first record-breaking best seller, *The Good Earth,* deals with the Chinese people, whom she has called "the easiest people in the world to love."

The cause of interracial understanding has always been close to Pearl Buck's heart. She is not, however, primarily a writer with a message; first and foremost she is a great and prolific storyteller, the author of forty-seven books. Her most recent interest is the theater; she is writing an original play, and is working with composer Frank Loesser on a musical comedy. She lives with her husband, Richard J. Walsh (who is also her publisher), on a dairy farm in Pennsylvania. They have five adopted children.

Condensations of two of her previous books have appeared in Reader's Digest Condensed Books: *The Hidden Flower* (Summer '52) and *My Several Worlds* (Winter '55).

TO·RENDER·EVERY
MAN·HIS·DUE

Wood Engravings by Bernard Brussel-Smith

THE FBI STORY

A condensation of the book by

DON WHITEHEAD

From the Black Tom explosion of World War I to today's undercover war against Communist subversion, the history of the FBI is studded with memorable incident: the pursuit of Dillinger, the Lindbergh kidnaping, the apprehension of Hitler's saboteurs, the Rosenberg spy case.

The FBI Story is the authentic, behind-the-scenes view of an agency that for more than thirty years has played a vital role in protecting American lives and freedom.

"This is one of the most absorbing narratives of crime and punishment I have ever read." — Charles Poore
in *The New York Times*

"As intriguing and fascinating a story as any 'whodunit.'" — Neal Stanford
in *The Christian Science Monitor*

Foreword . . .

For more than thirty years, as the FBI's director, I have watched the story of the Bureau being reported on a day-to-day basis by the press, radio and, now, television. Yet, through these past years, no one could find in a single volume the real story recounting the FBI's birth, development and struggles.

Permission to do such a book was requested by Don Whitehead, a newspaperman well known on the Washington scene, twice winner of Pulitzer Prizes for distinguished reporting. It was granted with our complete confidence in his integrity, ability and objectivity. He was given access to the record, and full facts were given him so long as they did not violate security. He has formed his own independent judgment on our policies, procedures and performance. This volume is his report.

My one regret has been that the author did not have the space to call the full roll of loyal men and women who have contributed so much to the achievements of the FBI. There have been many of them.

J. Edgar Hoover

1. *The FBI in Action*

A Colorado beet farmer had milked the cows and finished his chores for the day. He closed the barn door and turned toward the house, where supper was waiting. He noticed the blinking lights of United Air Lines Flight Number 629, eleven minutes out of Denver and heading for Portland, Oregon, with thirty-nine passengers and five crew members. The dark shadow up there was death hurtling through the heavens and winking at those some 5700 feet below.

Then the shadow was ripped apart by a terrible explosion. A ball of fire hung in the sky and streamers of flaming gasoline trailed down the curtain of night. A flare ignited and drifted down to illumine the scene with ghostly light. The wreckage of the DC-6B was strewn over two square miles. It was 7:03 p.m., November 1, 1955. The farmer in his barnyard had witnessed one of the most shocking mass murders in the annals of American crime.

When news of the crash reached Denver and was flashed across the nation, only one man knew that murder had been done. Only one man knew that a time bomb had been ticking in a battered old suitcase stowed aboard the plane. That man was tall, husky, sullen-eyed Jack Gilbert Graham, aged twenty-three, who had once told a neighbor, "I'd do anything for money."

Jack Graham had driven his mother, Mrs. Daisie King, to the Denver airport to put her aboard Flight 629, the beginning of a journey to visit a daughter in Alaska. He had carried her brief case, a traveling case and her battered old suitcase to the ticket counter to be weighed. The luggage was thirty-seven pounds over the sixty-six-pound limit. A ticket agent suggested that Mrs. King might save $27 by lightening her luggage. Mrs. King turned to her son. "Do you think I'll need all this?"

"Yes, Mother," he said. "I'm sure you will need it."

While Mrs. King was paying the overweight charge, her son fumbled with a machine which dispensed life-insurance policies — $6250 worth for each quarter dropped into the coin slot. He filled out two policies for $37,500 each, writing his own name as beneficiary. On two others, for $6250 each, he wrote the names of an aunt in Missouri and a half sister in Alaska. Mrs. King signed three of the policies but for some reason Jack didn't get her signature on one of the $37,500 policies. Perhaps the ticking of the time bomb was beginning to pound in his brain and he was becoming panicky. His mother's plane was behind schedule and time was running out. Flight 629 arrived eleven minutes late. Mrs. King gave good-by kisses to her son and his wife, Gloria, and their twenty-two-month-old son, Allen. She hurried aboard the plane.

For Jack Graham, there were twelve more agonizing minutes while the plane sat waiting for a tardy passenger. At last, at 6:52 p.m., the big ship roared from the runway.

The Grahams went into the airport coffee shop to eat. Jack

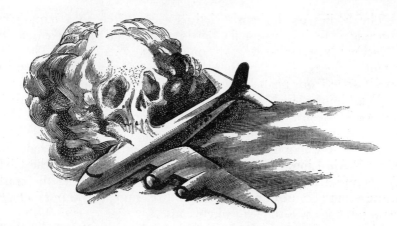

suddenly became ill and went to a rest room. He seemed to feel better when he came out.

The Grahams heard the rumor of a plane crash as they were leaving the airport. Gloria said later, "We finally heard his mother's name on the radio and Jack just collapsed completely."

Roy Moore, Assistant Special Agent in Charge in the Denver FBI office, was sitting at home watching television when news of the disaster was announced about 7:25 p.m. As usual in such tragedies, the United Air Lines (UAL) was advised immediately that the FBI was ready to help if help were needed. Then Moore notified FBI Headquarters in Washington.

Later that evening, the UAL flight surgeon asked the FBI's aid in identifying the bodies, and the Civil Aeronautics Board (CAB), which investigates plane crashes, requested an FBI Laboratory expert to help examine the wreckage. These agents arrived from Washington the next day.

The Colorado-crash inquiry was a remarkable example of how today's FBI operates. It shows what vast strides have been made in the FBI's techniques from the day in 1924 when J. Edgar Hoover took over command of an inept and politics-riddled Bureau.

This is how a murderer was tracked down by modern, scientific methods and the coöperation of government agencies, aviation engineers and private citizens.

The bodies of the crash victims were taken to a temporary morgue set up in a National Guard Armory, and nine were quickly identified by relatives, friends, or from personal effects. The FBI agents fingerprinted the other thirty-five and were able to identify twenty-one from prints on file in the FBI Identification Division in Washington. Five were identified by prints taken during their service in the armed forces. Others had been fingerprinted as government workers or employes in wartime defense plants.

The FBI Laboratory agent joined the investigators from the United Air Lines, the Douglas Aircraft Company and the Civil Aeronautics Board. Their job was to discover whether the crash came about because of mechanical failure, human error or sabotage. And sabotage was the least likely cause.

First, a surveyor marked a line through the center of the crash area in the direction of the plane's flight. At 1000-foot intervals, the line was bisected by 1000-foot lines to form a grid of squares, which were numbered. Teams of men went over the grid picking up pieces of metal, luggage, and anything else that came from the ship. Each piece was marked and its location on the grid carefully measured.

The tail assembly, virtually intact, looked as though it had been sliced away with a huge knife. The tail was a mile and a half from the point where the nose of the plane had torn into the earth.

These parts were taken to a Denver warehouse and placed on a scaled-down grid in the relative spots at which they had been found. The pieces were then carefully wired to a wooden mock-up of the DC-6B. Slowly the fuselage was reassembled. The big ship's shell became reasonably complete — except at one point. No pieces could be found to fit a jagged hole on the right side near the tail. This was the location of Number 4 cargo pit.

Engineers found that the metal at this point had been bent outward by some force more violent than a crash. They found shattered pieces of fuselage, burned on one side and discolored by a gray-and-white substance. Bits of metal had been driven through the soles and heels of shoes. Brass fittings from a suitcase had been driven into a stainless-steel container. No ordinary crash could hurl slugs of metal with such terrific force.

Experts added up the evidence. Clearly a violent explosion had occurred in cargo pit Number 4. There were no gasoline lines or tanks in this part of the plane. The CAB asked the FBI to begin a sabotage investigation. That was on November 7. Within twenty-four hours some one hundred agents in twenty cities were digging into the backgrounds of the plane's crew and passengers seeking a motive for murder, and checking freight manifests to determine whether there had been any illegal shipments which might have exploded accidentally.

Information poured in. There was no evidence of any illegal shipments. Agents studied the mass of information seeking some-one — a relative, a friend, a business enemy — who might have had a motive for murder and who could have caused the crash.

The face of Jack Graham began to emerge in dim outline.

The first small suspicion came when agents were unable to find Mrs. King's luggage except for a fragment here and there. They did find a handbag which she had carried on the plane. In it was a 1951 news clipping which said Graham was being hunted by police for forgery. Gradually attention began to center on Graham.

Jack Graham had been born in Denver in 1932. His father died when he was almost five years old. The mother, left penniless, farmed Jack out to an orphanage for six years. But they were re-united in 1943, when the mother married a well-to-do rancher, John Earl King.

Young Graham had better-than-average grades in school, but he was a restless boy with a vile temper. At sixteen he joined the Coast Guard by lying about his age. He was in the Coast Guard for nine months, during which he was AWOL for sixty-three days.

As they dug into his past, agents saw the pattern of a juvenile delinquent from a broken home who defied discipline and whose excesses were forgiven by a too-indulgent mother. In 1951, as a pay-roll clerk for a Denver manufacturer at $200 a month, Jack had forged the name of an official on company checks and cashed $4200 worth of them. He bought a flashy $2000 convertible and put the dust of Denver behind him in a five-state spree.

In Lubbock, Texas, young Graham was arrested for bootlegging, but only after he had crashed his car through a police roadblock in a hail of bullets. He was released to Denver authorities to answer the forgery charges. Daisie King couldn't bear to see her son in jail. She arranged to pay $2500 of the stolen $4200 and to have her son put on probation with the understanding he would repay the balance. For a time it appeared that Jack was going straight. He worked hard. In 1953 he married Gloria Elson, a Denver girl, and they had two children.

When Mrs. King's husband died in 1954, she invested $35,000 of her inheritance in a drive-in restaurant in West Denver and Jack managed it. She bought a home for her son and his family and, while in Denver, lived with them. When Jack wasn't at the restaurant, he worked in a garage. Gradually he reduced the forgery debt. Outwardly, he appeared to be a responsible citizen.

But in their investigations, FBI agents heard reports that Graham had stalled a pickup truck in front of a railroad train to collect insurance. There had been a gas explosion in the restaurant, too, which looked like another effort to collect insurance. And while Daisie King indulged her son, the two of them sometimes fought "like cats and dogs" over his management of the drive-in.

Agents questioned Graham on November 10. They asked about Mrs. King's luggage.

"I don't know what she put in her luggage," Graham said. "Mother liked to pack things herself. I do know she took some shotgun shells and ammunition. She was planning to do some hunting in Alaska."

No, Jack said, he hadn't put anything in the luggage himself.

Mrs. Graham verified her husband's story that Mrs. King liked to do her own packing. But Gloria said her husband had taken a gift-wrapped Christmas package to the basement just before they drove Mrs. King to the airport. The gift, she thought, was a set of drills, files and cutting tools which Jack had bought for his mother to use in her hobby of making jewelry and knickknacks from sea shells. Gloria supposed her husband had given the package to his mother before they left the house.

The agents were intrigued by the story. Graham had said nothing about a tool kit. But again it was mentioned by a neighbor, who told agents, "I heard Jack say he had searched the town to find the kind of kit he wanted, and he had placed it in his mother's luggage as a surprise."

Only two stores in Denver sold tool kits of the type used for cutting sea shells. A check at the stores disclosed that no one had bought such a kit during October. The flaws in the suspect's story had to be explained.

The second interview with Graham took place when he came with his wife to the FBI office on November 13, to identify fragments of leather believed to be from Mrs. King's luggage. Gloria stayed a few minutes and then returned home while Jack retraced with agents the story of his life. He consistently denied knowing anything about a Christmas gift package.

Late in the afternoon, Agent Roy Moore called Washington to ask about the analysis of the burned pieces of metal found at the crash scene. The FBI Laboratory reported that the metal showed traces of sodium carbonate, sodium nitrite and sulfur-bearing compounds — the residue left by an explosion of dynamite. Moore said later, "When I got this laboratory report, I knew we were on the right track."

At 6:40 p.m., Moore walked into the room where Graham was being questioned.

"I want you to know you have certain rights," Moore said. "The door there is open. You can walk out any time you wish. You can phone your wife or an attorney. You don't have to tell us anything — and if you do, it can be used against you in a court of law.

"Jack," he said, "we have gone over what you told us. You blew up that plane to kill your mother, didn't you?"

"No, I didn't," Graham protested.

"Then do you mind if we search your home?"

"No, I don't mind."

Graham signed a waiver which gave agents permission to search his home without a warrant. Moore dispatched agents to the Graham home, where they began a methodical search. An agent called in to say: "Mrs. Graham says Jack told her not to tell about the Christmas present. She signed a statement." Later the agents found the shells and ammunition which Graham had claimed his mother had packed.

These discrepancies in his story were ticked off by the agents. "What about it?" the youth was asked.

Graham finally admitted that he had bought a present for his mother, an X-Acto tool set, from "some guy" unknown to him. He said he paid $10 for it and two of his buddies at the garage were there at the time. He said he had slipped the box into his mother's suitcase. He had bound it with Scotch tape and put what was left of the tape in the glove compartment of his car.

Agents at the Graham house found no Scotch tape in the car, but they did find a roll of wire in one of his shirt pockets, wire of the type used for detonating dynamite.

At 10:15 p.m. the searchers found a $37,500 insurance policy signed by Daisie King payable to Jack, hidden in Jack's bedroom. This was the first time the FBI knew Graham had a policy on his mother's life. The insurance companies had provided copies of the insurance bought by passengers on Flight 629 — but somehow had overlooked the policies signed by Mrs. King.

The agents found something else of interest, too — stockings, a cosmetic bag, and some gifts which Mrs. King had intended for her daughter in Alaska. "Why didn't your mother take these things with her?" Graham was asked.

"I told her not to because her baggage was overweight."

At 12:01 a.m., agents reported that the two men who worked at the garage couldn't recall Graham's buying a tool kit. Graham was confronted with this report and with the report that the FBI Laboratory tests proved the crash was caused by a dynamite explosion. At 12:05 a.m., he asked, "Can I have a glass of water?"

An agent handed him the water and he took a long, gulping drink. He looked around sullenly and then said: "Okay, where do you want me to start?"

"Wherever you want to."

"Well, it started about six months ago. Mother was raising hell because the drive-in wasn't making money. . . ."

Without a trace of emotion he told of making the time bomb with twenty-five sticks of dynamite, two electric primer caps, a timer and a six-volt battery. He had worked at an electric shop for ten days to learn more about electricity before buying the dynamite

and timer. He had taken some things out of his mother's suitcase
and slipped the bomb in their places.

Graham talked for twenty minutes and then a stenographer was
called in to take his confession. At 1:42 a.m., a doctor arrived.
Graham was given a thorough examination so there would be
medical evidence that he had not been forced to confess by third-
degree methods, and so there could be testimony that he was in
sound mental condition, capable of giving a confession. He told
the doctor he had not been mistreated. He signed the confession.

At 3:42 a.m., Jack Graham was arrested for sabotage. Later he
was turned over to state officials to be tried for murder.

While he was in jail awaiting trial, Graham told a guard: "You
can send my mail to Canon City (Prison) until next month. After
that, you can send it to hell."

During the trial, Graham repudiated his confession. The evidence enmeshed him so tightly, however, that the jury required
only seventy-two minutes in which to decide that he was guilty
of murder in the first degree.

THE GRAHAM case is another baffling crime solved by the FBI.
But it is more than that. It is also a window that provides a glimpse
into the progress made by the FBI toward the goal of scientific
law enforcement by professionals trained to serve justice — and yet
preserve civil liberties in carrying out their tasks.

The FBI is almost half a century old. Its name is known to
millions as a symbol of integrity and efficiency. But it remains a
mystery organization to a great many Americans even though its
activities are interwoven with the protection of civil rights and the
security of the nation.

Few know how the FBI operates. Few realize that in protecting
the country the FBI also maintains a rigid around-the-clock system
of checks and controls over its own agents and their activities.
Hoover can and does pick up his telephone and within minutes
learn where an agent is, the case on which he is working and the
progress being made. The special agents in charge of the FBI's
fifty-two field divisions are responsible directly to Hoover for the
work within their geographic areas. In smaller cities surrounding

the field offices, the FBI has some 1200 resident agents who are responsible for the work in their subsections. This distribution of agents gives the FBI a well-deployed force which can move quickly to any given place, saving time and money.

At the main headquarters in Washington, the operation is highly centralized. For example, all bank-robbery reports come to one desk, where supervisors can tie together the investigative efforts in two, three or a half dozen cities; and so the operating method used in robbing a Chicago bank may be recognized by a supervisor as the identical method used a few days earlier in Los Angeles.

Around him, Hoover has gathered a group of top-flight executives. They are nine men who climbed from the ranks of the FBI's special agents. They came up through merit and not as somebody's political pets. Hoover has trusted them to make decisions. In turn, these men have repaid the trust with loyalty and fierce pride in the FBI. Though their names are not widely known, they hold in their hands much of the responsibility for the nation's safety.

These top lieutenants gather each Monday and Wednesday and if need be each weekday at 10:30 a.m. in what is known as "the FBI Executives Conference." The presiding officer is Clyde A. Tolson, who joined the Bureau in 1928. In 1947, Hoover gave him the title of Associate Director — formal recognition that Tolson was the Number 2 G-Man. Tolson serves in effect as Hoover's chief of staff. Like Hoover, he is a bachelor. The two men have become close friends over the years.

Two Assistants to the Director and six operating chiefs complete the inner circle. In the conference room, each is expected to say what he thinks. But he had better be ready to defend the position he takes. These are strong-willed men and there are, at times, clashes of opinion. When they walk out of the conference room, however, they walk out as a team. The decisions have been made and each man knows what he is to do. Their shoulder-to-shoulder teamwork is one of the keys to the FBI's unity and efficiency.

Another key to the FBI's efficiency is its attention to discipline. Through more than thirty years, Hoover has insisted on discipline in the ranks. This discipline is sternest, of course, in the special agent force of some 6200 men. But it is also maintained among the other 8000 employes. Obedience to official regulations is demanded to a degree that is astonishing to an outsider.

The life of a special agent isn't easy. He may be dismissed or disciplined if he violates certain rules. For example: He cannot drink intoxicants while on duty, and even off duty excessive use of intoxicants is banned, since the agent is subject to call at any time. He cannot disclose information to any unauthorized person, even his wife. He cannot accept rewards or gratuities in any form. He cannot fail to pay his taxes or to meet other financial obligations. And the list of rules goes on and on.

The newly appointed agent learns discipline from the day he reports to begin an intensive eighteen-week training course. The course is divided into two parts. There is classroom study of investigative techniques, FBI responsibilities and administrative work; also, at the FBI Academy at the Marine base at Quantico, Virginia, there is training in jujitsu and other tricks of rough-and-tumble fighting as well as instruction in the use of firearms.

Each agent, including the scientists who work in the Laboratory, must know how to take care of himself in a gun battle. He learns the "quick draw," in which a pistol is whipped from a holster in a stance which gives the steadiest position for firing accurately. ("Never shoot while running" is an FBI axiom.) He is taught to shoot from standing, kneeling, sitting and prone positions. He learns to handle a thirty-caliber rifle, a repeating shotgun and a submachine gun. The roll of eighteen agents killed in line of duty is a reminder that the battle against criminals is a dangerous one.

Despite the strict discipline, long hours and hard work, relatively few agents leave the FBI for easier, higher-paying jobs. There is something in the FBI which holds them, an intangible spirit of pride. In 1955, for example, the turnover among agents was less than one half of one percent.

Who then are these men called FBI agents?

They are a cross section of American life. Except for agents specializing in accounting — who must have three years' training in that field — or those highly qualified in certain other skills, such as languages, they are law-school graduates. But adaptability and versatility are as important as academic training in investigative work, and the FBI looks for young men whose interests are wide and varied. Some agents were once commercial artists. Some studied medicine and then decided they preferred the life of an agent. Some worked as musicians, pharmacists, bookdealers, teachers or farmers. Among them, they speak or read thirty different languages and dialects and their hobbies vary from art to sports. But certain similarities do emerge from a sampling of agents' biographies. And from the sampling comes the approximation of a so-called average agent named, let us say, John J. Jones.

John Jones is thirty-four years old and he has a wife and two children. His father is moderately well-to-do. His parents are the kind of people who say grace at mealtimes, and who teach their children to have respect for authority when it is properly used.

In high school, John had above-average grades. He was a good athlete and took part in debating and social affairs. He went to the State University and he worked at times during the summer. He graduated with an A.B. degree and then entered law school. John decided on an FBI career partly because it promised exciting and interesting work, and also because he felt he would be doing something worth while in an organization in which he could take pride.

These men form the FBI. They are professionals highly trained for their work and guided by the principle that establishing innocence is just as important as establishing guilt in their investigations. But this has not always been so. Undisciplined operations almost destroyed the Bureau in pre-Hoover days, and this is one reason for Hoover's insistence on discipline in the ranks.

The FBI traveled a long road to reach its present point. And there can be no understanding of the FBI without looking into the forces which helped in the past to shape its future.

Here, then, is how the FBI developed through the years.

2. *The Story Begins*

THE BUREAU officially came into being as a result of President Theodore Roosevelt's crusade, early in this century, against the "land thieves" in the West and the big-business "trusts" in the

East. Up to this time the Justice Department had "borrowed" agents from the Treasury Department's Secret Service, which had been organized after the Civil War primarily to combat a wave of counterfeiting. But in 1908, a Congress unsympathetic to Roosevelt's roaring battle against political and business corruption forbade the practice. This was a crippling blow to federal law enforcement. If federal laws were to be enforced, there had to be investigators to gather evidence of wrongdoing. Roosevelt countered the Congressional action with an Executive Order instructing the Attorney General to set up an investigative agency within his Department, reporting to him alone.

On March 4, 1909, President Roosevelt was succeeded by William Howard Taft. Twelve days later, Taft's new Attorney General, George W. Wickersham, gave the new investigative agency the dignity of a title, the Bureau of Investigation, by which name it was called until 1935, though we shall refer to it as the FBI prior to that date.

In its beginning the Bureau was disorganized and loosely directed, without character or discipline. Washington held little control over the agents in the field. There were no fixed standards of training or personal conduct. In the selection of agents, political endorsement carried more weight than experience or character.

When the storm clouds of World War I gathered in Europe, the Bureau was far from being prepared for the test. The small and inept force of 219 agents which existed in 1915 failed in its first great mission. It was totally unequipped to deal with German-organized espionage and sabotage. Saboteurs brought about such outrages as the 1916 "Black Tom" explosion in New York Harbor, which destroyed the United States' greatest arsenal with a roar heard for more than a hundred miles. Defense plants were destroyed with explosives, and wheat fields were fired in the West. With the call to arms in 1917, the Bureau was swamped with work. The agent force was increased immediately to 400. But this was a puny squad for policing more than 1,000,000 enemy aliens, protecting harbors and war-industry zones, helping to locate draft dodgers, and carrying on the regular duties of investigating federal-law violations.

After the war there were years of violent social unrest, when men preached anarchy, when mysterious bomb explosions spread terror, and when the Communist Party, advocating the overthrow of the government by force, was first formed in America. In combating violence, the Bureau's agents were not trained to protect civil liberties. Such affairs as the "Palmer Red Raids" of 1919, in which alien extremists were rounded up for deportation, caused great scandal. One of these raids, aimed at members of the Communist Party and the Communist Labor Party, took place one Friday evening in January of 1920. Agents in thirty-three cities, armed with warrants issued by the Bureau of Immigration, rounded up approximately 2500 aliens for deportation hearings. The outcry against injustices in this and other raids was to be heard for years.

The years after the war were also years when corruption spread through the country and into the government in Washington. And the time came at last when the Bureau itself was threatened with destruction by the indignant public reaction to dishonesty.

It was during the Harding Administration that events approached this climax.

Bluff, handsome Warren G. Harding had become President on March 4, 1921. He drew around him friends from Ohio, poker-playing pals who had helped chart his campaign.

It was hardly surprising that Harding named his old Ohio friend Harry M. Daugherty to the Cabinet post of Attorney General, and that Daugherty in turn appointed his old friend William J. Burns, known as "the famous international sleuth," as the new Director of the Bureau of Investigation. But the next three years were to be packed with surprises that would leave the country disillusioned with men in high places.

The Bureau's old records reflect the strong political influences at work in the Harding Administration. One memorandum to Burns, reportedly from a Senator, gave a breakdown on the party affiliations of the Bureau's Chicago agents.

Into this state of affairs strode the notorious detective Gaston B. Means, to become an agent of the Bureau of Investigation on October 28, 1921, by Burns's appointment. He quickly established the fact that he was Burns's favorite investigator and close friend

One young man at the Bureau clashed with Means almost immediately. Aged twenty-six, he had gone to work for the Department of Justice back in 1917 when he was a twenty-two-year-old lawyer. In the Daugherty shake-up of the Department, he had been transferred to the position of Assistant Director of the Bureau of Investigation. His name was J. Edgar Hoover.

Clashing with Means, Hoover asked Burns to order Means to stay out of his office. Hoover didn't like the man's spending habits or his morals. The New York *Sun* later took this notice of Means:

Means has been in the papers a long time. . . . He was an agent of Germany (in 1916) paid to embarrass British commerce. In 1917 he was accused of the murder of a rich widow, Mrs. Maude A. King, who was killed by a pistol bullet while in North Carolina with . . . Means. He was acquitted of the killing, only to be denounced in another court for filing a forged will which would have put the King estate practically at his disposal. Next we find this fellow an investigator in the Department of Justice. . . .

When too many people asked embarrassing questions, Daugherty and Burns finally solved the problem in this fashion: the Attorney General suspended Means as an agent "until further notice," then Burns put Means on the Bureau's pay roll as an informant, where he continued business as usual.

The country itself was sick, and running a high fever in the postwar adjustment. Jobless men were walking the streets by the millions. Congress began to demand an investigation of corruption within the Administration — corruption that included the infamous "Teapot Dome" scandal.

Soon after taking office, President Harding had turned over to the Interior Department the administration of naval oil reserves in California and Wyoming, the latter known as the Teapot Dome oil field. Secretary of the Interior Albert B. Fall signed a contract with private interests headed by Harry F. Sinclair and Edward L. Doheny, permitting them to pump and store the oil from naval reserves on a royalty basis. The transaction was defended on the grounds that Teapot Dome oil reserves were being drained off by nearby private wells, and that the new arrangement would protect the government's interests.

But soon Fall's neighbors in New Mexico noted sudden signs of prosperity at the Fall ranch. Later Sinclair and Doheny explained that they had "loaned" Fall more than $135,000. Doheny said his $100,000 share was merely "an accommodation to an old friend."

These explanations didn't satisfy Congress. Questions were being asked, too, about the handling of the Veterans Administration and the Alien Property Custodian's Office, and the Department of Justice's failure to prosecute alleged frauds in World War I contracts. Just as the storm was breaking over his Administration, Harding became ill, and died on August 2, 1923. Calvin Coolidge became President of the United States, inheriting a truly great mess.

Reports of corruption snowballed. An outcry was raised in Congress for Attorney General Daugherty's resignation, led, for one, by Senator Burton K. Wheeler of Montana. While the Senate was conducting its sensational investigation of the Attorney General, Wheeler himself was indicted by a Montana grand jury. He was charged with taking bribes from a syndicate of oil prospectors.

Wheeler immediately charged that he was the victim of a "frame-up" by the Department of Justice. A Senate committee and then a Montana jury found Wheeler innocent. The Philadelphia *Record* said the trial was "one of the most contemptible and vindictive political persecutions ever known in this country." Burns admitted that he sent three Bureau of Investigation accountants into Montana to help work on the Wheeler case.

The Daugherty investigation would never have been complete without Burns's old friend Gaston B. Means — and Means made his appearance a spectacular one, testifying to espionage directed against the Senators themselves. Means said he had arranged to have agents sneak into Senators' offices, open their mail, search their files and spy on them in an effort to find something damaging which could be used to stop their attacks on Daugherty. His testimony blended well with the general picture of corruption. As historian Samuel Hopkins Adams said later, the Department of Justice had "reached its lowest ebb in morale, morals and efficiency, and this in spite of many able subexecutives."

On March 28, 1924, President Coolidge demanded, and received, Daugherty's resignation as Attorney General. At last the time had arrived for the big house cleaning in government.

PRESIDENT Calvin Coolidge welcomed into his White House office one day in March 1924 a big New Englander with the plodding, deliberate gait of a countryman. The visitor was Harlan Fiske Stone, New Hampshire-born Republican, New York attorney and former Dean of the Columbia University School of Law.

The President talked to Stone for a long time. Here was the man Coolidge hoped would become his Attorney General, and whose rocklike integrity he believed could restore public confidence in the Department of Justice, which was being called, with reason, the "Department of Easy Virtue." When Stone left the White House that bleak March day he had agreed to take on the job of reorganizing the Department.

Attorney General Stone moved into the Department of Justice driver's seat and then looked around cautiously. One month and seven days after his appointment, he accepted the resignation of William J. Burns as Director of the Bureau of Investigation. The old era had ended for the Bureau.

Stone had been looking around for the right man to put in charge of the Bureau. He had mentioned his problem at a Cabinet meeting attended by Herbert Hoover, who was then Secretary of Commerce. Later Hoover told his assistant, Larry Richey, that Stone was looking for an intelligent young man to head the Bureau. Richey replied, "Why should they look around when they have the man they need over there right now — a young, well-educated lawyer?" Richey mentioned J. Edgar Hoover — not related to Herbert Hoover.

"You think he can do the job?" the Secretary asked.

"I know he can," Richey replied.

A few days later, Herbert Hoover told Richey that the Attorney General was going to "try young Hoover out."

The day after Burns resigned, twenty-nine-year-old J. Edgar Hoover was summoned to Stone's office. It was May 10, 1924. The news had already circulated that Burns was leaving. Hoover wasn't sure whether he would be next or not. Stone was known to be gruff and tough, and heads were falling.

Hoover entered Stone's office and saw the big man seated behind his desk, looking as though he'd been carved out of solid rock.

"Sit down," Stone said, scowling as usual. Hoover took a seat. The two men looked at each other across the desk. Then Stone said abruptly, "Young man, I want you to be Acting Director of the Bureau of Investigation."

Hoover realized the magnitude of the compliment. He knew that the Attorney General had rejected the argument that he was too young for the job. Far more important, he knew that Stone did not hold him responsible for the corrupt actions of those who had directed the Bureau of Investigation in the past. Finally he said, "I'll take the job, Mr. Stone, on certain conditions."

"What are they?"

"The Bureau must be divorced from politics and not be a catch-all for political hacks. Appointments must be based on merit. Second, promotions will be made on proved ability and the Bureau will be responsible only to the Attorney General."

"I wouldn't give it to you under any other conditions," said Stone. "That's all. Good day."

Thus it was, under the guidance of Stone, that Hoover took over the command of the Bureau, first as Acting Director, and then, seven months later, as Director.

In those first months, Hoover leaned heavily on Stone for support. And he received it.

Hoover believed strongly that the Department of Justice should have lawyers and accountants trained in collecting evidence. He recognized that the government's cases too often were not presented properly because the evidence was gathered haphazardly by untrained agents. Yet the collection of evidence was the basis for proving innocence or guilt.

Stone and Hoover had no difficulty over basic policies. Three days after Hoover's appointment, it had been agreed:

1. The Bureau would be a fact-gathering organization, limited strictly to investigating violations of federal laws.

2. Investigations would be made at and under the direction of the Attorney General.

3. Incompetents and unreliables would be discharged as quickly as possible.

4. No new appointments would be made without the Attorney General's approval — and preference would be given to men of good character and ability who had some legal training.

Hoover now had elbow room in which to work. He began issuing a rapid-fire series of orders to agents, who were startled by the sudden burst of attention from Washington. One of his first acts was to see that Gaston B. Means was fired, officially and finally.

The difficult job of reorganization developed as a two-pronged campaign. On one side was the fight to weed out the patronage hacks, to enforce the new code of conduct and to weld the organization into an efficient force. On the other side was the battle to convince Congressmen and political leaders that the Bureau was no longer a dumping ground for patronage appointments.

One of Hoover's first moves was to give the special agents in charge at the field offices greater authority. The old system in which agents sent individual reports to Washington was discontinued. Agents now reported to the special agent in charge and he made his reports to Washington. Thus a chain of command was established. Agents were reclassified on a basis of efficiency. The best men received the highest pay. Paper work was reduced. Office routine was systematized so that agents going from one office to another would find precisely the same methods of operation.

Hoover's code of conduct became a way of life for those who wished to stay in the Bureau. He forbade his agents to drink liquor either publicly or privately. (When Prohibition ended, this regulation was modified.) His men had to be neat in dress and discreet in their habits. He regarded them as representatives of the Bureau whether they were at work or enjoying an evening with friends. Even clerks and stenographers had to measure up to strict standards. Hoover and his men were called "college-trained flat feet" and jeered at as "Boy Scouts" in the field of law enforcement, but the new rules began to show results almost immediately. After seven months of watching Hoover's work, Attorney General Stone removed the word "Acting" from his title and on December 10, 1924, appointed him Director of the Bureau of Investigation.

It took Hoover roughly three years to perfect the Bureau's basic organization, which was to become renowned for its efficiency. Through all the formative years, Hoover maintained a close friendship with Stone, who remained in the Department of Justice for eleven months and then was appointed to the Supreme Court.

Frequently Stone would plod into the Bureau and say, "Edgar, I came by to inquire into your stewardship."

Some years later, Stone wrote Hoover:

It is always a comfort to me to see how completely you have confirmed my judgment when I placed you at the head of the Bureau of Investigation. The Government can now take pride in the Bureau instead of feeling obliged to apologize for it.

3. *The Battle Against Crime*

T HE SCANDALS of the Harding Administration had been mani-
festations of a general moral collapse. The country as a whole continued hell-bent on its way through the Roaring Twenties. Crime was breeding at an alarming rate throughout the country.

The gangsters shot and bribed their way into places of power and the FBI was virtually powerless to deal with such hoodlums as Alphonse "Scarface" Capone, who rose from an errand boy in a bawdyhouse to become the overlord of Chicago's underworld.

These were the years in which gangsters created invisible empires through alliances with crooked politicians, crooked lawyers, crooked doctors and crooked police. Gangsters' revenues from bootleg whisky, robberies, prostitution, gambling, narcotics and "protection" rackets ran to uncounted hundreds of millions of dollars. The income of Chicago gangs alone was estimated variously as from $100,000,000 to more than $300,000,000 annually at the peak of their power.

Curiously, the FBI was powerless to move against these underworld empires unless the gangs violated a federal law, such as the Antitrust Act, which forbids restraint of interstate commerce.

Capone was only in his mid-twenties when he took over full command of the Chicago underworld. Even when he "retired" to a plush Florida estate in 1927, he ruled the mob by remote control and men died at his command.

Capone was virtually untouchable. But finally he made a slip and the FBI went after him. In 1929 he pleaded illness as an excuse for failing to answer a subpoena to appear as a witness in a federal Prohibition case in Chicago. Claiming he had been bedridden for six weeks with bronchopneumonia, he produced a doctor's sworn statement as proof that he was in no condition to travel.

FBI agents checked into Capone's story. They found that during the time he was supposedly ill he had gone to horse races, taken a boat trip, flown to the Bahama Islands and visited public places with a glow of health on his cheeks.

As a result, Capone was cited for contempt of court and ordered before a federal grand jury in Chicago. He was arrested in Florida and released on bond in March 1929. Two months later, Capone was arrested in Pennsylvania and convicted of carrying a concealed weapon. When his one-year sentence expired, he was prosecuted on the contempt-of-court charge and given six months in jail. While Capone served his sentence, Internal Revenue Bureau agents took a close look at his financial affairs. He was charged with income-tax evasion. Convicted, he was sent to prison for ten years.

The reason for the rise of gangsterism in the 1920's is still disputed — but there is no dispute that its beginning coincided with the arrival of national Prohibition.

The country went "dry," officially, on January 16, 1920. At Norfolk, Virginia, Billy Sunday preached the funeral of John Barleycorn over a twenty-foot coffin. The evangelist shouted, "Good-by, John! You were God's worst enemy, hell's best friend!"

But John Barleycorn refused to be buried. Millions of Americans demanded spirits, and the bootlegger stepped in to supply them. Foreign ships anchored in international waters outside the three-mile limit and transferred their cargoes to the high-powered boats of rumrunners. These boats often sneaked quietly through the Coast Guard defenses, but sometimes they tried to fight their way through with machine guns blazing. The risk was great but so were the profits. A case of whisky bought for $15 at wholesale could be retailed for $70 to $80. At one time the ships on "Rum Row" outside New York Harbor were loaded with whisky estimated to be worth $225,000,000.

Congress gave the Treasury Department responsibility for enforcing Prohibition, and soon a small army of some 4000 agents was deployed from 105 offices.

With their huge treasuries, the gangsters corrupted city officials, police and federal agents. A $44-a-week Prohibition agent or policeman could earn hundreds of dollars a week merely by looking the other way. In New Jersey, a federal Prohibition administrator protested that all the agents in his office, except three, were accepting bribes and that he couldn't "lead an army into battle" when most of his soldiers were in the pay of the enemy. Another official reported that a brewery combine had offered a bribe of $300,000 a week if an agent wouldn't interfere with their operation.

Gangland massacres became commonplace. In 1926 homicides had reached the staggering rate of 12,000 a year. The crime bill mounted to billions of dollars. Political machines across the country were allied with the underworld. The federal government could act only in crimes where federal laws were violated, so the cleanup job was primarily one for the cities themselves — but indignation against corrupt and lax law enforcement was slow to develop.

Early in 1925, the FBI received complaints that Cincinnati was a graft-ridden city where the police were deeply involved in a conspiracy with the underworld. Saloons were operating openly within two blocks of the Federal Building, and narcotics were being peddled at an alarming rate. Conditions were so bad that city officials had finally appealed to the Department of Justice for help.

With Attorney General Stone's approval, Hoover ordered investigators to Cincinnati. Within two days, the agents found indications of a graft ring in the city's police department which involved violations of federal laws. Methodically they interviewed hundreds of witnesses. One narcotics peddler confessed he had grossed $455,056 over a thirty-month period and paid out $18,000 in protection money. A saloonkeeper admitted he had paid about $200,000 to the police over a three-year period.

In less than three months' time, the FBI was ready to act. A special federal grand jury was called and indictments were brought against forty-eight Cincinnati police and twenty-three "dry agents" from nearby villages. Some of the accused men fled. They were trailed as far as Miami and Los Angeles and brought back. Of the seventy-one indicted, seventy were tried and sixty-two convicted. One man escaped to Canada.

This investigation opened the way for a reform movement in Cincinnati which swept the old city-hall gang out of office along with the crooked police.

Soon after this cleanup, Hoover received the shocking report that Special Agent Edward B. Shanahan had been shot and killed by Martin James Durkin, an automobile thief wanted by the FBI. The agent had been about to make his arrest when Durkin had swept an automatic pistol from the seat beside him and shot Shanahan through the breast. For the first time an FBI agent had been killed in line of duty.

Hoover called in an aide. "We've got to get Durkin," he said. "If one man from the Bureau is killed and the killer gets away, our agents will never be safe."

The hunt for Durkin began.

Durkin killed a policeman and wounded another in Chicago. The FBI traced him to California and then picked up his trail when a Cadillac was stolen from a San Diego sales agency and a salesman identified Durkin's picture. The trail led from California into Texas. It was picked up, lost, and then picked up again.

At Pecos, Texas, Durkin had a close call. A suspicious sheriff checked on a parked Cadillac and saw a pistol lying on the seat beside the driver. The young man at the wheel said he was a deputy sheriff from California on vacation and that was why he had the gun. He would prove it, too, if the sheriff would permit him to go to his hotel for his identification papers. The sheriff agreed. Durkin roared off into the desert in the Cadillac, a woman companion by his side.

The sheriff at Pecos notified the FBI, giving a description fitting Durkin. Now the trail was hot. FBI agents scoured the desert. They found the Cadillac abandoned in a clump of mesquite. The car was the one stolen at San Diego. A nearby rancher recalled that a man and woman had come to his door and asked to be driven to a railway station. "I hauled them over to Girvin," the rancher said. "They talked about going from Girvin to Alpine to catch a train."

The agents checked with the ticket agent at Alpine. "Come to think of it," the agent said, "a young fellow and a woman got aboard No. 110 night before last. He bought tickets for San Antonio."

Through conductors, ticket agents and porters, the agents learned on the morning of January 20, 1926, that Durkin and his girl friend had boarded the MK&T "Texas Special," due to arrive in St. Louis at eleven o'clock that same morning. Hurried calls were made to the FBI office in St. Louis, and agents were given the number of Durkin's train compartment.

Special agents in St. Louis got in touch with city detectives and explained the situation. Oddly enough, the government couldn't prosecute Durkin for the murder of Shanahan because killing a federal officer was not then a violation of federal laws. He could be prosecuted for murder only in the state in which the crime occurred.

With city detectives coöperating, arrangements were made with railroad officials to have the "Texas Special" stopped outside St. Louis. Then if Durkin tried to escape, he would have to run across open plowed fields and would not endanger bystanders. When the "Texas Special" came to a halt, FBI agents and detectives boarded the train. They rushed into Durkin's compartment before he could reach for his pistols. He was taken from the train in manacles.

Martin Durkin, killer and thief, was captured a little more than three months after his gun felled Special Agent Shanahan. He admitted the killing and was sentenced to fifty years in prison.

By 1929, President Herbert Hoover had become so concerned with crime conditions that he named a national commission, headed by former Attorney General George W. Wickersham, to study the situation and report its findings. For two years the Wickersham Commission probed into the problems of law enforcement, covering a broad field. President Hoover said the work was the first official effort to envisage our crime problem as a national problem. When the Commission issued its report, the findings belabored police, politicians, Congress, crooks and the public for the crime conditions which existed. It stirred a controversy across the land — but the report did succeed in centering greater attention on law enforcement and crime.

Indirectly, the Wickersham report played an important part in shaping the future of the FBI because it emphasized the national character of crime. And when the people's revulsion against crime finally boiled over, Congress turned to the FBI for the cleanup.

A KIDNAP-MURDER in New Jersey, a gang massacre in Missouri and a kidnaping in Oklahoma were the crimes of 1932-1933 which shocked the nation and, by chain reaction, sent the FBI into guerrilla warfare against the forces of the underworld.

During the twenties most of the country had watched the rise of crime and gangsterism with a so-what attitude. But this tolerance was now to give way to angry demands that something be done about the menace. And the beginning of the change in attitude can be pinpointed as to time and place.

It began on March 1, 1932, near the little town of Hopewell, New

Jersey, sometime between 8:00 p.m. and 10:00 p.m. That was when a kidnaper stole through the darkness to the secluded home of Colonel and Mrs. Charles A. Lindbergh. Using a homemade ladder, he climbed to the window of the second-floor nursery where twenty-month-old Charles A. Lindbergh, Jr., had been tucked in bed. The man slipped in, lifted the blond, blue-eyed child from his crib, and disappeared with him into the night.

On the window sill, Lindbergh found a note which said:

> Have 50000$ ready 25000$ in 20$ bills 15000$ in 10$ bills and 10000$ in 5$ bills. After 2 — 4 days we will inform you were to deliver the mony. We warn you for making anyding public or for notify the police. The child is in gut care. Instruction for the letters are singnature.

The "singnature" was a symbol of two interlocking circles in which three holes had been punched.

In the days that followed, Dr. John F. Condon, a retired school principal, became the intermediary between the Lindberghs and the kidnaper as the result of an offer published in the Bronx, New York, *Home News*. Condon became "Jafsie" in the negotiations, the kidnaper became "John." On April 2, in St. Raymond's Cemetery in the Bronx, Condon turned over $50,000 in cash to "John." He received instructions that the boy would be found on a boat named "Nellie" near Martha's Vineyard, Massachusetts.

Even as this scene was being enacted, the child lay dead in a shallow grave only four and a half miles from his nursery. The body was found accidentally on May 12 by a truck driver's helper. Apparently the boy had been killed soon after he was kidnaped.

The brutal kidnap-murder angered the country as no crime had done in years. Three months after the kidnaping, Congress passed the Lindbergh Kidnap Law, which, as later amended, provided the death penalty for transporting a kidnaped person across a state line.

The investigation of the case developed into a coöperative effort between the New Jersey State Police, the New York City police and the FBI. The big break finally came on September 15, 1934

— two and a half years after the kidnaping — when a motorist handed a New York City filling-station attendant a ten-dollar gold certificate. On the bill the attendant wrote the car's license number — 4U-13-41. He didn't think of the Lindbergh kidnaping, but he was suspicious because gold certificates had been called in when the United States went off the gold standard in 1933.

Three days later, a bank teller spotted the bill as a Lindbergh ransom note. A check disclosed that the license had been issued to a Bruno Richard Hauptmann, of 1279 East 222nd Street, the Bronx. Hauptmann was arrested. A twenty-dollar ransom bill was found in his pocket. Another $13,000 of the ransom money was discovered in his garage. Dr. Condon identified Hauptmann as the "John" to whom he paid the $50,000. Evidence piled up. The accused man was convicted after a sensational trial and electrocuted on April 3, 1936.

In a curious side-line development, the FBI once again got onto the trail of that extraordinary man Gaston B. Means. Means had been so discredited by 1932 that it seemed unlikely anyone would believe his stories. Perhaps he was surprised himself when wealthy Mrs. Evalyn Walsh McLean, of Washington, D. C., sent for him three days after the Lindbergh kidnaping.

Mrs. McLean knew Means was a crook. But for that very reason she wondered if he might not have underworld contacts who could arrange the return of the Lindbergh baby. She put the question to him. Means didn't bat an eye as he solemnly told Mrs. McLean that her call was a strange coincidence. He said that a few days before the kidnaping, in New York, he had met an old pal from the Atlanta Penitentiary. This convict had urged him to join in a big kidnaping job, but of course he had refused.

When he read about the Lindbergh child, Means said, he knew this was the "big job" discussed by his friend. He was certain he could locate the gang which was holding the child. By the time Means finished his story, Mrs. McLean was under the extraordinary illusion that she had discovered the secret of the kidnaping.

Having "made contact" with the kidnapers, Means told Mrs. McLean the baby was well and the gang was demanding $100,000 ransom. Mrs. McLean gave Means the money. He promised not to pay the gang until the baby was safely in Mrs. McLean's hands. He devised an elaborate code. The baby was "The Book." Means was "Number 27." The gang leader was "Number 19," or "The Fox."

The weeks that followed were a cruel nightmare for the woman who trusted Means. Mysterious telephone calls came from Means and "The Fox." Once "The Fox" turned up at Mrs. McLean's cottage at Aiken, South Carolina, to discuss details. He wore suede gloves and carefully wiped off all polished surfaces that he touched, as though a fingerprint might have shown through his gloves. Always the gang was on the verge of delivering the baby — but always something happened to prevent it. Mrs. McLean paid Means another $4000. She was arranging to pawn her jewels to raise an additional $35,000 when her attorney discovered what was going on. At this point the FBI was called in.

The main problem was to find Means's confederate, "The Fox." Day by day, FBI special agents checked on long-distance telephone calls which had been made to Means and to Mrs. McLean. Most of them had been made from pay stations in North and South Carolina, Maryland, New Jersey and New York. But "The Fox" had made one slip in placing station-to-station calls from the same neighborhood to his own residence and to Means. In running down these calls the name of Norman T. Whitaker emerged. A check disclosed that Whitaker was an ex-convict and a disbarred attorney.

Whitaker was identified as "The Fox." Means and "The Fox" were convicted of a conspiracy to commit larceny and sentenced to fifteen years and eighteen months, respectively.

Hoover was in the courtroom when Means testified, insisting he had made desperate efforts to find the baby. Finally, he stepped from the witness stand and sat beside Hoover.

"Well, Hoover," he said, "what did you think of that?"

"Every bit of it was a pack of lies," Hoover retorted.

Means blinked his eyes. "Well," he said, "you've got to admit that it made a whale of a good story."

But a "whale of a good story" to Means was a cruel story to most people. In the outcry raised by the Lindbergh kidnaping, the country and Congress came to realize that federal laws were woefully weak in combating interstate crime. Criminals were operating with high-speed automobiles, machine guns and armaments which were better than those of the law-enforcement agencies.

By 1933 bank robberies were occurring at the rate of almost two a day. Kidnapings had increased alarmingly despite the Lindbergh Kidnap Law. The Attorney General had urged people to report kidnapings to the FBI by calling the special "kidnap" number — NAtional 8-7117, Washington, D. C.

Many of the gang operations were not in violation of federal statutes and there were curious inconsistencies in the laws. For example, a bank official who embezzled from a federal bank in 1933 violated a federal law. But a gang might rob a federal bank of $100,000, machine-gun the officials and escape to another state without violating a single federal statute. And the bandits could be reasonably sure that pursuit would end at the state line.

In 1933, also, FBI agents did not have the full police authority given to city and state police. The result was that agents often had to enlist the aid of local police when searches and seizures were to be made. In most cases, police gave invaluable help. But in some cities the FBI found that, when they confided their plans to local police, the plans were "leaked" to criminals.

Director Hoover explored the role of the federal government in the crime fight with President Franklin D. Roosevelt's Attorney General, Homer S. Cummings. Demands were being made that federal crime laws should be strengthened, though it was clear to Hoover that the federal government should not take over the nation's local police work.

Meanwhile, the insolence of gangsters toward law enforcement was never displayed more brazenly perhaps than in the "Kansas City Massacre" of June 17, 1933.

The day before this crime, FBI special agents had ended a long hunt by tracking down Frank Nash, an escaped convict and desperado who had eluded police for three years. Nash was seized in Hot Springs, Arkansas, by two agents and Police Chief Otto Reed of McAlester, Oklahoma, one of the most respected police officers in that part of the country. They boarded a train with Nash for Kansas City, Missouri, en route to Leavenworth Prison.

The news was flashed to Kansas City by the underworld, and a gunman named Vern Miller was told that the train would arrive at the Union Railway Station at 7:15 the next morning. Nash would then be transferred to an automobile for the ride to the prison. That night, as the FBI was to discover later, Miller enlisted Charles "Pretty Boy" Floyd and Adam Richetti, two of the most dangerous gunmen in the Middle West, in a plot to free Nash.

Nash and his guard arrived in Kansas City on schedule. They were met at the Union Station by two more FBI men and two Kansas City detectives. Special Agent Raymond Caffrey had parked his car across the street from the station.

"Get into the front seat," Caffrey told Nash.

Chief Reed and two FBI agents climbed into the rear seat. The two city detectives and an FBI agent were standing beside the car while Caffrey walked around to the door on the driver's side of the automobile. All the officers were armed.

At this moment, three gunmen, two with machine guns and one with pistols, suddenly approached the car. A voice shouted: "Up! Up!" The officers looked up into the muzzles of the machine guns. Then the command came: "Let 'em have it."

The hoodlums opened fire. The attack was so sudden and devastating the officers didn't have time to swing their weapons into action. Within a few roaring seconds, Chief Reed, Agent Caffrey and the two Kansas City detectives were killed. Two other FBI men were wounded. One agent escaped harm by some miracle. The killers leaped into a car and escaped.

And Nash died with a bullet in his brain, a bullet from the gun of one of his "liberators."

Public protests aroused by the shocking "Kansas City Massacre" had hardly subsided when gangsters again sneered at the law with the kidnaping of a wealthy Oklahoma oilman.

Shortly after midnight on July 23, 1933, a call on the special kidnap line flashed on the FBI's switchboard. The operator switched the call to the home of Director Hoover.

The telephone awakened Hoover. He picked up the receiver and Mrs. Charles F. Urschel of Oklahoma City spilled out the story that her husband and a friend, Walter R. Jarrett, had been kidnaped only a few minutes earlier. She and her husband had been playing bridge with the Jarretts on the Urschels' screened porch when two armed men had appeared. "Which one of you is Mr. Urschel?" one gunman asked. When neither Urschel nor Jarrett replied, the kidnaper said, "Well, we'll take both of them." The gunman warned the women not to use the phone. But when Mrs. Urschel heard the kidnapers' car drive away, she called the FBI.

Hoover immediately ordered agents from the Oklahoma City FBI office to the Urschel home. Within an hour FBI agents were converging on Oklahoma City from other points. They were under orders to coöperate with the family, and to do nothing that would jeopardize the safe return of the oilman. It is the policy of the FBI not to advise a family whether ransom money should or should not be paid. Those were decisions for the family to make.

Jarrett, disheveled and shaken, returned to the Urschel home two hours after the kidnaping. He said the kidnapers drove some ten or twelve miles northeast of the city, took $50 from him, put him out of the car and then headed south with Urschel.

Four days later, J. G. Catlett, of Tulsa, Oklahoma, a friend of the Urschels, received a package containing four letters, one in Urschel's handwriting. Another was a typewritten letter addressed to E. E. Kirkpatrick of Oklahoma City, also a friend of the Urschels. This letter demanded $200,000 for the oilman's safe return. There were instructions to place a classified ad in the *Daily Oklahoman* if the price was to be met.

The innocent-looking ad appeared in the newspaper:

For Sale — 160 Acres Land, good five room house, deep well. Also Cows, Tools, Tractor, Corn and Hay. $3750 for quick sale . . . Terms . . . Box H-807.

Further instructions were received in a letter, and Kirkpatrick left Oklahoma City carrying a handbag stuffed with $200,000 in twenty-dollar notes. Orders were followed to the letter, but the FBI had a record of the serial numbers of the ransom bills.

Kirkpatrick registered at a hotel in Kansas City, Missouri, on July 30. He waited in his room for the telephone call which finally

came, giving him the rest of his instructions. Late in the afternoon
he took a cab to the LaSalle Hotel, stepped out and walked west
A stranger approached him and said, "I'll take that bag." Kirkpatrick protested that he had to have a message for Mrs. Urschel
The stranger said, "The title deeds to the farm will be delivered
within twelve hours." He took the bag and walked away.

Urschel arrived home the next night, unharmed but exhausted
He gave FBI agents the story of his kidnaping in amazing detail
After his friend Jarrett was put out of the car, he was blindfolded
About daylight, the kidnap car drove into a garage or barn, and
he was transferred to a larger car which he judged to be a Buick
or a Cadillac. He was placed in the back on the floor.

About three hours after changing automobiles they stopped at a
gas station, where a woman filled the tank without noticing any
thing unusual. "How are crop conditions?" one kidnaper asked

"The crops around here are burned up," she said, "although w
may make some broomcorn."

Their next stop was another garage or barn and a kidnape
remarked that it was 2:30 p.m. Urschel was given a ham sandwich
and coffee, and he remained in this place until nightfall. Then h
was taken on foot to a nearby house. Next day he was driven t
another house about twenty minutes from the first one. He knew
it was a farm or ranch house because he heard the noises of chicken
cackling and cows lowing. He heard water being drawn by bucket
from a well he judged to be northwest of the house. He drank from
a tin cup without a handle and the water had a mineral taste. I
was in this house that he wrote the letter to Catlett.

Handcuffed to a chain and blindfolded, Urschel was able t
learn on occasion from his captors the time of day. Each mornin
about 9:45 and each evening about 5:45 he heard a plane pass ove
the house. But on Sunday, July 30, there was a downpour of rai
and he didn't hear the morning plane. The next day he was drive
to a point near Norman, Oklahoma, and released.

FBI special agents studied Urschel's recollections and decide
that their best chance to locate the kidnapers' house was tied i
with the account of the rainstorm and the failure of the plane t
follow its usual flight course. The woman at the filling station ha

alked of a dry spell, so any area drenched by a recent rainfall was mportant. They began a systematic check of the air lines, coupled vith a study of meteorological reports.

They hit pay dirt. They found that on Sunday, July 30, an American Airways plane on the Fort Worth-Amarillo run had been orced to swing north from its usual course to avoid a rainstorm. J. S. Weather Bureau records disclosed that this general area had een suffering from a drought until the July 30 rains came. A little alculation showed that the morning plane leaving Fort Worth nd the afternoon plane leaving Amarillo would pass a point near 'aradise, Texas, at the approximate times recalled by Urschel.

They found the house described by Urschel. It was the ranch ome of Mr. and Mrs. R. G. Shannon, the stepfather and mother f Kathryn Kelly. And Kathryn Kelly was the wife of the notorius "Machine Gun" Kelly, who reputedly could knock walnuts off fence with his machine gun at twenty-five yards.

Urschel identified the Shannon home. There was the well, the n cup without a handle and the chain to which he had been handuffed. He could never forget the mineral taste in that water.

The Shannons confessed they had helped guard Urschel. And iey admitted that the kidnapers were Kelly and Albert L. Bates. The FBI men tracked Bates to Denver, where he was arrested. .elly and his wife were traced to a house in Memphis, Tennessee. 1 the early hours of September 26, 1933, FBI agents and Memphis olice raided the Kelly hideaway. Caught without a machine gun 1 his hands, Kelly cringed and pleaded, "Don't shoot, G-Men!" Kelly's nickname for the FBI's agents stuck with them for years.

The interstate character of gangster operations was underlined 1 the Urschel case. The oilman was kidnaped in Oklahoma and eld captive in Texas. The ransom was paid in Missouri. One of the idnapers was caught in Colorado, and the other in Tennessee.

Insistent demands continued to be made for federal action gainst criminals. As a result, Attorney General Cummings laid efore Congress a series of major bills aimed at giving the government greater leverage in the fight against crime. Congress quickly pproved the crime bills and in May and June 1934 President oosevelt signed them into law.

These laws opened new avenues to the FBI. Now it was a federal crime to assault or kill a federal officer, a federal offense to rob a federal bank. It was unlawful to flee to another state to avoid prosecution or giving testimony in certain cases. Carrying stolen property worth $5000 or more across a state line was a federal offense. On special occasions, FBI special agents had been authorized to carry weapons. Now agents were given full powers of arrest and full authority to be armed in carrying out their duties.

And then it was that the FBI, literally, went to war against the underworld.

JOHN HERBERT DILLINGER led a kill-crazy gang which swept through the Midwest from September 1933 until July 1934, leaving a trail of ten men murdered, seven men wounded, four banks robbed, three police arsenals plundered and three jails from which prisoners were freed.

Dillinger was wanted in Indiana for the murder of an East Chicago policeman, and police throughout the country were alerted to watch for him. He was recognized in Tucson, Arizona, and arrested with three members of his gang. The Tucson police found, among other odds and ends at the Dillinger hide-out, three submachine guns, two rifles mounted as machine guns, five bullet-proof vests and more than $25,000, part of which was loot from an East Chicago bank.

Dillinger was returned to Indiana and placed in the County Jail at Crown Point — a so-called escape-proof jail — to await trial for the East Chicago murder. But he escaped on March 3, 1934. He always claimed he frightened the guards with a wooden gun which he had fashioned with a razor blade in his cell. The red-faced guards said he had a real forty-five which someone had slipped him.

The fact remained that Dillinger did force a guard to open his cell door. Then he grabbed two machine guns, stole the sheriff's automobile and headed for Chicago. The instant he crossed the Indiana-Illinois state line, he violated a federal law — the National Motor Vehicle Theft Act, which prohibits transportation of a stolen motor vehicle across a state line. Until then, Dillinger had

iolated only state and local laws. But now the FBI had the right
nd the duty to go after him.

Dillinger jeered at "the law" after his jail break. He wrote his
ister not to worry about him; "I am having a lot of fun." Then he
dded:

> . . . (the reports) I had a real forty five Thats just a lot of hooey
> because they don't like to admit that I locked eight Deputys up
> with my wooden gun. I showed everyone the wooden gun after
> I got a hold of the machine guns and you should have seen *thire*
> faces. Ha! Ha! Ha! Pulling that off was worth ten years of my
> life. Ha! Ha!

As it happened, the escapade cost Dillinger a great deal more
an just ten years of his life. He had only a few more weeks to live
hen he wrote the letter.

On two occasions, FBI agents thought they had Dillinger
apped. Each time he escaped in a barrage of machine-gun fire.
ut the circle was tightening. On the first of June Hoover called
pecial Agent Samuel P. Cowley into his office. Cowley was a
efty, thirty-four-year-old Utah lawyer who had served as a mis-
onary in the Mormon Church before he joined the FBI. He was
 take charge of the Dillinger search. Hoover told him: "Stay on
illinger. Go anywhere the trail takes you. Take him alive if you
n but protect yourself."

Cowley's search led him to Chicago. Dillinger was reported to
 in hiding there, recovering from a doctor's attempt to disguise
s features by plastic surgery. Cowley and Melvin Purvis, Special
gent in Charge of the Chicago office, worked closely with two
st Chicago policemen, Captain Timothy O'Neill and Sergeant
artin Zarkovich, in running down the scores of tips from people
ho thought they had recognized Dillinger.

The break in the case came on July 21. O'Neill and Zarkovich
ought a dark-haired, middle-aged woman to the FBI. She was
na Cumpanas, a Rumanian who had come to the United States
1914. Now she was known as Mrs. Anna Sage, and she wanted
make a deal. The Immigration and Naturalization Service

wanted to deport her as an undesirable alien because she was th
madam of a bawdyhouse. Her proposition was this: she would lea
the FBI to Dillinger — but she wanted a promise that she woul
receive a reward and also that something would be done to perm
her to remain in the United States.

The reward was promised. And Purvis told Ana Cumpanas th
her coöperation would be called to the attention of officials wh
handled deportation matters.

Ana Cumpanas disclosed that John Dillinger was planning
take her and his friend Polly Hamilton to a movie the next ev
ning. She wasn't sure which theater. She would let them know th
next day. How would other FBI agents, who hadn't seen he
identify her? Ana said she would be dressed in red.

With a squad of agents and East Chicago policemen, a trap w
planned for Dillinger.

Ana Cumpanas kept her word. She telephoned early in the ev
ning of July 22. The theater would be either the Marbro or t
Biograph. This meant that both places had to be covered.

These were Cowley's final instructions, as one agent recall
them in his report:

> Gentlemen, you all know the character of John Dillinger. There
> will be an undetermined element of danger in taking him. It is
> hoped that he can be taken alive, if possible, and without injury to
> any agent . . . yet he must be taken. Do not unnecessarily endange
> your own lives. If Dillinger offers any resistance each man will be
> for himself.

Dillinger decided to go to the Biograph, where Clark Gable w
playing in *Manhattan Melodrama*. The FBI men and the poli
men recognized him when he entered the theater with Po
Hamilton and Ana Cumpanas, who was to become known as "T
Woman in Red." Despite plastic surgery, the outlaw was identifi
beyond doubt. Cowley called Hoover, who was pacing the libr
at his home in Washington. The decision was made to take I
linger as he came out of the theater, rather than risk a gun ba
inside the crowded show house.

By prearrangement, Purvis lit a cigar when the trio emerged.
The trap began to close. Dillinger must have sensed something. He
glanced over his shoulder and saw an agent moving toward him.
He darted toward an alley, clawing a pistol from his pants pocket.
But before he could get his gun into action, three FBI agents fired
five shots. Dillinger pitched on his face. The chase was over.

Cowley was promoted to the rank of inspector for his part in
Dillinger's capture, but he didn't live long enough to receive the
full measure of recognition from his new title. Four months later,
Cowley and Special Agent Herman E. Hollis unexpectedly ran
onto two of Dillinger's old gang driving along an Illinois highway.
They were John Paul Chase and "Baby Face" Nelson, a killer who
had been labeled by the press as "Public Enemy Number 1." Nelson's wife, Helen, was with him in the car. The FBI agents and
the gangsters jumped from their cars, and in a gun battle Cowley
and Hollis were killed and Nelson wounded fatally. When Nelson
died a few hours later, Mrs. Nelson and Chase laid his body in a
ditch beside a highway.

In a curious revolt against reason, some people regarded Dillinger and Nelson as the heroes in these dramas, and the FBI men
as the villains. One Virginia newspaper editor assailed the FBI's
killing of Dillinger as the work of cowards who were afraid to
arrest him in the theater. "Any brave man," said the editorial,
"would have walked down the aisle and arrested Dillinger. . . .
Federal agents are mostly cowards."

Dillinger's girl friend, Evelyn Frechette, joined a carnival side
show. She told gaping crowds of her life with Dillinger. "He liked
to dance and he liked to hunt," she said. "He — excuse me if you've
heard this one — was a good shot. . . . He liked music but he never
sang. I think he liked gravy better than anything else. He liked
bread and gravy." Audiences heard the bread-and-gravy revelation
with open-mouthed wonder.

One of the more mawkish of the stories was an interview with
"Baby Face" Nelson's pretty widow. The story said, in part: " 'Baby
Face' Nelson died in the arms of his wife with a smile on his lips,
but with tears in his eyes for his two young children. . . ."

The widow was described by Nelson's sister as "one of the most

devoted mothers I have ever known," despite the fact that she an
Nelson had abandoned their children, who knew their mothe
only as an infrequent visitor called "Aunt Helen." A bare mentio
was made of the murdered Cowley and Hollis.

The sympathy that poured out for the dead gangsters outrage
J. Edgar Hoover's Presbyterian concept of right and wrong. H
referred to criminals as "scum from the boiling pot of the unde
world," "craven beasts" and "vermin." He took to the platform
of clubs, universities and conventions to hammer on the theme tha
criminals and those who associated with them were public enemie
He criticized "venal politicians" and lawyers who were allies (
the underworld. He spoke out against crooked police, and again
those who abused the states' parole systems by turning habitu:
criminals loose to commit more crimes.

Behind Hoover's bitter assaults on lax law enforcement was h
knowledge of gang operations, such as those of the notorio
Barker-Karpis gang, whose worst members were paroled convict

In the parade of criminals, Alvin Karpis in time was labele
"Public Enemy Number 1" — wanted for the $100,000 extortio
kidnaping of William Hamm, Jr., of St. Paul, Minnesota, and c
local charges of murder. Hoover frequently referred to Karpis as
"rat," and finally this riled Karpis. He sent word to Hoover that I
intended to kill him.

Hoover issued instructions that when agents received inform
tion on Karpis's whereabouts he was to be notified so that he mig
take charge of the case. FBI agents tagged Karpis as "the Bos
man."

Hoover thought his chance had come in March 1936. He r
ceived word in New York that Karpis was hiding somewhere
Hot Springs, Arkansas. He flew by special plane to Washingto
where he waited for further news. But the disappointing rep
came that Karpis had escaped — apparently tipped off by loc
police that the G-Men were closing in.

Hoover was again in New York on April 30, when he receiv
word that Karpis had been trailed to New Orleans, where he w
living in an apartment house on Canal Street. He flew to Ne
Orleans with a squad of special agents. The local police were

notified. No chances were taken on a "leak" flushing Karpis into flight.

As Hoover and his men approached the apartment by automobile, Karpis and a companion unexpectedly walked out the door. For a few tense seconds the FBI cars were blocked by a man riding a white horse, then the horse moved out of the way. Karpis climbed into his automobile. Hoover ran to the left side of the car and Assistant Director Earl Connelley to the right side. Hoover reached into the car and grabbed Karpis before he could reach for a rifle on the back seat.

"Put the handcuffs on him," Hoover ordered. But no one had remembered to bring handcuffs. An agent pulled off his necktie and tied Karpis's hands behind him. He was put aboard a special plane to be flown to St. Paul, Minnesota.

The plane had been air-borne a short time when Hoover noticed that Karpis's face was white. "Are you airsick?" Hoover asked.

"Go ahead and do it!" Karpis blurted. "Get it over with."

"What are you talking about?"

Karpis looked at Hoover wildly. "I know what you're going to do. You guys are going to throw me out of this plane and then say it was an accident."

"Don't be a fool," Hoover snapped. "We don't do things like that. You're going to stand trial. Nobody's going to hurt you while you're with us."

At Kansas City, where the plane stopped to refuel, one headline in a morning paper read: "Karpis Robs Bank in Michigan." Karpis laughed. "This is one time I've got a perfect alibi."

Thus the boss of the G-Men made his first arrest. Karpis was given a life sentence for the Hamm kidnaping.

Now the G-Men were glamorized by a wave of publicity comparable to the later "Davy Crockett" craze. Hollywood turned from gangster films to pictures of the G-Men who always got their man. Magazines and newspapers got on the bandwagon. Anything Hoover did became news, even when he went to a night club or attended a boxing match.

But while public opinion was on Hoover's side, he became a special target for attack, also. He began to be assailed as a headline hunter. One critic sneered at the FBI's use of five or ten agents to seal off avenues of escape while arresting a criminal, saying Hoover was using "a sledge hammer to knock a fly off the baby's nose." But another writer said: "We Americans no sooner set up a hero than we prepare to knock him down. It is working out that way with J. Edgar Hoover." And so it was.

At this same time a report gained wide circulation that "important New Dealers" were after Hoover's scalp, and that he might be ousted because "liberals high in the Administration regard the vaunting power he has built up with strong misgivings." Such rumors failed to note that Hoover had strong supporters in the White House inner circle: they were Steve Early, Roosevelt's Press Secretary; Major General Edwin M. Watson, Secretary to the President; and, most influential of all, Franklin D. Roosevelt himself.

When the assaults of the 1930's spent themselves Hoover was still solidly entrenched in his position.

4. *Behind the Scenes*

T HE 1930's also brought some important developments behind the scenes at the FBI.

The FBI Identification Division, the FBI Laboratory and the FBI Academy were all officially established during those years

Centuries ago, men recognized the distinctive patterns in finger-prints. In ancient China, a thumbprint in clay served as an identifying seal on legal documents. By 1902, England's Scotland Yard had begun to use fingerprints as a means of criminal identification. Soon after that the fingerprint system began to gain popularity in the United States as well. New York State adopted it for Sing Sing in 1903. In 1904 the Department of Justice authorized the warden at Leavenworth to "expend a sum not to exceed $60" for installing the system.

Still there was need for a centralized bureau of identification — a bureau which would serve all law-enforcement agencies and institutions, federal, state and local. Over the years there was much dispute about where this bureau should be located. But Congress finally and decisively settled the dispute in June 1930 with a law approving a permanent Division of Identification and Information within the FBI.

Identification work increased rapidly. The number of law-enforcement agencies coöperating in the program increased to 4712 in 1932 and climbed to more than 12,000 by 1956. Hoover made the program international through agreements with European police — thus giving police a check on crooks wanted in other countries.

The FBI's identification files began to balloon in numbers in 1933, when the Civil Service Commission turned over more than 140,000 fingerprints of government employes and job applicants. At this time a Civil Identification Section was set up, separate from the criminal files, and the FBI encouraged citizens to have their prints filed away as a protective measure.

While the FBI Identification Division became one of the strongest links in the chain of coöperation between federal and local law-enforcement officers, it also proved to be a protector of civil rights in many cases. In one instance, in 1937, the FBI received a letter from a Tennessee police department enclosing the photograph of what purported to be a latent fingerprint. In the same envelope were the fingerprints of a suspect. FBI experts spotted a fraud. The alleged latent fingerprint was actually a photograph of one inked impression of the suspect's fingerprint card. Someone in the police office had photographed one of the suspect's fingerprints on his card, and then had tried to palm it off as a fingerprint found at the scene of the crime. Had the trick succeeded, the FBI would have linked the suspect with the crime.

There is a never-ending drama in the FBI's work of matching fingerprints with people. In 1955, more than 13,600 fugitives from justice were identified from fingerprints. The work of the Identification Division goes on around the clock. When police need extraordinarily quick identification, they use a machine known as a Speedphoto Transceiver, by which prints may be transmitted direct to the Bureau. Within a matter of minutes, the FBI can identify the prints if they are on file.

As we have seen, the early 1930's were a nightmare in the history of crime in America — a nightmare in which criminals had better weapons, faster automobiles, greater range of movement and far more political influence than the poverty-stricken local police.

This was the period when demands came for a national police force which would take over the job of the local police. Hoover, however, fought for the principle that law enforcement in a democracy was primarily the responsibility of local officers and not the federal government. He believed the answer to the crime problem lay in taking police work out of politics, and in giving all policemen scientific training in law enforcement.

At that time, in the country as a whole, most rookie policemen received no training. They were simply given a badge and a gun and told to go to work. Few cities had any training program for police officers, and generally there was an attitude that none was needed. One chief of police commanding a force of more than a hundred men dismissed the idea of scientific police training with the curious comment: ". . . all that a policeman need know [is] the Ten Commandments."

In 1934, Hoover conferred on the problem with Attorney General Cummings, and together they carried a proposal for a national police-training school before the Attorney General's Crime Conference, which met in December. Hoover told the conference "The value of adequate training has already been proven in the training schools maintained by our Bureau for its own personnel

With but slight readjustment, these training facilities already established could be extended to the local law-enforcement agencies of the country."

The conference recommended that the school be established, and on July 29, 1935, the first class of twenty-three police officers gathered for twelve weeks of study. This was the beginning of the FBI's now famous National Academy.

In its first twenty-one years, the Academy gave instruction to more than 3200 officers of the law. Out of this number, more than 28 percent climbed to positions as executive heads of their departments back home.

The number of graduates is small when compared with the total number of police officers in the United States — some 250,000. But it is a basic purpose of the Academy that each graduate be qualified to organize police schools in his home town, and to share the knowledge he has gained with the other members of his force.

An Academy student is nominated by the head of his department. He must be not more than fifty years old and he must be in good physical condition. He must have the capacity to absorb information and then pass this information on to others. He must be a man with a good reputation, and a full-time officer, of at least two years' experience with a city, county or state law-enforcement agency. This agency, or the student himself, pays all expenses for transportation, food and lodging during the session.

The Academy has been a success from the beginning. Applications have poured in at the ratio of about seven applications for each student admitted.

Two twelve-week sessions are held each year — sessions in which some eighty students attend classes from nine to five, five days a week. After-dinner hours are taken up with the typing of notes and study. The Academy's regular instructors are well-trained FBI teachers. Other FBI special agents are available to teach highly specialized courses. Lectures are given by educators, criminologists, lawyers and others. The subject matter ranges from the proper method of keeping police records to the lifting of a fingerprint from the scene of a crime, police photography, and the calculation of an automobile's speed from skid marks.

Some graduates have returned to their home towns to find fellow officers resentful and unwilling to coöperate in starting training schools. But in other cases, graduates have found their colleagues eager to learn new techniques. They have managed to overcome obstacles and get training schools under way. Civic clubs, business firms and universities have helped.

Perhaps more than any other single program, the FBI's National Academy brought closer coöperation between the FBI and local police. The FBI agents and the students came to know each other and to have a better appreciation of the others' problems. Local officers saw the FBI men in an entirely different light — and the FBI's agents gained a new perspective by looking at the local men's problems.

There was, for example, a heavy-set officer from the sagebrush country, who came to the Academy and refused to associate in off hours with either the instructors or the other students. He was overweight when he began training, and the pounds dropped off at an alarming rate. But he didn't complain. At mealtime, and at night, he went off by himself. He became the Academy "lone wolf."

At the close of the session, he came to the office of the training director and blurted out his story: "I know you all think I'm pretty strange, acting like I have. Well, here's the reason for it. I had to mortgage my house to get enough money to come here and at the same time take care of my family. After I bought my railroad ticket and took out the money for the hotel, I had thirty-five cents a day for food. I couldn't afford to eat with the others. That's why I went off by myself."

The FBI man said, "But why didn't you tell me? We could have worked out something."

The officer shrugged. "Pride, I reckon. I guess I was ashamed to say anything. But it's been worth it. I figure I'm a better man for what I've done." He shook hands and walked out.

This, of course, is a side of the policeman which the public seldom sees. Hoover told a visitor of this incident and said: "I've seen this kind of thing so often it makes me sick. They ask for law enforcement which will be honest, efficient and intelligent. And then they offer a starting salary to a rookie policeman as low as

$1770 while a messenger for the federal government starts at $2960. In one Eastern city, they give their policemen a starting salary of $3725 — and the starting pay for a garbage collector is $3950. It's an outrageous insult."

ANOTHER division of the Bureau, the FBI Laboratory, founded in 1932, has become a vital institution in American law enforcement.

In the quarter of a century since the Lab started, the FBI's scientific tools for use against crime have become more and more complex and effective. For example, specks of dirt no larger than a pinhead, clinging to a man's shoe, may place him at the scene of a crime. This might be done by the Lab in this way: the speck of dirt from a suspect's shoe and another piece of dirt from the scene of the crime are placed in one of the FBI-constructed twin furnaces. As the controlled temperature rises in the furnaces, the two specks of dirt undergo physical changes which are recorded automatically on a graph. If the graph lines are identical, it means the two specks of dirt underwent changes at precisely the same moments under the same degrees of temperature; and this sameness shows that the two specks were composed of similar mineral elements — and, therefore, could have come from the same place.

Among the important laboratory aids to crime fighting are the "reference files," which include type specimens from virtually every make of American typewriter; animal hairs, including wallaby and wombat; rubber heels and tire prints; samples of the paints used by automobile manufacturers; and about 42,000 different records of watermarks in paper. Day after day, these files provide the clues which help to link a suspect with a crime.

The FBI's scientists and technicians have done a tremendous amount of research on human hair, because hair is so frequently important in investigating crimes. The FBI Laboratory can take hair from an unknown source and determine the person's race and indications of age and sex.

One stiff challenge to the laboratory was in the making when a crack Navy test pilot climbed into a strange-looking aircraft and hurtled into the stratosphere. The sleek craft was an advanced jet fighter still in the secret stage of development and it had to be proved out in a hundred different ways. Sensitive instruments built into the plane automatically recorded pressures, speeds and a vast amount of vital information.

And then, suddenly, something went wrong. The aircraft went crazy in that crazy world beyond the sonic barrier, where forces buffet a plane at times with maniacal fury. The pilot's voice came clearly to those listening in by radio. "Going to have to leave it!" he said. His words trailed off into a gibberish of sound. And then there was silence.

Searchers found the pilot's body and bits of the plane. But no one could unscramble his last words as the ship screamed toward earth. Yet this babble of sound might provide a priceless clue to what had gone wrong in the plane or why the pilot had not bailed out.

The recording was finally sent to the FBI Laboratory, where specialists went to work on it. Their first steps were to prepare an exact working copy of the recording tape in order to preserve the original, and to determine the precise speed at which the original recording had been made.

One of those who helped untangle the mystery recalled the highly technical laboratory work in these words:

> We found an extremely high noise level in the background of the pilot's voice. I suppose it was due to the screaming dive of the plane. In a series of tests, we were able to filter out the noise frequencies above and below the normal voice frequencies and at the same time amplify the voice. This improved the signal, but the pilot's final words still were not intelligible.
>
> We tried another tack. We transferred the recording to a disk and in this way we could vary the speed at will. You probably have slowed down a phonograph record and noticed that the pitch of the music was lowered. When the record was turned too fast you got a high, squeaky sound. In either case, the sound was distorted.
>
> We used an instrument called a Sona-Stretcher which permitted us to speed up or slow down the record without changing the pitch. We were able to make the voice speak slower without changing

pitch and this again improved the signal. But even though we knew we were getting close, the words still were not clear enough.

Then we began manipulating the speed during the actual transcription — that is, speeding it up and slowing it down. This was the solution and finally we had the pilot's voice reproduced.

Excitement spread through the Laboratory. Technicians gathered to hear the completed recording — the voice, filtered out of all the sounds of a plane in its last dive, saying:

"Can't bail out . . . can't . . . bail . . . out!"

These few terrible words were the clue which led to the discovery of a defect in the plane — intelligence which meant that the lives of other brave men could be saved.

Another little-recognized result of the FBI Laboratory's work has been the sifting of the innocent from the guilty.

Hardly a day passes in which the FBI Laboratory doesn't make a report saying in effect: "This bullet was not fired from this gun." This means in many, many cases that someone, somewhere, is no longer a suspect.

Circumstantial evidence can sometimes play tragic tricks. Such was the case on the night of February 13, 1950, when Mrs. Robert F. Parks ran from her home at Luray, Virginia. Near collapse, she pounded on the door of a neighbor. Her husband, she said, had been shot. Luray police were called. They found Parks, a former Army captain, lying dead in a bedroom which opened onto the dining room. A bullet had passed through his right arm and smashed through his heart, lodging in his left side. In the dining room, an automatic pistol was lying against the wall opposite the bedroom door. A cartridge case was jammed in the gun.

There were no powder burns and it was obvious, because of the direction from which the bullet entered Parks's body, that he couldn't possibly have held the weapon himself.

When Mrs. Parks was composed enough to talk, she told police: "I was standing in the kitchen when I heard the shot. I ran to the bedroom and Bob was standing there. He said, 'Honey, the gun backfired.' And then he fell."

Police learned that the Parkses had had violent arguments.

Witnesses said that two or three weeks before the shooting Mrs. Parks had telephoned San Francisco. They heard her ask someone to send her a bus ticket. The circumstantial evidence all was against her. She was arrested and charged with murder.

But the investigation continued. On the third day, an alert policeman looked at a metal grille over a hot-air duct in the bedroom doorway. It had a bright dent in it. A bit of the brown paint had been knocked off. The police wondered if the dent could have been caused by the gun found in the dining room. There was brown paint on the rear of the gun slide. They decided to send the grille, gun, bullet and cartridge case to the FBI Laboratory.

The gun picked up in the dining room was the death weapon. This was proved by an examination of the fatal bullet. The brown paint on the grille was similar to the paint on the gun slide. It was found that the gun could be fired when dropped on the rear part of the slide and the hammer.

The indentations in the grille matched marks made by the rear sight and knurling of the hammer. And when the rear sight and hammer were placed against the markings on the grille, it became evident that the gun in this position would have been pointing in the direction of the bedroom where Parks stood.

The findings pointed to the strong possibility that Parks shot himself accidentally. Investigators reasoned that Parks, in a fit of temper, had thrown the gun against the grille; it had fired; the slide had jammed against the grille, preventing ejection of the cartridge; and the gun had skittered across the floor of the dining room. The murder charge against Mrs. Parks was dismissed.

As one FBI scientist said, "There's a new, challenging problem each day in this business. I guess that's the reason I stay with it."

5. *The Enemy Within*

F ORCES of fear and subversion were on the march in the summer of 1936. In Germany, the one-time paper hanger, Adolf Hitler, talked of peace while he planned for war. The Japanese war lords stood astride Korea and Manchuria. Mussolini was carving out his empire in Africa. Spain was torn cruelly by civil war. In Soviet Russia, Stalin was continuing his blood purges, adding new victims to the millions already liquidated by guns and starvation. And in the United States, nine million jobless walked the streets while the reactionary forces of Fascism and Communism were enlisting recruits to their causes.

This, in bare outline, was the gloomy state of the world on the morning of August 24, when FBI Director J. Edgar Hoover left his headquarters to go to a White House conference, the first of three which would remain secret until this writing.

Hoover was shown into Franklin D. Roosevelt's office. The President smiled. "Sit down, Edgar," he said. "I called you over because I want you to do a job for me and it must be confidential."

Roosevelt said he had become increasingly concerned about the activities of Communists and other subversive groups. He felt that he should have more information and he wondered if he could be provided with a broad intelligence picture of Communist and Fascist activities alike in relation to our political and economic life.

"Mr. President," Hoover said, "there is no government agency compiling such general intelligence. Of course, membership in the Communist Party is not a violation of the law and we have no specific authority to make such general investigations."

The President said, "It seems to me there must be some way this could be done, Edgar. Have you any suggestions?"

"Yes," Hoover said. "The FBI has authority to undertake an investigation for the Department of State when requested by the Secretary of State. We could make the investigation should the Secretary request it and the Attorney General approve his request."

At Roosevelt's request Hoover returned to the White House at 1:45 p.m. the next day to meet with Secretary of State Cordell Hull. Roosevelt again stated his belief that the FBI should undertake a quiet investigation of Communist and Fascist activities.

"Edgar says he can do this," the President said to Hull, "but the request must come from you to make it legal."

The tall, distinguished Secretary of State from the hills of Tennessee turned to Hoover and said: "Go ahead and investigate the —— !" The President threw back his head and laughed.

Roosevelt discussed at length the international character of Communism and Fascism. He said that he didn't like the reports that Constantine Oumansky (counselor for the Soviet Embassy) had been running around the country, spending very little time in Washington. He thought the State Department had a right and a duty to know what was going on in such cases.

"Do you want the request in writing?" Hull asked.

Roosevelt said no, he wanted the matter to be handled confidentially. He thought the FBI should coördinate this investigation with the War Department's Military Intelligence Division, the Office of Naval Intelligence and the State Department.

One week later, on September 1, final arrangements were made. Hoover sent confidential letters to his special agents in charge on September 5. Attorney General Homer Cummings, who had been out of Washington, studied Hoover's report on the White House conferences on his return and approved the investigation.

So the FBI, quietly and without publicly disclosing the source of its authority, began to check on Communist activities and to chart the rise of Fascist movements in the United States. These investigations would later stir up a hornets' nest of criticism to the effect that the FBI was meddling in the political beliefs of persons merely because they held views contrary to those held by Hoover.

More than three years before Roosevelt ordered this intelligence operation, the FBI had at times been requested to look into pro-Nazi activities. Under such authorization an investigation was made, a report was submitted, and that ended the matter until another request was made.

A curious chain of events had led to the first of these limited investigations. The German Embassy had received a letter in March 1933 signed "Daniel Stern," saying that, unless President Roosevelt rebuked the Hitler government for its outrages against Jews, then, "I shall go to Germany and assassinate Hitler." The German Ambassador, F. W. von Prittwitz, enclosed the letter in a communication to Secretary Hull requesting an investigation. Hull sent the letters to the Department of Justice and the FBI was instructed to investigate.

The German Ambassador probably wished in the weeks to come

that he had never written to Secretary Hull, because his request was a diplomatic fumble. It gave the FBI an oblique look into the doings of the pro-Nazi organizations in the course of seeking "Daniel Stern," who, incidentally, never was found.

During the late 1920's and early 1930's, pro-Fascist agitation in the United States had been confined largely to propaganda. But as the situation steadily deteriorated in Europe and Asia, the propagandists were joined by espionage agents. From 1933 to 1937 the FBI investigated an average of 35 espionage cases a year. In fiscal 1938, the total jumped to 250.

The first major espionage case in this period started when War Department Intelligence received a warning from an American military attaché in London that an effort would be made by an unknown foreign agent to steal our secret East Coast defense plans. The FBI was called in on the case.

Soon after this warning, New York City detectives and State Department special agents arrested a man who had attempted to obtain American passport forms by representing himself as Secretary of State Hull in a telephone call to the New York Passport Bureau. The man was identified as Guenther Gustave Rumrich. A deserter from the U. S. Army in 1936, Rumrich had entered the German espionage service. A note found in his pocket showed him to be the agent who would attempt to steal the coastal-defense plans.

Rumrich was turned over to the FBI, and revealed to agents a Nazi plot for obtaining information on America's military strength and the secrets of the new aircraft carrier, the *Enterprise*. Unfortunately, the story of Rumrich's arrest was leaked to the newspapers and his confederates scattered. Eighteen persons were indicted, but only four were convicted. The others were listed as fugitives from justice.

The FBI worked with the Office of Naval Intelligence to nail another spy, John Semer Farnsworth, a graduate of the U. S. Naval Academy who was dishonorably discharged from the Navy in 1927 and then became a spy for the Japanese from 1933 through 1936. The first tip on Farnsworth's activities came from Fulton Lewis, Jr., a newsman who heard and believed Farnsworth's drunken talk of a spy career. Rather than expose the case as an exclusive story, he took the facts to the FBI — a practice followed by other reporters over the years when security was involved. Farnsworth, the FBI learned, received some $20,000 for giving the Japanese stolen Navy blueprints, code books and other information.

Then columnist Heywood Broun caused a flurry in March 1937 when he wrote that the activities of the German-American Bund had reached a point where "actual recruiting is going on, and there is already a considerable body of storm troops here in America."

The FBI was directed to study the Bund. A lengthy report was submitted to the Department of Justice early in 1938, but the investigation came to a dead end. The Department apparently decided that, while the Bund's teachings tended to be subversive, they did not violate any law of the United States.

Meanwhile, a fight blew up over the question of primary jurisdiction in investigations of subversion. This was settled when President Roosevelt sent a confidential directive to Cabinet members on June 26, 1939, which said that the investigation of all espionage, counterespionage and sabotage matters was to be controlled and handled only by the FBI and the Intelligence Divisions of the War Department and the Navy. The President declared that other government agencies should report subversive activities to the nearest FBI office.

This directive sorted out the lines of responsibility. The decision came none too quickly, because on August 24 Germany and Russia signed their ten-year nonaggression pact, and on September 1 German panzer divisions drove into Poland. France and Great Britain declared war on Germany on September 3.

On September 6, President Roosevelt disclosed publicly that the FBI had been instructed by him "to take charge of investigative work in matters relating to espionage, sabotage, and violations of the neutrality regulations." But for overseas intelligence operations there were still no clearly defined areas of responsibility. The pressing need for a decision in this field grew more evident as the months passed. Finally an agreement was worked out which, roughly, gave the Navy responsibility for intelligence coverage in the Pacific; gave the Army responsibility for coverage in Europe, Africa and the Canal Zone; and gave the FBI responsibility in the Western Hemisphere, except for Panama.

Early in 1940, the FBI stage-managed a strange counterespionage drama which began when William Sebold, a naturalized American, returned from a trip to his native Germany. Sebold disclosed to the FBI that the Gestapo had threatened injury to his relatives — his grandfather was a Jew — unless he returned to the States as a spy. He had agreed and they had taught him how to use a short-wave radio, supplied him with a secret code and given him instructions to pass on to other German agents in the United States.

Sebold played his role so well that a ring of spies in America was lured into a carefully set trap. First the FBI arranged for Sebold to send a message advising the Gestapo that he had arrived safely. Then FBI engineers built a short-wave radio station at Centerport, Long Island. It was registered as an amateur station just in case any radio "hams" became suspicious. At 7:50 p.m. on May 20, a contact was made with the Gestapo station in Hamburg, Germany. A flow of messages began which gradually led the FBI to the largest spy ring to be uncovered before Pearl Harbor.

Each message transmitted from the Long Island station, which was manned by FBI agents, contained enough authentic information to be convincing. The Germans never suspected the hoax.

The FBI had established Sebold in a mid-Manhattan office after certain "props" had been installed. A mirror on the wall reflected the image of anyone sitting in the chair by Sebold's desk — but in the adjoining room this mirror became a window through which agents took movies. Hidden microphones recorded each spoken word. On the desk was a clock (and behind it a calendar), so the movies showed the precise time and date when Sebold had visitors.

German agents drifted in and out of the office to receive instructions from Sebold and to turn over messages for transmission to Germany. Among the callers was Fritz Duquesne, an adventurer and German agent whose spy career went back to the early 1900's. Duquesne was particularly interested in sending information to Germany on war materials, ship movements to and from England, aircraft production and the delivery of aircraft to Britain.

This game of cat-and-mouse continued until the FBI was certain the entire espionage ring was known. Then agents closed in. Thirty-three persons were convicted, including the suave Duquesne. "It was like shooting fish in a barrel," one agent said.

Meantime, the FBI was making preparations for a wartime emergency — just in case. At the request of the Army and Navy, the FBI surveyed more than 2200 key industrial plants in the United States in addition to arsenals and aircraft factories. Ways of tightening security were recommended. Methods of sabotage were studied and preventive measures outlined. A team of FBI special agents was dispatched to England in 1940 to study British civil defense and the security lessons learned in the Battle of Britain.

The FBI was also keeping a watch on the activities of German, Italian and Japanese consular officials as well as the officials of the Soviet Union. The FBI gave the Administration evidence that German and Italian consular offices throughout the country were being used as centers of propaganda and espionage, and in June 1941 the State Department ordered these offices closed.

6. *The FBI Goes to War*

ON SUNDAY morning, December 7, 1941, the bombs were still falling on Pearl Harbor when the Honolulu Special Agent in Charge, Robert L. Shivers, called the FBI Headquarters in Washington. It was about 2:30 p.m. there. The telephone girl at Head-quarters switched the urgent call to the FBI's private line to New York City, where J. Edgar Hoover had gone for the week-end. Then she put in a call to Griffith Stadium, where Assistant to the Director Edward A. Tamm and other top FBI officials were watching a pro football game.

Tamm reached the telephone in time to hear Shivers tell Hoover, "The Japanese are bombing Pearl Harbor. No doubt about it — it's war. You may be able to hear the explosions yourself. Listen!" Over the telephone Hoover and Tamm heard the crash of bombs.

Hoover ordered Shivers and Tamm to put into effect immediately the war plans which had been worked out months before; then he sped to La Guardia Field to catch a plane to Washington.

Two days earlier, Hoover had instructed his agents to be ready at any time for "the immediate apprehension of Japanese aliens in your district who have been recommended for custodial detention." Now the whole FBI organization was alerted. But Hoover and his men couldn't move on this job until President Roosevelt had issued an emergency proclamation and Attorney General Francis Biddle had signed directives giving the FBI authority to act.

Quietly the FBI had been assembling a list of aliens who were likely to prove most dangerous in time of war. The list included some 770 Japanese. FBI field offices knew precisely where these people could be found.

When President Roosevelt ordered the detention of enemy aliens that Sunday evening and Biddle signed the necessary papers, an urgent message went over the FBI teletype system. Across the nation and in Hawaii, Alaska and Puerto Rico, FBI agents began the roundup of Japanese, which was to be followed the next day by the arrest of German and Italian enemy aliens.

The roundup was a remarkable performance on the part of agents and local police squads trained by the FBI in anticipation of the emergency. Careful advance preparations made it possible to take into custody 3846 enemy aliens in the first seventy-two hours of the war with no violence. In sharp contrast to World War I days, machinery existed for each arrested alien to have a hearing before a civilian board and to be represented by counsel.

Hoover ordered the FBI on a twenty-four-hour schedule. Annual leaves were canceled. Protective guards were placed at the Japanese Embassy and consulates. FBI offices were instructed to alert industries with war contracts to be on guard against espionage or sabotage.

EVEN as the oily black clouds of destruction mushroomed above the shattered fleet at Pearl Harbor, a thin spire of smoke was rising from the yard of the Japanese Consulate in Honolulu. Consul General Nagao Kita and his Vice-Consul, Atojiro Okuda, were burning the Consulate's secret code books and the messages which had passed between Kita and Foreign Minister Togo in those last days before treachery reached its climax.

Behind the curtain of diplomatic immunity Nagao Kita had supplied Tokyo with a running account of last-minute ship movements in and out of Pearl Harbor. And now that the blow was struck, he was trying to destroy the evidence.

But paper in bulk burns slowly. While the flames at the Consulate were being fed, Special Agent in Charge Shivers asked the Honolulu Police Department to place a guard at the Consulate. The guard saw the papers being burned. He rushed in and grabbed a code book and a bundle of messages from the protesting Japanese.

The papers were turned over to Shivers, who gave them to the Navy to decode, along with Consulate messages obtained from the commercial communications companies. When Shivers saw the uncoded messages, he exclaimed, "If we'd only had these earlier!" One of the messages read:

FROM: KITA   3 December, 1941
TO: FOREIGN MINISTER, TOKYO

Re signals I wish to simplify communications as follows:
1. *Code*
    1. Battle force, including scouting force, are about to put to sea —
    2. Several aircraft carriers plan to put to sea
    3. All battle force has sailed 1st-3rd dates inc.
    4. Several aircraft carriers have sailed (1st to 3rd)

5. All aircraft carriers have sailed (1st to 3rd)

6. All battle force have sailed, 4th-6th dates inc.

7. Several aircraft carriers have sailed (4th to 6th)

8. All aircraft carriers have sailed (4th to 6th)

2. *Signal*

Light in Lanikai beach house at night —

One light from 8 p.m. to 9 p.m. indicates "1." From 9 p.m. to 10 p.m. indicates "2." The below signals until midnight, in order to indicate 3 and 4. Two lights, according to the time, indicates 5, 6, 7, 8. When not in accordance with (lights) above 1 full automobile headlight and one half indicates 1, 2, 3, 4. Two full lights indicate 5, 6, 7, 8.

2. On the Lanikai coast during daytime from 8 a.m. until noon every hour 1 piece linen cloth (sheet) indicates 1, 2, 3, 4. Two pieces linen cloth indicate 5, 6, 7, 8.

3. In Lanikai bay during daytime in front of harbor (offing) a star boat with one star on sail indicates 1, 2, 3, 4; a star and "III" indicates 5, 6, 7, 8.

4. Light in dormer window of Kalama house from 7 p.m. to 1 a.m. every hour indicates 3, 4, 5, 6, 7, 8. . . .

Clearly, Kita had arranged for someone to signal Japanese submarines and give them information on the American fleet. The finger of suspicion pointed to Otto Kuehn as Kita's confederate because Kuehn had a house at Lanikai, a house at Kalama with a dormer window and a boat with a star on the sail.

Otto Kuehn, a German national, had first come to the FBI's attention in 1939 because of persistent rumors that he had an abnormally large income for a man with no known business connection. He had once been a member of the Nazi Party. The FBI had begun to suspect that Kuehn's income had come from Japanese sources in Berlin. Still, there was no tangible evidence of espionage until the Consulate messages had been translated.

Then Kuehn confessed. He admitted he had originated the code for signaling to the submarines, but he claimed it was never used so far as he knew. When he gave it to Kita he had advised the Consulate that there were seven battleships, six cruisers, two aircraft carriers, forty destroyers, and twenty-seven submarines in Hawaiian waters. Kuehn told of receiving some $30,000 in 1940-1941 from sources in Tokyo.

A military commission under martial law listened to Kuehn's story and sentenced him to be shot to death "by musketry." However, the sentence was later commuted by the military governor to fifty years at hard labor. After the war he was paroled from Leavenworth Penitentiary for deportation. In 1948 he left the United States for Argentina.

KUEHN was one of ninety-one persons convicted of spying against the United States from 1938 to 1945. And the shame of it was that sixty-four of them were American citizens betraying their own country. The greater number spied because of loyalty to Germany. A few others were mere adventurers. A few were recruited by threats of death to loved ones held by the Nazis.

One spy was the improbable "doll woman," who wrote such gentle and disarming letters about her dolls. But then one of her letters was returned from Buenos Aires marked "Unknown at This Address." The name of Mrs. Sara G., of Portland, Oregon, was given as the return address. The letter was dated May 20, 1942. Mrs. G. brought the letter to the FBI. "I never saw it before," Mrs. G. said. "I don't know anyone in Buenos Aires."

The letter looked innocent enough. It said, in part:

I just secured a lovely Siamese Temple Dancer, it had been damaged, that is tore in the middle. But it is now repaired and I like it very much. I could not get a mate for this Siam dancer, so I am redressing a plain ordinary doll into a second Siam doll. . . .

After other doll letters had been intercepted by censors, cryptanalysts in the FBI Laboratory decided that "Siamese Temple Dancer" meant "aircraft-carrier warship" and "doll" meant "warship." The talk of dolls assumed a sinister meaning:

I just secured information of a fine aircraft-carrier warship, it had been damaged, that is torpedoed in the middle. But it is now repaired and I like it very much. They could not get a mate for this so a plain ordinary warship is being converted into a second aircraft carrier. . . .

Agents noted that this letter had been written a few days after the aircraft carrier USS *Saratoga* left Puget Sound for San Diego.

But the gentle doll lover made a mistake. In a moment of spite, she used as one return address the name of Mrs. M., with whom she had had a spat. An FBI agent called on Mrs. M.

"Do you have any idea who might use your name?" he asked.

Mrs. M. thought for a moment and then her eyes blazed. "I'll bet it's that Velvalee Dickinson in New York. I bought some dolls from her and because I couldn't pay her right away she's been after me with nasty letters." Agents compared letters written by Velvalee Dickinson and the "doll woman." They were written on the same typewriter.

At first Velvalee Dickinson claimed that the $100 bills she was withdrawing from a safe-deposit box were part of her husband's estate. Then she changed her story, saying that her late husband had been paid $25,000 by the Japanese Naval Attaché on November 26, 1941, to furnish information to the Japanese. She insisted she had not supplied information herself, although the FBI's evidence all pointed to Mrs. Dickinson and not her husband. Mrs. Dickinson was indicted on espionage charges, but the U.S. attorney handling the case decided to accept her plea of guilty to violating censorship because the evidence was "circumstantial."

In uncovering spy activities, the FBI also uncovered espionage tools resembling a magician's props. One enemy agent was caught with a box of ordinary-looking safety matches. Four of the matches turned out to be tiny pencils which wrote invisibly. Messages were sealed into fountain pens whose barrels had to be broken to extract the notes. Codes were concealed in books and magazines by minute pinpricks through certain letters.

One of the FBI's most exciting achievements was uncovering the Nazi secret of the "micro-dots," perhaps the cleverest espionage weapon of World War II.

Early in 1940 the FBI received a tip from a double agent who told of attending the Nazis' espionage school at Klopstock Pension, Hamburg. In a final lecture the school's director had said:

> The greatest problem of der Führer's agents in North and South America is keeping in touch with us . . . but before long we shall be communicating back and forth throughout the world with impunity. . . .

The double agent said a new photographic process had been developed by which full-page messages would be transmitted on dots no bigger than the head of a pin. He had been shown one under a microscope and told to watch for these dots in messages. But he could give no further information.

Then a young Balkan arrived in New York from South America. He checked into his hotel and didn't appear surprised when he found two FBI agents waiting for him in his room. Though he had been recruited by the Germans as an espionage agent, it can now be revealed that he was working for the FBI.

"Did you bring them?" an agent asked.

The young man pulled from his pocket four blank telegraph messages. The papers were sent to the FBI Laboratory in Washington and under a fluorescent lamp a Laboratory technician saw tiny black dots embedded in the paper. He pried one loose; it was a dot no bigger than the period at the end of this sentence.

Under a microscope that enlarged the tiny object two hundred times, the technician saw a full-page message reproduced. He pried other "periods" loose from the papers and found all of them were messages reduced to midget size. One of the dots brought by the Balkan agent bore the message:

> There is reason to believe that the scientific works for the utilization of atomic-kernel energy are being driven forward into a certain direction in the United States partly by use of helium. Continuous information about the tests made on this subject are required and particularly: 1. What process is practiced in the United States for transporting heavy uranium? 2. Where are tests being made with uranium? (Universities, industrial laboratories, etc.) 3. Which other

raw materials are being used in these tests? Entrust only best experts with this.

This was the secret of the "dots," a triumph in photography.

Discovery of the micro-dot secret put the FBI onto the trail of espionage agents, a trail that led through the United States and South America, and helped the FBI break up a ring in Mexico in coöperation with the Mexican government.

One of the most successful double agents developed by the FBI had the code name of ND98. He was operating an import-export business in Germany in 1941 when he was summoned one day to the Hamburg office of the Abwehr — the intelligence department of the Nazi general staff. He was ordered to Uruguay, there to set up a radio transmitter. "Contact us when you have the radio ready," the Nazi official said.

ND98 had a pleasant voyage to Montevideo. There he met a U. S. State Department official. ND98 was willing to sell his services. Was the United States interested?

A few days later ND98 advised his Nazi espionage bosses:

Impossible to establish radio station desired. Am going to United States where I can operate more freely. Will contact you.

And then he proceeded to New York City, where, under FBI guidance, he made radio contact with Germany on February 20, 1942, from a secluded Long Island transmitter similar to the one the FBI had set up for double agent William Sebold. The Nazis quickly asked for information on aircraft, ship and arms production, troop and cargo movements and new weapons. And ND98 began feeding information to Germany — information carefully prepared by the FBI and screened or furnished by the Joint Security Control operating under the Joint Chiefs of Staff.

In August of 1943, Hamburg grumbled that while ND98's information was good, it was certainly expensive. By this time the Nazis had paid him approximately $34,000, which was turned over to the Alien Property Custodian.

ND98 replied: "Sorry you regard information as expensive. If not satisfactory, will be glad to withdraw as strain is great." The Abwehr hurriedly assured ND98 that not only was his work satisfactory but he would receive another $20,000 in due time.

ND98 acknowledged the bonus with a message in November broadly hinting that the United States planned a large-scale attack against the Northern Kurile Islands, a message which was close to the truth. The attack on the Kuriles, however, was to be a feint while the main American force hit the Marshall Islands. As expected, the Germans relayed the message to Japan. The Joint Chiefs later advised the FBI that there was reason to believe that ND98's information had contributed to the successful attack on the Marshalls in February 1944.

Among the final hoaxes played on the Nazis was a series of messages sent just before the Allied invasion of Normandy on June 6, 1944, telling the Germans that invasion plans had been delayed by a breakdown in the production of invasion boats. At least ND98 added to the confusion of reports fed to the Germans on Allied invasion plans.

The success of the Long Island radio operation is reflected in the fact that the Germans doggedly maintained contact with ND98 up to the time the British captured Hamburg on May 2, 1945. For his efforts, double agent ND98 received from the United States government $32,000 in salary and expenses. The $55,000 supplied by the Germans was more than enough to cover the cost of the operation.

Hitler had boasted that his armies were invincible. But even at the peak of the Nazi power in Europe, the German High Command was secretly worried. Air Marshal Hermann Goering and S.S. Chief Heinrich Himmler, among others, were complaining bitterly about the failure of the Abwehr to establish reliable agents in the United States.

The Abwehr chiefs were in an embarrassing position. Something had to be done to replace their agents who were being trapped by American counterespionage, and also to sabotage the American industrial giant before it became too great a threat. The Abwehr decided on a bold gamble: agents who had once lived in America would be chosen, men who knew the country well. Some would be trained in espionage and others in sabotage. Then they would be slipped into the United States by submarines with enough money and supplies to last them for two years.

The plan was laid before Admiral Doenitz. He agreed to co-operate if the agents would supply information of value to the German Navy. The Abwehr agreed and the task of recruiting two of the sabotage teams was given to pudgy, bull-necked Lieutenant Walter Kappe, who in the 1930's had helped to promote the German-American Bund. Kappe had returned to Germany from the United States in 1937 and had joined the German intelligence service.

Kappe picked eight men from a group of prospects. The oldest was George Dasch, thirty-nine, a radio monitor in the German Foreign Office. Dasch could have become an American citizen in September 1939 by taking the last step in obtaining citizenship, the oath of allegiance to his adopted country. But before he was notified to appear in court, he had returned to Germany. The Reich had financed his return.

Dasch and his seven companions-to-be entered the Nazi sabotage school at Quentz Lake, near Berlin, in April 1942. They were taught how to use explosives, incendiaries and detonators. They were taught how to wreck an industrial machine or an engine with abrasive material, and how to place an explosive charge to get the maximum damage to a bridge or a plant. Each man memorized the location of his targets. They rehearsed phony life stories documented with false birth certificates, draft-deferment cards, social-security cards, and automobile-drivers' licenses.

At last the men were ready. Lieutenant Kappe took his pupils to the submarine base at Lorient, France, where final preparations were made. Dasch was the leader of team Number 1, which included Ernest Burger, Heinrich Heinck and Richard Quirin, all in their thirties. Team Number 2 was under the command of thirty-two-year-old Edward Kerling. His companions were Herman Neubauer, thirty-two; Werner Thiel, thirty-five; and twenty-two-year-old Herbert Haupt.

Kappe gave each team leader $50,000 for a general fund, plus another $20,000 to be divided among the men as needed. In addition, there was a money belt for each containing $4000 and a wallet stuffed with $400 in small bills.

Kerling and his team slipped out to sea on a submarine on the night of May 26. Two nights later, the U-boat *Innsbruck* left carrying Dasch and his team. Each group carried four boxes containing high explosives, TNT molded to look like pieces of coal, fuses, detonators and other equipment.

After reaching the States, the men were to split up in pairs. Some of their sabotage targets included the Aluminum Company of America plant in Alcoa, Tennessee, and the locks on the Ohio River from Pittsburgh to Louisville, Kentucky. One team was to concentrate on railroad sabotage, placing explosives in the Pennsylvania Railroad station at Newark, New Jersey; blowing up a section of the Hell Gate bridge across the East River in New York City; and disrupting facilities of the Chesapeake and Ohio Railroad.

Sixteen nights after leaving Lorient, on Friday, June 12, the *Innsbruck* surfaced off the beach near Amagansett, Long Island, in heavy fog. The motors were stilled. Near midnight, seamen scrambled on deck and inflated a rubber boat. The four saboteurs, dressed in German Marine fatigue uniforms, climbed into the boat. Two seamen manned the oars and the boat rode through the surf; the Germans scrambled onto the beach. In the confusion the boat was swamped, but the equipment was hauled to safety. The seamen struggled frantically to empty the boat of water while the saboteurs changed to civilian clothes.

At about the same time, twenty-one-year-old Seaman 2/c John Cullen left the Amagansett Coast Guard station, alone and unarmed, to make the midnight beach patrol. The fog swirled around him on the lonely stretch of sand; his flashlight beam was a white cone stretching into gray nothingness. He could see only a few yards in any direction.

Dasch saw the light approaching. He was horrified. The man must not see the uniformed submariners at the water's edge. He intercepted Cullen and recognized his Coast Guard uniform.

"What's going on here?" demanded Cullen. He saw two men struggling with an object in the water.

Dasch said casually, "We're fishermen. Our boat ran aground and we're going to wait here until daylight." He explained that he and his friends had left East Hampton to go to Montauk Point when they became lost in the fog.

"Do you know where you are now?" Cullen asked.

"I thought you should know," Dasch said. "Where is your station?"

"It's right up there. My station is Amagansett."

Dasch, who knew Long Island, realized that the skipper of the *Innsbruck* had crossed three thousand miles of the Atlantic and missed his target of East Hampton by only three miles. But that three-mile error was endangering the entire expedition. For a moment Dasch considered the idea of shanghaiing Cullen aboard the submarine. He decided to try bribery instead.

Cullen said, "It's four hours till sunup. You'd better come to the station."

Dasch walked up the beach with Cullen but then he stopped. "Wait," he said. "I'm not going with you."

"You'll have to go," the youth retorted.

"Now, listen," Dasch growled. "How old are you? Do you have a father and mother? I don't want to kill you. Why don't you forget all this? Here is some money. Go have yourself a good time."

"I don't want the money," Cullen said. Then from out of the fog a man ran up to Dasch and said something in German. Dasch snapped, "Shut up!"

Cullen was thoroughly alarmed now. He didn't know how many men were out there in the fog or what they might do.

Dasch grabbed Cullen by the arm and said, "Come over here!" He shoved a wad of bills into the Coast Guardsman's hand. "Look in my eyes! Would you know me if you ever saw me again?"

"No," Cullen said. He backed away. "I never saw you." Once out of sight of Dasch, Cullen ran for his station to sound the alarm.

Dasch returned to his companions. "It's all right," he said. "I fixed everything."

Quickly the four saboteurs buried their clothing and boxes of equipment in the sand dunes. Then they walked across the dunes to a macadam road and waited for daybreak.

Back at the Coast Guard station, Cullen aroused four of his mates and told them what had happened. He showed them the money — $260. The men armed themselves and went back to the beach but they found nothing. At daybreak, Coast Guardsmen finally found footprints and followed them to the buried cache of equipment and German uniforms. The saboteurs had been too excited to smooth the sand and cover their tracks. A truck was called and the boxes were taken to the station for closer examination.

While the Coast Guardsmen were discovering the boxes, Dasch and his companions were walking to the Long Island Railroad station in Amagansett. But the station was locked. They sat on the platform waiting. It was 5:30 a.m. Finally the ticket agent came and Dasch bought four tickets. "You're out early," the agent said genially.

"Yes," Dasch said, "we've been fishing."

The saboteurs boarded the 6:57 for New York. In the city, Dasch and Burger registered at the Governor Clinton Hotel. Heinck and Quirin checked into the Hotel Martinique.

Warning that enemy agents had landed on Long Island reached the FBI shortly before noon. Coast Guard and Naval officers agreed that the FBI should take over the responsibility of running down the spies. Director Hoover ordered the FBI into action.

The day after landing, Dasch and Burger sat in their hotel. The blood-pounding excitement was gone now. They knew they were hunted men, and their courage was oozing away. Dasch told Burger, "I'm going to notify the FBI in Washington." Burger nodded.

On Sunday evening, an agent in the New York FBI office received a mysterious telephone call.

"I am Franz Daniel Pastorious," a man said. "I want you to know that I shall get in touch with your Washington office next Thursday or Friday. I have some important information." There was a click, and the line went dead. The agent shrugged. Another screwball call. But he made the usual memorandum for the record.

At 10 a.m. on Friday, June 19, the man who called himself Pastorious rang the FBI Headquarters and asked to speak to Hoover. "I called your New York office last Sunday," he said. "My real name is Dasch. I have just arrived from Germany with some important information. I am in Room 351 at the Mayflower Hotel."

Within minutes, FBI agents were at the hotel. They brought Dasch to Headquarters, where he poured out his story. He told them of Edward Kerling and the other sabotage team, who, he supposed, were loose somewhere in the States. He gave the agents a handkerchief on which had been written, in secret ink, the names of persons to contact in the United States.

Where had he been since calling the FBI in New York? He had been shopping and playing pinochle with old friends.

Kerling had better luck in landing than Dasch. His team landed undetected just before dawn on June 17 at Ponte Vedra Beach about twenty-five miles south of Jacksonville, Florida. They buried their equipment near the beach and caught a bus into Jacksonville, where they spent the night in hotels. Kerling and Thiel went to New York by way of Cincinnati, Haupt and Neubauer to Chicago.

From the records of previous investigations made of persons who had returned to Germany before the war, FBI agents located relatives and friends of the saboteurs and kept them under surveillance. Burger was followed in New York City, and led agents to Heinck and Quirin. Kerling and Thiel were caught in New York when Kerling contacted a man who was listed on Dasch's handkerchief. Neubauer was found in Chicago registered at a hotel under an alias.

As the net closed, young Haupt made a bold effort to throw agents off his trail. One day he walked into the Chicago FBI office. "I understand the FBI has been inquiring about my selective-service status," Haupt said. "I went to Mexico to avoid being forced into marriage and that caused trouble with my draft board. But I've got it all straightened out now and I'd like permission to go to work."

"We're no longer interested in your case," the agent in charge told Haupt. "Since you've got things straight, you're free to do whatever you wish."

But when Haupt walked from the office he was followed. Before arresting him the FBI wanted to know whether he had made any contacts with other agents. Fourteen days after the first saboteurs had landed on Long Island, all eight of them were in the custody of the FBI. The Nazis' grandiose scheme of sabotage had failed.

The announcement of the capture of the saboteurs jolted Nazi hopes that they might establish an apparatus for espionage and sabotage such as the Germans had established in World War I. Throughout the war years, the FBI investigated 19,649 cases in which sabotage was suspected. They found, for the most part, industrial accidents caused by fatigue, carelessness or spite, but not a single case of enemy-directed sabotage.

7. *The FBI South of the Border*

OR MORE than sixteen years the FBI has remained silent about its amazing operation in Central and South America, in which special agents often risked their lives in helping smash the Nazis' World War II spy networks in the Western Hemisphere.

The story began in 1940, when President Roosevelt and others in his Administration realized with grave concern that South America had become a staging ground for Nazi spies being slipped into the United States. Clandestine radio stations were pumping military, political and economic reports to the Nazis. And some Germans had turned from daydreams of *Lebensraum* to the practical planning of ways to conquer South America for Hitler.

Long before Hitler's star had risen, Germans had migrated to South America and settled in colonies which, for the most part, clung to German customs and language. The Nazi movement took hold in these colonies. Germans wore the uniforms of storm troopers and carried the Nazi flag on ceremonial occasions.

The FBI, through its own counterespionage and from reports by other intelligence agencies and the British, realized that these spy nests in Latin America must be wiped out. This called for skill and diplomacy as the coöperation of the Central and South American governments had to be enlisted.

Hoover discussed the problem with Assistant Secretary of State Adolf A. Berle, Jr., and with General Sherman Miles, Assistant Chief of Staff of Army G-2, and Admiral Walter S. Anderson, Director of Naval Intelligence. Out of these meetings came a proposal for a Special Intelligence Service (SIS) to operate in the foreign field.

Berle laid the plan before the President, and Roosevelt decided that Hoover and his men would be responsible for nonmilitary intelligence coverage in the Western Hemisphere. On June 24, 1940, he issued a directive setting this forth. In less than thirty days the FBI organized an SIS operation and agents were soon drifting south. Most of them were men with special skills in undercover work, and they went south secretly. Later, others were openly attached to embassies or were stationed with national and local police forces, with approval of the governments involved.

One undercover agent went to South America as a soap salesman for an American concern whose officials never suspected his role with the FBI. He sold so much soap within a few months that the company had to expand its import and distribution operations and then settle a dispute over the franchise. A local businessman who had been with a firm which had given up the franchise was howling to get it back. Meantime the demon soap salesman had made valuable contacts in business and government circles.

One young man became a stockbroker, bought a membership in the stock exchange and sent out a stock-market report that drew favorable attention in Argentine business circles. He had wire communications with New York and soon his margin accounts for customers dealing with the New York Stock Exchange were well above $600,000. He turned a neat profit, but his reports to the FBI were even more informative than the reports to his stock customers.

Most of the Central and South American governments willingly helped in the counterespionage program, but there were places, such as Argentina, where hostile police and government officials made the work difficult and dangerous. There agents were frequently shadowed, and informants caught by police told of inquisitions with the *picana eléctrica,* the electric spur, which caused an agony of pain when inserted into a sensitive part of the body.

Until Argentina severed relations with the Axis in 1944, the SIS kept a battered old motor launch hidden on the Rio de la Plata in Buenos Aires harbor. Frequently at night an undercover agent or an informant sought by the police would slip through the shadows along the water front. There would be a whispered conversation with the boat's skipper. And soon "Crandall's Navy," as FBI agents had dubbed the boat in honor of the agent who conceived the escape idea, would slide out and, dodging the harbor patrol, carry the hunted man upstream toward the safety of Uruguay.

SIS agents penetrated the "Green Hell" of the Chocó jungle in Colombia trailing platinum smugglers. They tramped rugged coasts looking for submarine hiding places. They traveled by canoe on the dangerous headwaters of the Amazon. They helped track down hidden radios and, with the State Department, Army and Naval intelligence, the British, and local police, pieced together the story of one of the Germans' greatest spy networks.

Out of the mass of information came a clear picture. The Nazis' intelligence apparatus in the Western Hemisphere was centered primarily in Brazil, Argentina, Chile and Mexico, although it extended into every Central and South American country. The United States' own "soft underbelly" was exposed, and the war clouds were gathering.

Brazil severed diplomatic relations with the Axis in early 1942. That was the signal for SIS agents to join forces with Brazilian authorities in their cleanup of Nazi rings which operated six clandestine radio stations in Brazil alone. Messages between these stations and German stations in Europe had been intercepted for months by FCC and FBI monitoring stations. Most of the Axis agents and their cover names were known to the Americans. In March 1942, Brazilian police armed with SIS information began the roundup of the Nazi agents. The six radio rings were broken up and eighty-six agents were convicted in Brazilian courts.

The arrests smashed the Brazilian spy net, but then the Nazis' headquarters for espionage shifted to Argentina and Chile. The SIS task was especially difficult and sensitive in these countries because the SIS men could not interfere directly with the Axis agents' operations. All they could do in most cases was collect the information and pass it on to the American Ambassadors, who then laid the facts before the governments concerned.

The danger of enemy radio stations to the Allied cause is illustrated in the case of the great liner the *Queen Mary,* which became a troop transport and a prize hunted by the U-boats.

The big ship arrived in Rio de Janeiro on March 6, 1942, en route overseas with 10,000 troops. That same day an FBI station intercepted a message from the Nazi station CIT which said: "Queen Mary arrived here today at 10:00 ... she must [go] to the cellar."

Two days later, another station, CEL, informed Hamburg: "Queen Mary sailed on March 8, 18 o'clock local time." And the next day CIT's operator pounded out a message: "With Queen Mary falls Churchill. ... Good luck."

So the sea raiders were alerted that the *Queen Mary* was in the Atlantic with a cargo whose loss would be a staggering blow to the Allies. And she was traveling without a convoy.

The intercepted messages were turned over to the State Department, the Office of Naval Intelligence and Army Intelligence by the FBI. The American Embassy reported the messages to the British Embassy in Rio de Janeiro.

On March 15, the official Italian news agency Stefani broadcast a report which said:

In Argentine maritime circles it is affirmed that the British transatlantic [liner] *Queen Mary,* which left Rio de Janeiro a few days ago with 10,000 North American soldiers aboard, was torpedoed. The ship was damaged heavily and tried to reach the British base at Falkland Islands.

But the *Queen Mary* had dodged the U-boats, saved by the prompt warning which resulted from the intercepted messages.

At the peak of the SIS operation, the organization had a total of 360 agents. Nine of the ten republics of South America had asked that agents be assigned to act as technical advisers on counterespionage. These agents made security surveys of more than 150 industrial plants, utilities and other centers regarded as highly important to the Allied war effort, and they recommended measures for tighter security.

Of all SIS activity, perhaps none produced more effective results than the battle of wits against platinum smugglers.

Platinum is essential in equipping and maintaining a war machine. Only five nations produce it in quantity — Colombia, Canada, Russia, the United States and the Union of South Africa. The German war machine needed platinum badly, and the Nazis reached out to Colombia to get it because Colombia was the only one of these countries not at war with the Reich in 1942.

About 22,850 troy ounces of Colombia's annual platinum production came from the dredges of the Choco Pacifico Company and another 12,150 ounces came from some 30,000 natives who panned it from streams, much as Klondike miners panned gold.

From 1936 until 1941, a German named Theodore C. Barth had about cornered the "native" platinum production by paying 20 to 30 percent above the official price. But Barth's monopoly collapsed when German funds were frozen in 1941. The smugglers moved in. The price of platinum jumped to $2338.10 a pound in the black market in 1942. A four-and-a-half-inch cube weighing sixty-six pounds was worth $154,314.60.

The United States, by agreement with Colombia, was supposed to receive all the country's platinum. There was no difficulty about the production from the Choco Pacifico Company, but controlling the native production was the key to blocking the flow of platinum to the Germans. And the natives in the back country were usually willing to sell to the highest bidder. The Colombian government threatened severe punishment for those who failed to turn in their platinum to the government, but there was no effective machinery for enforcement and the smugglers knew it. And so the SIS moved in.

The trails in smuggling cases reached from the jungles of Colombia to a luxurious home near the smooth greens of California's Monterey Peninsula Country Club.

One day in March 1943, SIS agents in Quito, Ecuador, notified FBI Headquarters in Washington of "possible platinum smuggling" by a man named Harold Ebury, said to be a British citizen. Ebury had often been in Ecuador claiming to be dealing in wheat. The FBI searched its files. They found a prewar report on Ebury after he arrived in Seattle from the Orient carrying a considerable amount of Japanese currency. He had claimed to be an international banker, but the British had advised the FBI that Ebury was a suspected smuggler.

The agents in Quito were ordered to give the Ebury case "preferred attention." They dug into the doings of the mysterious Mr. Ebury and his South American associates, to find that a ring was organized to smuggle platinum from Colombia by way of Ecuador to Argentina. The end of the line, so far as the agents could learn, was a tailor's shop on Florin Street in Buenos Aires.

As lead after lead developed, it became clear that Ebury, from California, was directing smuggling operations in South America. Agents trailed one smuggler to Argentina to learn the route. He was permitted to sell the metal and it was traced to a refining firm with a German name.

The FBI closed in on July 17, 1943. Agents found Ebury at his Monterey Peninsula home. He ushered them into his living room and, quite coolly, talked of his travels and his plans to go to Ecuador to establish an import-export business. The agents pressed him for more details and it became obvious to Ebury that these men knew more than he had realized. Finally he smiled, leaned back and said, "Yes, gentlemen, I smuggled platinum to Buenos Aires. I'll tell you everything."

Ebury reckoned that during his career he had handled perhaps a half ton of platinum. He admitted that when he used the word "cloth" in his correspondence he was referring to platinum, and that the figure $1300 meant 1300 grams of platinum.

While SIS agents were marking the Ebury case closed, they were opening nineteen new smuggling cases as a result of leads turned up in that one investigation.

In tracing platinum from 1942 to July 1, 1944, SIS agents were able to account for all but 2507 troy ounces of the metal. Presumably that amount could have reached Germany. But the German war machine in that period, according to official estimates, needed 137,500 troy ounces. The barriers set up by the Colombian government based on information furnished by the SIS limited the Nazis to less than two percent of their platinum needs.

The Special Intelligence Service was disbanded after the war, when the government set about revising its foreign intelligence operations. So the FBI's days of working in this field came to a close. But now the story of those days can be told as it has been here. As Adolf Berle, Jr., wrote to Hoover soon after the war, "It is the story of a great piece of work."

8. *War's Aftermath*

Hoover had foreseen that the FBI and local law officers would be confronted by a staggering crime problem in the wake of World War II.

One barometer was the rising rate of wartime juvenile delinquency. During the war, the migration of workers from small towns and farms to cities and defense centers often brought a moral letdown. Parents' authority over children relaxed. Families were crowded into slumlike areas where children had little chance for normal life, and teen-agers began looking for excitement without a steady hand to guide them. The problem wasn't confined to those living on the wrong side of the tracks. It was found in the better neighborhoods, too, when well-to-do parents and children drifted apart and suddenly found they didn't understand each other.

Much of the crime increase could be accounted for by the increase in the nation's population. But that wasn't the whole answer, because the percentage increase in crime in the postwar years was greater than the increase in population. From 1945 to 1955, population increased 24.3 percent while crime increased 44.5 percent. And the most shameful part of the record was the number of teen-age children involved in major law violations. The bare statistics gave the frightening impression that young people were running wild. Such an impression was false, of course, but the situation was disgraceful and there was confusion across the land. Almost every state had its own definition of a juvenile delinquent and its own legal rules for handling youthful violators.

The FBI's early interest in the youth problem was rooted primarily in the fact that, until juvenile delinquency was controlled, there was little likelihood that the adult crime problem could be solved. Records show that the juvenile delinquent frequently becomes the adult criminal. As early as 1946, Hoover considered the problem so pressing that he directed the organization of an FBI Juvenile Delinquency Instructors School, a broad research project supplemented with lectures by authorities in delinquency. The agents — many already possessing a practical background in working with young people — equipped themselves to lecture to local police groups on the latest developments in handling juveniles, the psychological problems involved in delinquency, how to organize boys' clubs, and related subjects.

Along with the increase in juvenile delinquency, there was a steady increase in bank robberies. Old-time gangs like Dillinger's no longer roamed the country. But professional bank robbers still operated, and they had been joined by a growing number of amateurs even more vicious and dangerous than the professionals because they were less predictable in handling weapons.

The FBI found that greed for easy money wasn't confined to any age bracket. Bank robbers, the records show, came in all ages from teen-agers to grandpas. And even some families tried it. In Wisconsin, a mother, her twenty-four-year-old son, fourteen-year-old daughter and two others outside the family planned a robbery and carried it off, escaping with $11,533.93. The daughter, who carried a gun in the robbery, afterward returned to her grade school with a note for the teacher, signed by her mother: "Please excuse Marguerite, she was sick with a cold." The brother was quite proud of his young sister. "I think she would have done all right if somebody had started shooting," he said after the gang's arrest.

The FBI found, too, that some robbers shuddered when they saw that a bank had women or elderly men as tellers. "You never know what they're going to do," one robber, Clyde Milton Johnson, told agents after his arrest. "I'll tell you what I mean. I went into a savings-and-loan-company office and pointed my gun at this old man sitting there in his cage. You know what he did? He just sat there. I shoved the gun under his nose and said, 'I mean business!'

"He said: 'I don't have anything to do with the money,' and he pointed to the guy in the next cage. Well, I figured the old guy would stay put, so I put my gun on the other guy. Then this old man got up and started toward the door. I yelled: 'Where the hell do you think you're going?'

"He looked over his shoulder and said, 'I'm going for a policeman,' and he kept going."

Johnson shook his head. "What are you going to do with people like that?"

In another case a bank robber exhibited a pistol to a woman teller and pushed a note through the window: "Fill this bag with money or die." The woman exclaimed: "Why pick on me?" Then she calmly squatted down behind the protection of her counter. The baffled robber fled.

Another persistent crime problem for the FBI was the tremendous number of automobiles stolen and then transported in interstate commerce. In 1955 alone, there were 227,150 automobile thefts. Thefts such as those in which youngsters steal a car for a joy ride have been local police problems. The FBI concentrates largely on tracking down those who have stolen cars for use in crimes, and also professional automobile rings who make stolen cars a lucrative criminal business.

While the FBI's assault against postwar criminals was a spectacular part of the Bureau's work, the G-Men were by no means entirely absorbed with crime. They were responsible also for fact finding in a broad range of civil litigation. A book could be written about this field of FBI activity alone, in which special agents produced evidence to save the government more than $600,000,000 from 1945 to 1955 by exposing such things as false claims and fraud against the government.

Many of these investigations were intricate exercises in accounting and finance. Others involved documenting evidence to refute false claims. Such was the case of a veteran, a farmer, who claimed payment for a total disability.

A special agent drove into the country and spent several hours observing the farmer. He was plowing with a team of mules, keeping his plow in a deep, straight furrow. After plowing a while, he picked up heavy sacks of fertilizer and carried them across the field. He was spreading the fertilizer when something frightened the mules and they broke away. The farmer took out after the mules, ran them down after a hundred-yard sprint, and brought them back. Then he went on with the plowing.

The agent's photographic record of this busy day was a convincing argument. The veteran's claim was not allowed.

Fact finding in civil-rights cases has been another facet of the FBI's work. There has been no area more sensitive for the Bureau than this one, where investigations touch jealously guarded States' rights and where the passions of men are easily aroused.

Unless a federal law is violated, the FBI has no jurisdiction. The two basic statutes which more or less form the framework of the FBI's responsibilities in the field of civil rights are found in Sections 241 and 242 of Title 18, United States Code. Section 241 deals for the most part with involuntary servitude, peonage and voting rights. Section 242 applies largely to the actions of law-enforcement officers who, "under color of law," willfully deny a person the rights guaranteed by law and the Constitution.

One great barrier encountered by the FBI in civil-rights violations has been local prejudice. Juries have refused to convict even when defendants confessed. Witnesses' lips have been sealed by fear. Authorities have refused to coöperate. And public opinion has been apathetic toward seeing justice done.

A shocking case of a jury's refusal to convict occurred in 1947 in South Carolina, after a cab driver was fatally stabbed. A Negro suspect named Willie Earle was arrested and taken to the Pickens

County jail for questioning. He protested his innocence. The word spread that Earle was being held for the crime. Angry cab drivers began to discuss the death of a brother driver. Soon the crowd had become an armed mob and the mob was racing for the jail. They pushed their way into the jailer's living quarters and forced him to unlock Earle's cell.

Earle was dragged out and pushed into an automobile. Near the Saluda Dam the caravan halted and the prisoner "confessed." Then he was taken to a point in Greenville County. There the mob beat and stabbed him. Finally shotgun blasts snuffed out the last small flame of life. Then the self-appointed executioners went home.

The Justice Department authorized the FBI to conduct a full investigation because of the possibility that Earle's civil rights had been denied by the jailer's willingly helping the mob. The FBI's investigation exonerated the jailer.

The FBI joined forces with local officers in the investigation and twenty-eight persons were identified as having been in the mob. They were arrested on state warrants charging them with murder — and twenty-six of the defendants confessed to taking part in the lynching. South Carolinians generally were outraged. The defense offered no testimony. But the jury found all twenty-eight defendants "not guilty," despite the confessions.

Civil-rights enforcement has led the FBI into sharp conflict at times, not only with police officers with whom the FBI has worked for years, but also with the governors of states. On the other hand, much of the time the FBI has found local law-enforcement officers willing to coöperate. Some police departments, such as that of Dallas, Texas, notify the FBI immediately whenever a civil-rights complaint is made against an officer. An attitude has developed — and is growing — that, if a police officer has treated a prisoner brutally, then the officer deserves to be exposed, punished and fired. But if the charges are untrue, then the officer's innocence should be established beyond doubt.

Obviously the Bureau cannot make investigations on the basis of whether or not the FBI's popularity will be affected. If that were the case then the FBI would never check into civil-rights cases involving public officials. There probably would never have been any investigation into the powerful Pendergast political machine in Kansas City, Missouri.

Tom Pendergast ran Kansas City's politics and its underworld. His power was legendary and he seemed untouchable, until the federal government cracked down on the Boss and his stooges for corrupting the ballot boxes in the November 1936 election.

A committee of citizens who had revolted against boss rule had watched the violations of election laws and given their evidence to the United States attorney. A federal judge ordered a grand-jury investigation. On the face of it, something was wrong, because Kansas City had a population of less than 400,000, and there were some 270,000 registered voters. The FBI was called into the case.

FBI agents piled up damning evidence of fraud, stuffed ballot boxes, intimidation and thievery of votes by the changing of markings from Republican candidates to Democratic candidates. One precinct captain was heard to say, "I've had a hard day. I've been in the basement and those damn Republicans certainly write heavy. It was a tough job erasing."

The FBI found proof of erasures on ballots. Crosses had been made on different ballots by the same person. Fingerprints of defendants were found on ballots which they had had no right to handle. Indentations showed that ballots had been marked while lying one on top of another. The evidence was overwhelming, and 256 defendants were convicted. It was the beginning of the end for one of the most corrupt political machines in American history.

The FBI's oldest enemy in the field of civil liberties has been the Ku Klux Klan, the hate group which FBI agents have been fighting for more than thirty years. The fight has forced the FBI at times to move against officers of the law who joined a mob or did nothing to halt mob action.

In one case at Hooker, Georgia, in 1949, a mob of fifty to seventy-five persons dressed in Klan robes burned a cross near the home of a Negro woman whom they accused of giving "wild parties." In her home were six Negro men, aged from nineteen to thirty, who had come to see one of her sons. The mob took the visitors onto a hill, flogged them, and told them, "Get on over that hill and get out of here."

Among those watching the cross-burning were Dade County Sheriff John William Lynch and Deputy Sheriff William H. Hartline. Hartline helped the mob load the Negroes into automobiles and the sheriff stood by without uttering a word of protest.

A federal-court jury in Rome, Georgia, found Sheriff Lynch and Deputy Hartline guilty of violating a federal statute by failure to protect the Negroes. They were each fined $1000 and sentenced to a year in prison. The Supreme Court refused to review their case.

By far the most unusual part of the episode was the resolution adopted by the federal grand jury at Rome, composed of local residents, which said:

The members of the Federal Grand Jury . . . hereby resolve: That the following agents of the Federal Bureau of Investigation . . . by their great fidelity and singleness of purpose in developing the information in the Dade County, Georgia, conspiracy trial have gone far beyond the line of duty to aid, assist and protect the citizens of the United States and to further the cause of equity and justice in America.

9. *The Cold War*

ON OCTOBER 14, 1949, at 11:10 a.m., a whisper ran through the federal courtroom at Foley Square in New York City, "The jury is coming in! It's a verdict!"

In his black robes Judge Harold Medina mounted the bench. From his high-backed chair he looked down at the eleven defendants — the top commanders of the Communist Party of the United States, who had been tried on charges of teaching and advocating the overthrow of the United States Government by force and violence.

Their trial had lasted nearly nine months. It dramatized what has been by all odds the strangest chapter in the history of the FBI its fight against Communism.

The trial had been one of the longest criminal trials in federal court history. And some in the courtroom believed the defense attorneys had deliberately tried to bring about a mistrial by the use of insolence, delaying tactics, and disobedience of the Court's orders.

"You may bring in the jury," Judge Medina said to the clerk.

The jurors filed into the jury box, where they sat in the red upholstered chairs from which they had followed the testimony for so many weeks. "Shall I proceed, your Honor?" the clerk asked.

"Yes."

The jurors' names were called and they answered present. And then the clerk turned to Mrs. Thelma Dial, Negro foreman of the jury, and said: "Madam Foreman, have you agreed on a verdict?"

"We have."

"How say you?"

"The jury finds each of the defendants guilty."

A murmur was heard through the room. That was all.

The clerk polled each juror separately: "You say you find the defendants Eugene Dennis, John B. Williamson, Jacob Stachel, Robert G. Thompson, Benjamin J. Davis, Jr., Henry Winston, John Gates, Irving Potash, Gilbert Green, Carl Winter and Gus Hall guilty as charged."

All the replies were in the affirmative. Judge Medina thanked the jurors, praised them for their patience, and dismissed them.

"Now," said Judge Medina, "I turn to some unfinished business." He called the names of the six members of the defense counsel, and asked them to rise.

"... I find," said the Judge, "that the acts, statements and conduct of each of the defendants [counsel] constituted a deliberate and willful attack upon the administration of justice, an attempt to sabotage the functioning of the federal judicial system and misconduct of so grave a character as to make the mere imposition of a fine a futile gesture and a wholly insufficient punishment. . . ."

He sentenced three of the lawyers to six months' imprisonment, two to four months' and one to thirty days'. A babble of protest arose from the six men, who shouted angrily at Judge Medina as they had shouted day after day with insinuations that the Court was guilty of racial prejudice, bias, corruption and partiality.

Judge Medina broke in to say: "Let these contempt adjudications be notice that there is power in the judicial system of the United States under its Constitution, and there are laws to protect and maintain the dignity of the Court and the orderly administration of justice."

So ended the trial which claimed attention around the world.

THIS DRAMA had begun more than ten years earlier, when, under Franklin D. Roosevelt's direction, the FBI began assembling evidence that proved that the Communist Party leaders were not advocating peaceful political revolution, but were conspiring to bring about the violent overthrow of the United States Government.

From the first, J. Edgar Hoover had looked on Communism as an international conspiracy. The Party was no "fraternal society" espousing liberalism and it was not a political party in the accepted sense. This was a dangerous mechanism organized on an interlocking world-wide basis to wreck the existing social system after it had been weakened by subversion. The men in command at the FBI had no illusion about the *Communist Manifesto* and the writings of Lenin and his successors. Some saw them as intellectual exercises to be classified only as opinion. The FBI saw in these writings what they saw in *Mein Kampf* — the battle plan for conquest. The FBI leadership accepted the Soviet chiefs at their word; they knew that Communism threatened to destroy the freedoms and the government which FBI men were sworn to defend.

In 1946-1947, the FBI assembled a 1350-page legalistic brief, with 546 exhibits, which contained the evidence gathered over the years against the Party and its leaders. Two supplemental briefs added another 500 pages and 300 exhibits. These pages and exhibits were the product of untold days of investigative work and they formed, perhaps, the most complete summary ever put together of the Communist Party's activities and aims in the United States.

The brief was sent to Attorney General Tom C. Clark in February 1948, and the Department of Justice decided to move against the twelve members of the Communist Party's National Board. After more than a quarter of a century, the government aimed a massive blow at home-grown Communists.

A federal grand jury in New York City returned an indictment on July 20, 1948, charging the Party leadership with a conspiracy in violation of the Smith Act. The Smith Act, passed by Congress in 1940, said in part: "It shall be unlawful for any person to knowingly or willfully advocate, abet, advise, or teach the duty, necessity, desirability, or propriety of overthrowing or destroying any government in the United States by force or violence."

Federal Judge Vincent L. Leibell signed bench warrants for the arrest of the defendants and FBI agents began the roundup which the Communist *Daily Worker* promptly labeled "a giant frame-up."

Hoover recognized that it would be necessary to uncover some of the confidential informants whom the FBI had planted in the Party years before, and to make them available as witnesses if prosecutions were to be started.

The trial of the eleven Party leaders opened in Judge Medina's courtroom in January 1949. (National Chairman William Z. Foster was indicted also, but not tried because of illness.) Perhaps the greatest shock to the defendants and to Party members was the dramatic appearance of young Herbert A. Philbrick as a government witness. Philbrick had become known in Boston as a trusted member of the Communist Party's inner circle; no one, not even his wife, had been aware that he was also an undercover agent for the FBI.

In 1940, at the age of twenty-five, Philbrick had helped organize a youth group in Boston and had become chairman, only to find the group was secretly controlled by young Communists. He discussed the situation with the FBI and agreed to continue in the work to help uncover what he could about the Communists' operations. He worked his way deeper and deeper into the Party. In this weird double life, Philbrick played the role of a dedicated Communist while keeping the FBI informed on the Party's maneuvers, until the time came for him to testify at Foley Square. He was one of six FBI confidential informants who testified for the government.

Witness after witness spread before the jury the Communist teachings which were summed up by Stalin's statement that a revolution in the United States was "impossible without the violent destruction of the machinery of the bourgeois state." The defendants were linked in the testimony with a conspiracy to put these words into action. Across the courtroom echoed the words of an ideology which had drawn nation after nation into slavery.

The trial was a bitter struggle in which the defense claimed the eleven men on trial had only been exercising their right of free speech and freedom of thought.

The jury thought otherwise.

The verdict of guilty was upheld by Circuit Judge Learned Hand, who said in part:

> We know of no country where they [the defendants] would have been allowed any approach to the license here accorded them; and none, except Great Britain, where they would have had so fair a hearing. Their only plausible complaint is that freedom of speech, which they would be the first to destroy, has been denied them. We acknowledge that that freedom is not always easy to protect; and that there is no sharp line which marks its scope. We have tried to show that what these men taught and advocated is outside the zone. . . .

On June 4, 1951, the United States Supreme Court also affirmed the Communist leaders' conviction in upholding the constitutionality of the Smith Act.

The Supreme Court's decision was the signal for four of the eleven convicted Communists to jump their $20,000 bail and go into hiding. Gus Hall, Robert Thompson, Henry Winston and Gilbert Green disappeared. FBI agents began the search for them.

Hall, the Party's national secretary, slipped into Mexico with the help of the Party's underground. He dyed his blond hair, eyebrows and eyelashes dark brown. He shaved his mustache and thinned himself by forty pounds. But the disguise didn't work. Mexican police found him in a tourist court. His papers were not in order, and he was escorted to the border at Laredo, Texas, where FBI agents took him into custody on October 10, 1951.

After more than two years, Robert Thompson was tracked down

to a cabin hide-out high in the Sierra mountains. He had grown a mustache, dyed his hair, and taken the identity of John Francis Brennan, who had fought in the Spanish Civil War and then committed suicide in New York in 1938.

Thompson's arrest shocked the Communists, and the Party began a frenzied search for the "traitor" who had disclosed the hide-out. But they never learned how the FBI had managed to find Thompson.

The remaining two fugitives, Winston and Green, remained at large until early 1956, when, individually, they surrendered voluntarily at the Federal Courthouse in New York City.

With the top command of the Party convicted, the FBI went after seventeen "second-string" Communists, again piecing together the evidence to prove that Marxism-Leninism was not merely a social theory but a guide to revolutionary action. In a trial lasting nine and a half months, thirteen of the seventeen defendants were convicted.

The trials of the Communist leaders were part of a broad attack by the government against Communism in the Cold War years. President Harry S. Truman's Federal Employees Loyalty Program was another part of the same attack. Into the Great Debate over the issue of "Communists in Government," which this program called forth, there exploded the Hiss case. The FBI's part in this was to investigate the charges of Whittaker Chambers, who admitted having been a Communist from 1924 to 1937, that Alger Hiss, brilliant young State Department diplomat, had been a member of the Party and of the Soviet espionage apparatus. Hiss denied the charges. In all, 263 agents at one time or another worked on the investigation in forty-five of the FBI's fifty-two field divisions.

On December 15, 1948, a federal grand jury in New York City indicted Alger Hiss for perjury. His first trial, which began the following May, resulted in a hung jury, but in the second trial, held in November 1949, Hiss was convicted and sentenced to serve five years on each of two counts.

The FBI had found over the years that in the development of the Communist movement in the United States — as elsewhere — the

Party exposed only part of itself to public view. Part of it was open and above ground and its leaders made no effort to conceal their connection with it. But there was always a hidden part known to Communists themselves as "the illegal apparatus," working secretively and hiding the identities of its members. Some members worked only in the underground, some above ground, and others in both organizations.

Late in 1946, as the Cold War developed, the Communist Party shifted its center of gravity toward the underground. By October 1947 the Party had completed arrangements for an effective underground organization, according to reports received by the FBI. And by late 1948, state groups had reached agreement on the use of certain "fronts" for their activities. Party members began disappearing from their old haunts and turning up in other cities under assumed names.

When the Party's top leaders were convicted in the New York trial, lesser leaders began arranging for hide-outs and renting offices and residences as fronts for future meeting places. One Party chief sent his wife and child into hiding, stored his furniture, and then disappeared himself. When he came out of hiding he used an assumed name.

FBI agents discovered that in preparing for underground operations, the Party had adopted these security measures among others:

1. Membership cards were eliminated.
2. The basic Party unit, the club, was limited to no more than five members. Members of one group were not to know the identities of those in other groups.
3. Use of telephones and the mails was restricted and members were encouraged to use code words and double talk. The courier system was expanded.
4. Party records were destroyed or hidden.
5. Duplicating machines and quantities of paper were bought and hidden in the homes of trusted members.

In piecing together the story of the underground, the FBI learned that in 1948 three Communist leaders had been chosen to expand the hidden apparatus. Each of the three was instructed to name three subordinates, and this system was to be extended down through the district, state, county, city and club units. Thus one layer in the underground would know only the next layer above and below; and penetration to the top by the FBI would be more difficult.

By mid-1956, the FBI estimated that the Communist Party, USA, was stripped down to a hard core of about 20,000 members.

Through the fabric woven by the FBI's investigations of Communist activities ran one continuous thread: the dedication of the Party to the interests of Soviet Russia. Whenever the interests of the United States and those of Russia clashed, the Party stood with the Soviet interests.

In the tense days following the North Korean Communist Army's invasion of South Korea in 1950, the United States Communists accused their own government and "Wall Street" of being responsible for the war. Recognizing that the American Communists' loyalty was doubtful if Russia should openly enter the war, the FBI assigned more agents to the coverage of Communist underground activities.

The first break in the pattern of underground activity came in 1955, in the afterglow of the Geneva Conference, when the Russians began to promote in the name of "friendly coexistence" the hope that Communism and capitalism could live at peace in the same world.

In this atmosphere fugitive Communists suddenly reappeared to take up open Party activity again. FBI informants reported that many Communists themselves believed another "friendly" era was ahead and that the smiles of Khrushchev and Bulganin meant an easing of tensions.

But then the FBI received information late in 1955 disclosing that Party leaders had been thrown into confusion about the Party "line."

The stern facts of life became clear when the Communists met in Moscow in February 1956 for their Twentieth Congress. Khrushchev and other leaders talked of the peaceful evolution of Communism. But Khrushchev also told the Congress:

In the countries where capitalism is still strong and has a huge military and police apparatus at its disposal, the reactionary forces will, of course, inevitably offer serious resistance. There the transition to socialism will be attended by a sharp class, revolutionary struggle....

The Party "line" was clear as far as the FBI was concerned.

IN THE same year that the top Communist leaders were tried, another history-making story erupted.

The story went back to December 3, 1943. The United States Fifth Army in Italy was slowly hacking a bloody path toward Cassino. On the Russian front, the tide had turned against the Germans in the battle for Stalingrad.

From out of the Atlantic, the British transport *Andes* steamed into the sheltered waters of Norfolk, Virginia. The long, hazardous voyage from England was over. At the ship's rail a group of British scientists laughed and joked as preparations were completed for them to go ashore. Tonight, New York City! A city that fairly sparkled with lights when compared with blacked-out London, a city with no enemy planes droning overhead ...

But beneath the excitement of arrival was another, greater excitement, generated by being part of a war effort so secret that only a handful of people knew its real meaning. Even within their own select group, none of these men could know that in the pooling of their knowledge with the Canadians and Americans they would harness the atom as a military weapon in the incredibly short time of nineteen months. Not even the brilliant, sallow-faced young physicist at the ship's rail could imagine such an achievement.

Klaus Fuchs had never been in the United States before. He knew no one well here other than his sister, who lived in Cambridge, Massachusetts. He had fled to England from Germany in 1933 after Hitler had risen to power. When Germany and England went to war, after being interned briefly as an enemy alien, he had gone to work for the British in nuclear research. Now he had British citizenship. Already he had established a reputation as an extraordinarily brilliant physicist and mathematician.

But though Fuchs knew no one in America, somewhere out there among the millions of people a stranger was waiting for him. Fuchs knew that one day he and this man would meet and recognize each other.

On docking, there was no bothersome checking by security officers. The Army had exclusive responsibility for clearing personnel assigned to the Manhattan Engineer District, which directed the atomic-energy program. The British had assured the Army that Fuchs had been screened and found trustworthy. These assurances were accepted.

Within a short time the British group was en route to New York, to enjoy the city's glitter and then to plunge into the atomic unknown.

But one member of the group was not entirely engrossed with atomic problems. A few weeks after his arrival, Klaus Fuchs strolled from the Barbizon-Plaza Hotel on a windy Saturday afternoon. A few minutes later he stepped from the subway in New York City's Lower East Side. He carried a white tennis ball in his hand.

Then Klaus Fuchs saw the Stranger. He knew him instantly by the gloves in his hand and the book with the green binding. He was middle-aged and solidly built. His eyes flicked to the tennis ball in Fuchs's hand. He spoke, and the two of them went to a restaurant on lower Third Avenue. The Stranger said, "I am Raymond." Never was he to let Fuchs know his real name, Harry Gold.

Fuchs told his companion of the supersecret Manhattan Engineer District. He talked of the goal of harnessing the atom's energy to a military weapon. He promised specific details later, and so they parted.

In those few, fleeting minutes, early in 1944, Klaus Fuchs and the Stranger had unlocked a door leading to the theft of atomic secrets for Soviet Russia.

In September 1949, the struggles on the battlefields of Europe and the Pacific were a four-year-old memory. No longer an ally, Russia was the Cold War enemy of the Western World.

At his desk in the Department of Justice building in Washington, FBI Director J. Edgar Hoover studied a top-secret report — and his face flushed with shock. Here was information, reliable beyond doubt, that agents of a foreign power had stolen the secret of the construction and detonation of the atomic bomb. Here was information of a crime so shocking that it was to be called "the crime of the century."

The FBI, not the Army, was now responsible for atomic security. Hoover reached for the telephone. He gave a series of orders. In essence, these orders were: "The secret of the atomic bomb has been stolen. Find the thieves!"

Hoover's men swarmed into the Los Alamos atomic plant near Santa Fe, New Mexico, and other plants. They dug into records and personnel files, interviewed hundreds of people. Within a few days, the FBI concluded that the key figure in the crime had very likely been a member of a foreign mission, probably a physicist. The British were notified of these conclusions.

During this manhunt, President Truman jolted the nation with his announcement that the government had "evidence that within recent weeks an atomic explosion occurred in the U.S.S.R." The United States no longer had a monopoly on the atomic bomb.

Near the end of September, the coil of evidence was tightening around Klaus Fuchs. On the known record, it seemed impossible. He was now the respected head of the Theoretical Physics Division of Britain's atomic-energy establishment at Harwell, a man with a brilliant future. But then a small alarm bell sounded. An agent digging through old Nazi records seized during World War II spotted an entry. Translated, it said: "Klaus Fuchs, student of philosophy, December 29, 1911, Russelsheim, RSHA-IVA2, Gestapo Field Office, Kiel." This Klaus Fuchs in the Gestapo file had the same birth date and birthplace as the British physicist. RSHA stood for *Reichssicherheitshauptamt,* Central Office of Security Police; IV designated a department of the RSHA; A2 identified the file into which the Gestapo dropped the names of Communists.

The Nazis undoubtedly had accused many innocent persons of being Communists. Still, the file couldn't be ignored.

Sifting through every record they could find, agents turned to the file of the 1946 Canadian case of Igor Gouzenko, the cipher clerk who had fled from the Russian Embassy at Ottawa. In this file was a copy of an address book picked up by Canadian police. Among the names was the entry: "Klaus Fuchs, University of Edinburgh, Scotland."

Hoover notified British Intelligence (MI5) of this development. MI5 agents shadowed Fuchs. By the end of October the British had decided he was the atomic spy — or at least one of them.

It was December 1949 when William J. Skardon, Harwell Security officer, tapped on Fuchs's door. Inside, he told Fuchs he was suspected of passing information to the Russians.

Fuchs seemed surprised. "I don't think so," he blurted. Skardon persisted. He told Fuchs he had precise information.

"I do not understand," Fuchs said. "I have not done any such thing."

Fuchs continued to deny his guilt. But on January 24, 1950, he sent word to Skardon that he wished to see him. Skardon came to Fuchs's rooms. The scientist was plainly under emotional stress. At last the confession came tumbling out. Yes, he had given the Russians atomic secrets from 1942 until a year ago. He had sought out the Russians on his own initiative. Before he went to the United States, he was told how to meet the Stranger. Shortly after he returned to England in 1946, he had accepted £100 from the Russians as a "symbolic payment" to signify his "subservience to the cause."

At his trial, Klaus Fuchs pleaded guilty to charges of giving "to persons unknown" information useful to an enemy.

Lord Chief Justice Goddard, after hearing the evidence, said to Fuchs: "You have betrayed the hospitality and protection given to you with the grossest treachery. . . . The maximum sentence ordained is fourteen years. That is the sentence I pass upon you."

Fuchs was led away to Wormwood Scrubs Prison.

FROM THE time Fuchs confessed, the FBI concentrated on getting the answer to one question: who was the Stranger, the man to whom Fuchs slipped information on at least ten occasions in New York, Santa Fe and Cambridge?

The single clue was a vague description by Fuchs of a man in his middle years. About five feet ten. Solidly built. Round face. Not a physicist. A man who knew something about chemistry. Perhaps a chemist. He called himself "Raymond," but obviously that wasn't his real name.

Beyond this shadowy image, Fuchs could give no further help.

This is a big land. There are millions of middle-aged, solidly built, round-faced men who are not physicists. Where to start?

"Perhaps a chemist . . ."

Agents of the FBI called on Fuchs's sister, Mrs. Kristel Heineman, in Cambridge. She and her husband recalled that in January 1945 a stranger had called at their home asking for Klaus, who hadn't yet arrived for his vacation with them. The man was middle-aged and solidly built. He returned the following month, and he and Klaus talked for quite a while. The visitor seemed fond of children; he had promised their son a chemistry set. The Heinemans could recall no name.

There again was the reference to chemistry. Through days and weeks, agents pored over files of chemists. The task was enormous. For example, in 1945, New York City alone had issued 75,000 licensing permits to chemical firms. But by the slow process of elimination, the possibilities thinned to 1000 . . . 100 . . . 20 . . . and then at last to Harry Gold.

Gold's name had come up in 1947, during an investigation which grew out of information supplied by Elizabeth T. Bentley, a self-confessed Communist courier. The file showed that Gold was a chemist. A further check disclosed that Gold now worked at the Philadelphia General Hospital. On May 15 — some six weeks after Fuchs's conviction — two FBI agents visited the hospital and asked Gold if he would give them an interview.

"Of course," Gold said. "Would you come back this evening?"

The agents returned after dinner. Gold recalled that he had been questioned by the FBI on another occasion, and he asked what they wanted to know this time. He was shown a picture of Klaus Fuchs and exclaimed, "This is a very unusual picture. He is that English spy!" Then he added that he didn't know Fuchs, of course, but he had recognized his face from the newspapers.

No, he didn't know the Heinemans in Cambridge or anyone in Santa Fe. As a matter of fact, he had never been west of the Mississippi River. He answered questions willingly, but the agents noted small evasions and discrepancies in his story.

A week passed. Gold was questioned several times, and finally he said to the agents, "I've told you everything I know. I've nothing to hide. If it will help, go ahead and search the place." He gave his written consent for the search of his house.

At Gold's suggestion, the agents started their search in the bedroom, the room where he had most of his papers and books. Gold made himself comfortable in a chair. One of the agents looked behind a bookcase which obviously hadn't been touched in years. He picked up a Chamber of Commerce tourist map. It was a map of Santa Fe.

The agent spread it open. "You said you had never been west of the Mississippi?"

Harry Gold stared at the map. For a long minute no one spoke. The agents waited. Then suddenly Gold seemed to crumple, like a man too bone-weary to carry his burden another step. He said, "I . . . I am the man to whom Klaus Fuchs gave his information." He told of meeting Fuchs in New York and Cambridge and Santa Fe. After picking up information he gave it to Anatoli A. Yakovlev, Russian Vice-Consul in New York.

But why? Gold's explanation was an old, familiar refrain: confused idealism leading to treachery. He said: "I began spying for the Soviet Union in 1936. I thought I would be helping a nation whose aims I approved." His reaction to working with Fuchs was: ". . . I felt that, as an ally, I was helping the Soviet Union obtain information that I thought it was entitled to."

Doubt had finally come to Gold. But by then it was too late to turn back.

NINE MONTHS after J. Edgar Hoover flashed the warning that atomic secrets had been stolen, the whole wretched story of espionage was known to the FBI.

Agents had followed the trail from Fuchs to Gold. From Gold, the trail branched into a maze of treachery. One path led to a twenty-eight-year-old ex-Army sergeant, David Greenglass, who lived with his wife, Ruth, and their two children at Apartment No. 6, 265 Rivington Street, New York City.

Greenglass was at home when two FBI agents called on him on June 15, 1950. They showed identification, then said, "We are trying to locate information on materials lost, misplaced or stolen at the Los Alamos project. You worked at Los Alamos, didn't you?"

"Yes," Greenglass said. "But I can't help. I know nothing about it."

Later an agent left the apartment with pictures of Greenglass and his wife, including a snapshot taken while Greenglass was in uniform during World War II. The agent took the pictures to Gold, who said: "This is the man I contacted at Albuquerque."

For a time Greenglass protested his innocence. But finally his part of the story spilled forth. Piece by piece, the parts fell into place and formed the clear picture of espionage. In its essentials, this is the story:

On November 29, 1944 — three months after T/4 Sgt. David Greenglass's transfer to the secret Los Alamos project — Ruth Greenglass arrived in Albuquerque, New Mexico. David met Ruth at the Hotel Franciscan. It was their second wedding anniversary. David had wangled five days' leave from his job as a machinist at the project. One day while they were out walking, Ruth told him about a talk she'd had in New York with Julius and Ethel Rosenberg. Ethel was David's sister. Ruth said that Julius and Ethel had dropped their Communist Party activities. David was surprised. "But why?"

"Because at last Julius is doing what he always wanted to do — giving information to the Soviet Union!"

Ruth said that Julius knew that David was working on the top-secret atomic bomb. Julius and Ethel wanted David to give them information about his work.

David was scared. "I can't do it, Ruth," he said. But next day he agreed. Julius and Ethel had persuaded him to join the Young Communist League when he was fourteen. Julius was his hero. David didn't want to see him fail at anything he tried.

David gave Ruth a description of the Los Alamos layout which she memorized and repeated to Julius Rosenberg when she returned home. Two months after this, David returned to New York on leave. At Julius' request he made a number of sketches of a lens mold being used in atomic experiments. A day or so later, at the Rosenbergs' apartment, Julius said to Ruth Greenglass, "How would you like to go to Albuquerque to live?"

"I would be very happy," Ruth exclaimed.

"You are going to be there," Julius said. The money for expenses would be a gift — from the Russians.

Later they talked about how David might identify any stranger who came to get information for Julius. Going into the kitchen, Julius cut the side from a Jello box and then cut the cardboard into two notched parts. He gave one half to Ruth Greenglass. Ruth put it into her wallet. Julius kept the other half.

David and Ruth returned to New Mexico and Ruth found an apartment in Albuquerque where David could come on his days off from Los Alamos. They were at home one Sunday when a stranger knocked on the door, a man whose name they would later learn was Harry Gold.

Only a few days before, Gold had met Soviet Vice-Consul Anatoli Yakovlev in New York. The two men had discussed Gold's trip to Santa Fe, where he was to pick up information from Klaus Fuchs. Then Yakovlev told Gold that after seeing Fuchs he must go to Albuquerque.

Gold protested. The additional trip to Albuquerque might endanger the arrangement with Fuchs. But Yakovlev cut him short: "It's an order!" He gave Gold a sheet of paper with the name "Greenglass," an address, and a notation: "Recognition signal. I am from Julius." He next handed Gold a piece of cardboard cut from a Jello box and an envelope containing $500 for Greenglass.

Gold arrived in Santa Fe on June 2, 1945. Having time on his hands, he wandered about town. At a newsstand he picked up a Chamber of Commerce map. He tucked the map in his pocket, a single careless act which five years later would shatter his composure when an FBI agent found the map behind his bookcase.

But Gold wasn't thinking of the FBI as he strolled through Santa Fe toward his meeting with Fuchs. He saw the scientist driving toward him in an old car. The car stopped and he got in. Within a few minutes, Fuchs had given him a thick packet of information on atomic-bomb secrets. With this part of his mission completed, Gold left Santa Fe for Albuquerque.

Next morning, the Greenglasses had just finished breakfast when the stranger knocked. David opened the door. Gold stepped in. He said, "I come from Julius."

"Oh! You arrived sooner than I expected," Greenglass said. From his wife's purse he fished out the piece of Jello box. Gold produced the other half. The pieces matched.

Gold said, "Have you any information for me?"

David said: "I have some but I will have to write it up." He went to work, drawing more sketches of the lens mold on which he had been working, and describing how the lens was used as a triggering device in atomic experiments. Gold took the information from Greenglass and left behind the $500.

Greenglass was back in New York on furlough in September 1945. The atomic bombs had been dropped on Hiroshima and Nagasaki. Japan had surrendered. The war was over.

This time David gave Julius a sketch of a cross section of the Nagasaki-type bomb as he visualized it from his own knowledge of the triggering device and from discussions he had heard between scientists. Julius was pleased. "This is very good," he said. He told Greenglass he had stolen a proximity fuze while working at Emerson Radio. Later he boasted that he had research information about atomic-powered airplanes as well as a "sky platform."

At one time Julius urged Greenglass to enter college where he could study engineering and cultivate friendships with students of nuclear science; the Russians would furnish whatever money he needed beyond the GI Bill of Rights aid.

Then the British announced Fuchs's arrest on February 3, 1950. Julius Rosenberg came to the Greenglass apartment and talked with David. He told him about Gold's connection with Fuchs and said that he figured Gold would be caught next. He said that Greenglass had better leave the country.

After Gold's arrest, Julius again urged David to leave, gave him traveling instructions and $5000. But Greenglass didn't go.

Julius and Ethel Rosenberg, David Greenglass and Morton Sobell, another spy involved in the conspiracy, were indicted by a federal grand jury on charges of violating the Federal Espionage Act of 1917. Greenglass pleaded guilty. The Rosenbergs and Sobell pleaded not guilty.

The trial opened on March 6, 1951, in the United States Court House in Foley Square, New York. The trial judge was Irving Robert Kaufman. Kaufman made it clear from the first that he was aware of the profound implications in the case — the chances that prejudices, religious or political, might color a juror's thinking. He questioned prospective jurors closely. Where he noted the slightest doubt of objectivity, he excused the prospect, and thus the prosecution and the defense were saved a challenge.

The jury found the Rosenbergs and Sobell guilty of violating the Espionage Statute, which provided that those found guilty "shall be punished by death or by imprisonment for not more than thirty years." The courtroom was hushed on the day Judge Kaufman was to pass sentence — April 5, 1951. The black-robed Judge centered his attention on Julius and Ethel Rosenberg.

"Is there anything defendants wish to say?"

Julius Rosenberg said, "No, sir."

The Judge looked at Ethel Rosenberg. "Do you care to say anything?"

"No, sir."

Judge Kaufman began speaking. His words were those of a man who had reached a decision only after searching the law for long, weary hours; only after probing deep into his own heart.

. . . I consider your crime worse than murder. Plain deliberate contemplated murder is dwarfed by comparison with the crime you have committed. . . . I believe your conduct in putting into the hands of the Russians the A-bomb has already caused the Communist aggression in Korea, with the resultant casualties exceeding 50,000, and who knows but that millions more of innocent people may pay the price of your treason. . . . What I am about to say is not easy for me. I have searched the records — I have searched my conscience — to find some reason for mercy. I am convinced, however, that I would violate the solemn and sacred trust that the people of this land have placed in my hands were I to show leniency.

It is not in my power, Julius and Ethel Rosenberg, to forgive you. Only the Lord can find mercy for what you have done . . . you are hereby sentenced to the punishment of death.

Judge Kaufman sentenced Sobell to thirty years, and Greenglass to fifteen years.

Before the Rosenbergs died in Sing Sing Prison's electric chair, their case was to be given one of the most careful reviews in American criminal history. It was reviewed sixteen times, on various points, by the United States District Court. There were seven appeals to the Circuit Court of Appeals, seven petitions for review to the Supreme Court, and two applications to the President of the United States for executive clemency.

Judge Kaufman's decision stood. Julius Rosenberg was executed at Sing Sing Prison at 8:05 p.m., June 19, 1953. Ethel Rosenberg was executed ten minutes later.

The path of treason had led to Klaus Fuchs . . . to Harry Gold . . . to David Greenglass . . . to Julius and Ethel Rosenberg . . . and then to the death house at Sing Sing. That was the end of the trail.

10. *A Look at the Record*

WHEN President Theodore Roosevelt ordered an investigative force organized in the Department of Justice in 1908, there were dark warnings that the move was leading to political espionage and the suppression of civil liberties.

And almost half a century later the question was being heard at times: "Is there danger the FBI will become a Gestapo?"

Sometimes this question was asked for political purposes. Often it was asked by Communists and their sympathizers with the deliberate intent to undermine the FBI's position. But in some instances the question was asked because the American people, abhorring the idea of a "spy system," knew little about the "mystery" organization called the FBI.

The Gestapo was Hitler's secret-police system which had the power to make arrests, hold prisoners incommunicado, make searches without warrants, execute without trial, and persecute anyone whose political thinking and racial background didn't conform to the Nazi ideology. It was the twin of the secret-police system of Soviet Russia and her satellites.

To compare the FBI with these foreign police systems is as absurd as to compare the independent judiciary of the United States with the courts of the Soviet Union.

No one who studies the FBI operation from the inside — reading the orders from J. Edgar Hoover to his agents, leafing through the policy directives, and watching the transformation of a politically corrupt agency into a force struggling to achieve an ideal — can come to any other conclusion but this:

The FBI cannot become a repressive arm of government or of a clique as long as —

— the President of the United States is a man who rejects the idea of a secret political espionage system.

— the FBI is manned and directed by men of integrity who respect the spirit of the law as well as the words, who believe that establishing innocence is as important as establishing guilt.

— Congress watches the FBI's policies with a critical eye and the Budget Bureau checks on how the FBI spends its money.

— the judicial branch of the government remains free to question investigative procedures, to review evidence gathered by agents, and to protect the rights of the accused.

— the nation's press has the freedom to expose wrongdoing.

— the Bureau is kept free of politics.

There is one condition under which the FBI could become a Gestapo. This could only happen if the traditional checks and restraints were corrupted or eliminated by a dictatorial government, and the FBI was then used as a political tool.

But it is inconceivable that all these restraints could be corrupted or eliminated.

The FBI is not a robot of efficiency. It is a human organization, subject to mistakes in judgment and procedures. In every case of error — and they are a minute fraction of a percentage in the total of FBI investigations — the FBI has held a "fire drill" to tighten up its procedures to insure against the same thing happening again. And the failure has been one of mechanics and not the result of intent.

It isn't difficult to pick out flaws and mistakes in almost half a century of Bureau operations. But the important fact is that the FBI has moved forward in the protection of civil rights just as the nation has made progress in this direction.

The history of the FBI, in reality, is the story of America itself and the struggle for an ideal. It isn't perfect, but it has made progress in giant strides, and it's incomparably better than it was thirty years ago.

There is nothing magical about the way the FBI operates or the methods used to unravel mysteries. The facts are that the most baffling crimes are solved by hard grinding hours of labor and that the FBI never closes a case until it is solved.

Under Hoover's direction, the FBI has become known as an organization that is efficient and incorruptible. He has operated it on the private-corporation principle of delegating authority and responsibility. And no other agency in government, perhaps, keeps a closer check on its employes and the quality of their work.

During seven of the worst years of the Prohibition era, when the Prohibition Bureau, local law-enforcement agencies, and politicians were being corrupted by the bootleg millions, only one FBI agent was known to have "gone bad." He accepted $350 in a bankruptcy case, was caught by the FBI and was promptly prosecuted.

One of the strengths of the FBI has been in the continuity of its leadership, which has meant a continuity of policy. The basic policies established by Hoover under the direction of Harlan Fiske Stone in 1924 have remained unchanged.

In most agencies and departments of government, a new head has arrived every few years to establish new policies. But Hoover has remained at the helm of the FBI during the administrations of five Presidents and eleven Attorneys General.

Over the years, one interesting strand of the story has been the FBI's relationship with some of the liberals and intellectuals. By all

logic, every liberal should have stood shoulder to shoulder with
the FBI in its fight to expose Communism as the most reactionary
and imperialistic movement the world has ever known.

Many liberal intellectuals did speak out to suggest that there was
nothing contrary to liberalism in supporting the FBI as the professional agency equipped to deal with espionage, sabotage and subversion. But among others there was antagonism, as though the
FBI were invading a realm of political sophistication which was
outside the understanding of law-enforcement officers. One myth
which was planted by the Communists was that an attack on
Communism was an attack on freedom of thought. The suspicion
gained headway in some quarters that the FBI was an agency of
reaction and a symbol of intolerance.

But an attack on Communism is not an attack on freedom of
thought. Communism did not spring from the workers as a liberal
movement for personal and intellectual freedom. Communism is
a brilliantly thought out plan to destroy the old world and build
a new one in which "The Party" will be the central, all-powerful
brain ruling the world's millions. It is a dictatorship by the "scientific" mind, which uses the workers as a means to an end.

The top command of the FBI has no illusions that Communism
can be destroyed in the United States by the investigation, prosecution and conviction of Communist Party leaders. That is merely
one phase of the job to be done in a world-wide struggle.

The bigger job lies with the free world's philosophers, professors,
scientists, scholars and students. These people are the ones who
can and must convince men that Communism is evil. The world's
intellectuals must see that Communism is the deadliest enemy
that intellectualism and liberalism has ever had. They must be as
willing to dedicate themselves to this cause as the Communists
have been to dedicate themselves to their cause.

America's top labor leaders have never had any illusions about
Communism. They have fought the Communists in their ranks
for years and with few exceptions have succeeded in kicking them
out of places of influence. These leaders know that wherever Communism has taken over a country the "toiling masses" have lost
their rights and whatever chance they had for personal dignity.

In a 1956 address to the FBI National Academy graduating class, President George Meany of the American Federation of Labor and Congress of Industrial Organizations said:

> Any system of government in which a party is the government — particularly when there is only one party with absolute power over every walk of life — cannot be government by law. And without government by law there can be no freedom. . . .

The record seems crystal-clear. Communism was conceived by reactionaries, and Communism must be destroyed by true liberals who have the intellectual capacity to reach the minds of men with a counterlogic to Communism, which strengthens man's faith in himself, his free institutions and the ideal that personal freedom and government by law shall not perish from this earth.

In the whole struggle, the FBI represents the people's effort to achieve government by law. It is an agency of justice. And the FBI in the future will be as strong or as weak as the people demand it to be. No more. No less.

Don Whitehead

DON WHITEHEAD has been a journalist since 1931, when he joined the Associated Press as a local correspondent in Harlan, Kentucky. Since that time his assignments have taken him all over the world. His by-line became especially well known during World War II, when he accompanied Allied troops in Africa and Europe and made six assault landings. He was with the first troops to reach Korea in 1950, and received a Pulitzer Prize in 1951 for his Korean War coverage.

Mr. Whitehead also has done extensive reporting in and around Washington, covering the Senate and politics. After the 1952 election, he was one of three correspondents who accompanied Mr. Eisenhower to Korea, and his story of the President-elect's departure and the precautions taken to insure his safety won for Whitehead the 1953 Pulitzer Prize for distinguished reporting on national affairs.

Since 1956, he has been chief of the Washington Bureau of the *New York Herald Tribune*.

MISSION
TO BORNEO

A condensation from **THE SPIRAL ROAD**

By JAN DE HARTOG

YOUNG doctor's formidable first assignment is a native village in Borneo — a nightmare of tropical jungle, deadly disease and Stone Age savages. Filled with the potential strengths and weaknesses of the very young, Anton, the totok (the newcomer), finds himself teamed with — and pitted against — crusty old Dr. Brits-Jansen, whose name is a legend in the Netherlands East Indies. Their relationship is the moving, comic and profound core of this episode from Jan de Hartog's new novel, *The Spiral Road*.

"A rich and rounded reading adventure." — Florence Haxton Bullock, *New York Herald Tribune Book Review*.

HE ARRIVAL in the Dutch East Indies was a disappointment. Young Anton Zorgdrager, M.D., fought against a brief, unreasoning sense of gloom as he tumbled out, bag and baggage, late at night in front of the YMCA hostel. All during the long voyage from Holland, he had looked forward to his first encounter with the Orient. Then the ship had been late arriving, so they had moored in darkness, with nothing in the least exotic or Eastern to welcome them. Surrounded by sharp cones of floodlights shining down on warehouses that were the same the world over, the passengers had debarked, just like passengers in any port of the mid-1930's.

Anton meanwhile had looked in vain for someone to meet him among the waving crowd at the quayside. His orders from the Government Health Service had said: "Report at once to the Head of the Service." But it was dead of night, he did not know where the office was, there was no one to tell him — so he had given up, had decided to join his three young cabin mates from the ship just as they hired a taxi to take them to the YMCA in the city of Batavia. And even the taxi ride there had been a disappointment:

outside the car, Java was a lurching darkness, smelling of petrol, and, in the short silence while they waited at a grade crossing, there was no strange music to be heard, no scent of unknown flowers, no bright bird or giant bat caught in the beam of the head lamps.

At the hostel they sat glumly in a room no different from the same thing back in Holland, except for the mosquito netting over the bed. On the ship a deep friendship had grown up between the four "totoks," as newcomers were called in the Dutch Far East — Anton, the newly qualified doctor; Witzenburg, a Dutch Reformed minister on his way to a church in Medan; Frolick, a junior civil servant bound for Celebes; and Enters, with nothing in his pockets but the address of a cousin's sugar plantation.

Now they had arrived, they had nothing to say to each other. "It's funny . . ." Frolick started to speak, and then stopped. Silently they watched Enters open the bottles, beer for three of them and soda water for Witzenburg. "Plop!" said a beer bottle. "Tee-tjak!" said a lizard. It darted with short, flashing movements across the wall like a little electric toy in which the current was switched on and off. In the silence they could hear the foaming of the beer; it was a smoldering, fatiguing silence, throbbing with the hum of myriads of mosquitoes dancing in the darkness outside.

They needed a lot of beer to chase that silence away. But finally they all talked together and laughed at every joke; it was amazing how many they remembered from as far back as grammar school, about making funny noises during history and letting loose a mouse in the girls' gymnasium when they were rehearsing Greek ballet for graduation, and about the stink bomb that exploded during practical physics. Anton told a story from medical school, about a farmer who took away the doctor's lantern when his wife was being delivered of triplets, saying: "Blast, they're coming for the light!" Witzenburg told a story about a woman who wanted a library book for her husband who was ill: "Do you want a religious book?" asked the librarian, and she answered, "No, thank you, he's getting better." They wept with laughter, and when they could remember no more jokes, they started telling stories from their youth, pointless stories full of street names the others didn't know, and the silence threatened to get the upper hand again.

Trying to ignore the day that lay ahead, when all of them would disperse in four directions to begin their new lives, they battled against sleep as if they were guarding a treasure. When at last they separated for bed, they wished one another good night with a strange feeling of farewell, as if only now were they really leaving Holland, forever.

Anton's room was bare and hot. There was a framed motto on the wall: *Tomorrow may be too late.* Alone at last, he stood with heavy thoughts, like suitcases he didn't know where to put down.

Tomorrow may be . . . He fell on his bed without undressing, and gazed at the ceiling, his hands under his head.

Tomorrow . . . He took out his wallet, and from it his passport: *Zorgdrager, Anton.* Distinguishing marks: none. The face of a middle-class boy; a face one met everywhere in Amsterdam, three to every streetcar. Fair hair, gray eyes, an irresolute chin. *Tomorrow* . . .

For so many years he had looked ahead to this phase of his life. He had seen himself as a white-coated young savior among the suffering natives of the tropics, practicing medical science in the purest realization of its divine calling. He had pushed himself through long, lonely, poverty-stricken years in medical school, just to arrive at this point.

His mind went back to some words spoken to him by a fellow passenger on the voyage out: an older man, one of those experienced, boisterous Dutch colonials who had at first bewildered him, then impressed him. He and the planter had been having drinks together. "Three things you've got to know in the Far East," the planter had said, gazing over the sea to the scorched coast of Africa. "To drink, to let drink and not to get drunk. You're going to a hellish paradise, a mad world, Doc, full of madmen who want to make you mad too. Say, 'Hello, boys' but think, You won't get me.' Then you'll be all right. That's it — yes," he had gone on with sudden, startling grimness, "however hot hell may get, say, 'You won't get me.' Those are the people God looks after. Believe in God?"

"No," Anton had begun. "Theology, as I see it — "

"You'll soon get cured of that," the planter had said. "In the jungle, God takes people who say He doesn't exist on His pitch-fork and makes them squirm. He is different in the East; in Holland you can ignore Him, but in the jungle you'll hear Him humming."

Hear Him humming. . . . Anton stirred restlessly. How could he believe in God? His mind went back to the false piety of his child-hood, and memories of his father, who had been a country parson, rose in his mind. He saw himself as a thin child at the supper table in the old vicarage, trying not to listen as his father talked endlessly against the darkness, the wind and the loneliness beyond the shutters: "Professor I could have been. . . . Fame and riches could have been mine. . . . But God punisheth those He loveth; your mother had to die, my ambition and selfishness had to die, I had to shoulder the cross as a parson in the bleakest corner of this bleak country, so that in the end I might live like Jesus, saving souls. . . ." And his own cool child's reflection: liar, windbag, he talks about saving souls, but he doesn't leave any cheese for me.

The dislike for his father came back to him for a moment like a cold draft, and with it came the desolation of the motherless child, the memory of waking up sobbing from feverish dreams that his mother had come, and put her hand on his forehead, and asked what fairy tale he would like to hear, and he had answered "The Little Mermaid. . . ."

Turning restlessly on the bed in the YMCA hostel, he chased the chill of these memories with a wave of affection: he remem-bered Dr. Bakker, that great untidy giant of a country doctor with a wild mustache and sky-blue eyes that radiated friendliness. He loved that man; God knew how his life would have turned out without him. Dr. Bakker had befriended him as a child, had taught him to catch fish in the canals, had let him tag along as he visited patients, had blinked tears of joy when Anton had told him that he wanted to become a doctor. After Anton's father had died, Dr. Bakker had comforted him when he found himself helpless with inexplicable grief; he had helped Anton find a job that gave him enough money to go to the University; and he had helped Anton to win his medical-school scholarship.

The scholarship was given by the government and required young men to sign a contract saying that they would serve ten years in the Dutch East Indies after they qualified. When Anton won it, he and Dr. Bakker had celebrated in a real man's restaurant in Amsterdam, finishing up with cigars and coffee. They had day-dreamed without stopping about the jungle and the tigers and the coconut trees and you watch out, boy, for those brown girls.

So he had begun medical school; and so he had met the two other important people in his life: Bertha — Bert — the medical student who had become his best friend; and Els, the girl who had become his fiancée. He had known he would miss Bert and their endless serious conversations about everything from films to trau-matic neurosis; but Els, with her graceful innocence, her silvery laughter — he could not imagine life without Els. How would he have ever gotten through medical school without her?

Feeling nearer sleep now, Anton turned out his light. In the darkness Els's image hung before his eyes: her guileless child's face, her halo of blond hair, her cornflower-blue eyes. She was the daughter of a teacher in whose home Anton had rented a room. It seemed incredible that such an elfin creature could be the daugh-ter of two ponderous, proper parents — but she was; it seemed incredible that she could fall in love with him — but she had; it seemed most incredible of all that she had consented to marry him — but she had. Thank God for Els, he thought, for her loyalty, her warmth, her sweetness and tenderness; yes, thank God for Els.

He tried then to daydream ahead to the time when Els would join him, and live as a doctor's wife at the edge of the flowered jungle, in a little pavilion with a gallery and a native servant and perhaps a pet cockatoo. . . . The sound of bare feet padding along the corridor broke his train of thought, distracting him from the fantasy. The invisible feet receded and died away in the distance. With a dry throat, he stared up toward the ceiling. Then, abruptly, with a feeling of starting a nightmare, he fell asleep.

THE NEXT morning, he was taken to the Government Health Service Office in a sado, a sort of buggy; and it was a drive full of surprises. After he got over his wonder at the tiny horse, he marveled at the Dutchness of an old canal with seventeenth-century gables; at the cool dignity of the government palaces; at the shabbiness of the Head Office of the best-organized colonial medical service in the world — somewhere in a back alley, dirty white, at the far end of a tunnel of foliage, cracked pots with dead dwarf palms lining the drive. An old Javanese led him to the end of a corridor, to a room with an enormous fan buzzing on the ceiling.

Anton saw a desk covered with telephones and stacks of papers, behind the desk a man in shirt sleeves, and behind the man a big map of the East Indian islands. Dr. Kramer, the Head of the Service, was an ordinary man with an ordinary voice, who welcomed Dr. Zorgdrager to the Far East; a pity that Dr. Zorgdrager hadn't come into the office the night before because now time was getting rather short: the boat for Borneo was to leave in three hours' time. He was sorry this would not give Dr. Zorgdrager a chance to get acquainted with the Service first, and he was aware that it was unusual to send a newcomer out on an expedition before getting acclimatized, but he was forced to improvise because the circumstances were unusual. A plague outbreak had been reported in central Borneo; the district doctor had unfortunately succumbed Dr. Brits-Jansen had taken his place four weeks ago, but he had not been heard of since. It was most urgent that someone go there at once, with sixteen tins of anti-plague vaccine. Dr. Zorgdrager could refuse, of course, because it was a tall order and would put him to a severe test. But on the other hand, it was a fine chance to get to know the islands a bit. As for the route . . .

Dr. Kramer turned round and traced the route on the map behind him with a pointer: by mail steamer to Bandjermasin on the Borneo coast, where he would hire sixteen coolies; then by coastal steamer to Rokul, where he would commandeer four prahus, as the native boats were called; then three weeks up the River Kali-Woga to Rauwatta, where he would find, if all was well Dr. Brits-Jansen and the plague epidemic. Dr. Brits-Jansen was one of the oldest doctors in the Service, the foremost leprosy specialist in the world; a newcomer could not be in better hands

It wasn't much of a trip, really; and if Dr. Zorgdrager managed to cope with it satisfactorily, it would of course be a splendid recommendation for someone new to the Service. He would hear all the details from Dr. Martens, Head of the Expeditionary Department; just one other thing: he should not tell the coolies that they were on their way to a plague epidemic, for then they would all beat it like bats out of hell; and that would not be funny, of course: to find oneself alone in the jungle, a couple of weeks up a river, with sixteen tins of anti-plague vaccine. Well, so long, Dr. Zorgdrager. Have a nice trip, and all the best; Dr. Martens will help you on from here. . . .

Dr. Martens: tall, thin, sickly, bags under his eyes and a croaking voice: "Well, what a job to give a totok! Brinkman has already gone west in that plague epidemic; if Brits-Jansen is still alive, you may thank your lucky stars. Do you realize? Four weeks, and not a sound — how like the old man to . . . Well, let's get cracking. Mandur! Ambulance!"

There followed an unnervingly fast drive in a clanging ambulance to a hospital like a barracks: swarms of native male nurses in white sarongs, shuffling soundlessly through the dim corridors on bare feet; the stench of closed-in heat and disinfectant; then an immaculate native doctor with a white skullcap and a stethoscope around his neck like a witch doctor's amulet. "Dr. Sardjono — Dr. Zorgdrager." A handshake. "What was it you wanted, totok? Oh, yes: sixteen anti-plague and four P.G. . . . Mandur!" and an apelike male head nurse shuffled out of the shadows.

"*Ambil itoe ampat kaleng pest sama itoe ampat P.G.*"

"*Baik,* tuan doctor . . ."

"Sit down, colleague," Dr. Sardjono went on. "Your first job in the Service?"

"Yes."

"Well, give Brits-Jansen my love, will you? Tell him that I'm keeping a real beauty of a *lepra tuberosa* on the ice for him."

Martens was sitting in a steel chair, topee on the back of his head. "How's business this morning?" he asked Sardjono. Anton listened with awe to the ensuing conversation about operations, exactly the same as in the clinic in Amsterdam, only the numbers were different: in Amsterdam four per morning, here nineteen.

The mandur came trotting back from the shadow. "Tuan . . ."

"Did you put the tins in the car?"

"*Saja,* tuan doctor . . ."

A hurried good-by from Dr. Sardjono: "Well, we're sure to meet again. If you get a chance in Bandjermasin, say hello on my behalf to van der Waard. Will I be seeing you, Martens?"

"Yes, I'll put baby on the road, then I'll be right round. You can start putting the ruptures aside for me."

"Well, have a nice trip. Send me a picture post card, haha!"

Outside the sunlight hit them like a wave of hot water. They drove back from the hospital far too fast, Martens at the wheel, chattering like a woman. Anton looked at impressive avenues, cool and dark underneath the crowns of the royal palms; native families walked in the shadows, in single file, the man leading. "That just goes to show you that civilization is nothing but a veneer, my boy," said Martens. "The natives trot along in our European towns as if they might change back into the jungle any moment, and, let me tell you, they aren't far wrong either. I saw it happen myself, in

Celebes: they started a mine, built a whole village, then the mine turned out a dud and within a month the village had turned back into jungle: alang-alang in the sinks, snakes in the beds, vines on the church steeple — Blast! Nearly hit that coolie. They always do that, cross the road without looking, just like the rabbits in the woods back in Holland. . . . Oh, here we are."

After a mad rush of collecting an expedition kit for Anton, sorting out such things as instrument case, flea boots, netting, compass, maps, another frantic drive: this time to the quayside. A screaming, crashing, steam-hissing madhouse. "Mind your head!" Whining cranes, barking klaxons, Martens exploding: "Ye gods, where's that ape with the tins?" At last, when Anton was shaking with nerves, they arrived on board a white ship, a bedlam of running people bellowing commands, and hoarse quarrels from ship to shore over the whining of the winches. The door to Anton's cabin was blocked by a fat, pipe-sucking dreamer, his topee tipped over his nose, who said, "Sorry," and stepped aside. A hurried good-by from Martens, who was cursing the native porter in a frenzy of haste, in a cabin like an oven with two bunks and a whirring ventilator: "Here, *traperduli,* those tins in the bottom bunk — the chest in . . . *manah itu lain lima goddam kaleng?!* Well, old boy, chin up, everything will turn . . . *Skrobbi,* bungler, the chest up there, I said! . . . will turn out all right; but don't forget . . . Holy mercy, that's the siren! Well, old boy, keep smiling; and don't forget . . . Yes! I'm coming! . . . and take good care of the P.G., for they are the most important. . . ."

T HE LONELINESS, all of a sudden, with sixteen tins of anti-plague and four of P.G. that were the most important, but heaven only knew what was inside, was a relief at first, then an oppression, and suddenly a panic as the siren howled three times and the glinting roof of the shack behind the porthole began to slide past. Almighty heaven, here he was: on his way to a plague epidemic three weeks up a river in the heart of the island of Borneo, and nobody had considered it worth while to tell him how to hire coolies or commandeer prahus, or what language one should speak, or how to know where one was; only "Don't tell the coolies you're on your way to a plague epidemic, or they'll beat it" and "If Brits-Jansen is still alive, you may thank your lucky stars."

He stumbled outside, shaken with fear. He saw the quay, the harbor, the jetty glide past, and he was about to be sick with nerves and exhaustion when the fat pipe sucker stretched, knocked out his pipe on the rail and said: "God bless Batavia. The bloke who invented that town deserves a statue."

"Yes," said Anton, bravely, and swallowed. "But I'll settle for Holland any time."

"Holland?" the fat man asked. "I don't believe it exists any more. A lie my mother told me, like the stork. Going to Tarakan?"

"No, Bandjermasin, and then inland. I'm a doctor. Government Health Service."

"I see. Something wrong in the jungle?"

"Yes."

"What is it this time?"

"Plague."

"Well, every man to his own taste. Speaking for myself, I get dizzy if I see a boil. What about a drink?"

"Thank you," said Anton. "My name is Zorgdrager."

"How do you do," the fat man said. "Flabbinga. Oil."

WELL, here it was. This was exactly what he had imagined so often, back in Holland, while lying on his back in his bedroom staring at the slatted light of the street lantern on the ceiling: our hero, on an expedition into the interior to save a grizzled old doctor trapped in the magic forest. But Lord, how he longed to look at that slatted light again, instead of at this iron ceiling dripping with moisture above his bunk.

In the daytime he was all right. Then he could think about it all dispassionately. He wrote several letters to Els, which made him feel that the expedition was not so bad as it seemed, that he would pull through all right. After all, he had been a Boy Scout. He wrote to her about his experiences in Batavia, the jolly people he had met there, the wonderfully stimulating atmosphere of action and realism in the Government Health Service; he told her that the Dutch East Indies were extraordinarily like the United States of America as far as the white population was concerned; that both communities showed a hospitality and a directness in making friendships that was heartening and virile. That first day, before leaving for Bandjermasin, he had already made two friends who he was sure would remain friends forever: a wonderful old character called Martens, and a most intelligent, sensitive Javanese doctor called Sardjono. He wrote about ten pages of this, and ended with: *I have to stop now for good old Flabbinga is calling me.* Good old Flabbinga hadn't done anything of the kind. Good old

Flabbinga hadn't opened his mouth since they left Batavia, except to snore and to yawn; for thirty-eight hours now he had lain blind drunk in his bunk.

Yes, the days were all right; it was the nights that began to unnerve him. For then, in the sweltering heat, as he lay sweating in the darkness with swelling eyes and parched lips, he began to see a vision. A strange, schizophrenic vision: he saw himself as an onion, being peeled in the hands of God. He had thought he didn't believe in God. The words of the planter came back to him: "You'll soon get cured of that."

The onion was a symbol; he couldn't make out quite what it meant, but it was sure to have some hidden meaning. All of his thoughts, at night, were taken up by fear and by that onion, dancing on the misty edge of the dark lake of sleep. An onion being peeled, layer after layer, until only the little white heart was left, robbed of the protective armor that twenty-eight years of careful education had put around the defenseless white manikin inside.

If only he had somebody to talk to, somebody of whom he could ask things. It would have been quite easy to start talking with the ship's officers or his fellow passengers; yet he could not bring himself to do it. For everyone seemed to assume that he was a man who knew exactly what he was doing, in no need of any advice. He must look like the real thing. So much like the real thing that he did not dare open his mouth and ask, "By the way, how does one hire coolies?" for fear of making them laugh at him.

By the second morning, he found himself thinking over and over again about Bertha Waterreus, his friend at medical school. Bert. She was as manly as her nickname, with a defiant lock of hair on her forehead, an earnest boy's face, owlish glasses, square shoes and that shapeless skirt she wore. The one thing she could not control, that remained feminine despite her passionate efforts to appear sexless, was the sensitivity of her nostrils, finely chiseled and touching in their secret nervousness.

She had never known her parents, who were officers of the Salvation Army in a leper colony in Indonesia. Up to the age of sixteen, she had been in a Salvation Army home in Rotterdam; then an uncle in the Far East had sent her money to pay for her medical studies. She told Anton almost nothing of her youth but he guessed a great deal from her loathing for hymns accompanied by a harmonium, her suspicion of the sincerity of the Salvationists' children as they talked about "conversion" and "salvation," her hankering after truth, her desperate clinging to facts, like someone drowning in a swollen river of emotions. Every night she read Marx's *Das Kapital* instead of the Bible; she had scolded as hotly during Communist debates at the University as her fellow orphans had prayed during holiness meetings. He and Bert had disagreed endlessly about politics — but something, some similar feeling about life, and religion, and medicine, had drawn them into friendship. It had always been a solution to any problem or mood to go to see Bert; to drink tea beside her little oil stove, to smoke a cigarette with her, to have his ears boxed with facts proving that he was a decadent individualist. It had been a good friendship.

Suddenly, on an overwhelming impulse, he sat down in his cabin to start a letter. *Bert,* he scrawled, *I must write to you or I'll go nuts. I am on my way to Borneo with sixteen tins of anti-plague and four P.G. What the hell can P.G. be? Could you look this up and let me* . . . He rubbed his eyes and dropped his pen. He must be mad. Long before she received this letter, he would have found out himself what P.G. meant.

Flabbinga gave an enormous belch in the half-open coffin of his bunk, and a furry voice asked: "What's the time?"

It gave him quite a shock. Those were the first words his cabin mate had spoken since the ship had left. "Eleven thirty," he said.

Flabbinga said, "No kidding." There was a long silence, then he started snoring again.

Anton crumpled the letter to a ball and threw it out of the porthole. Now the day was as bad as the night: there was no sign of land on the horizon, but Borneo was inexorably drawing nearer.

THAT EVENING Flabbinga woke up, at last. Bright as a daisy, he stuck his head with the three days' beard in the washbasin, made hearty bubbling noises, trumpeted like an elephant and started to sing. If it hadn't been nine o'clock at night, this behavior would have seemed normal; just a happy man waking up to a new day, full of vim and vigor. He sang "Tiptoe Through the Tulips with Me" and the Dutch National Anthem. Then he shaved, and after shaving he trilled "Sheep May Safely Graze"; then he put on a white tropical drill suit and made for the bar.

Anton was waiting outside the cabin and, the moment the fat man appeared in the doorway, he virtually threw himself upon him, crying: "Hello! Good morning! How do you feel?" Flabbinga asked: "Morning? I see, drunk again. I'll have to catch up with you. Come on." So both of them went to the bar.

Half an hour later, Anton couldn't understand why he hadn't thought of this before. The bar was the solution. Three whiskies, and the prospect of Borneo looked as harmless as a child's picture book. Four whiskies, and he realized that Flabbinga was one of the funniest, most generous, most experienced pioneers of the jungle. Five whiskies, and he became religious; he was sure he had attained more than any monk had attained after forty years of fasting and praying; he loved everybody, he was full of courage, compassion and hope. Six whiskies, and he passed out.

The night was dreamless, onionless and refreshing. He was awakened in warm, pleasant sunlight by Flabbinga singing, in French, "I believe in Thee, O nature's Master." They had breakfast together on deck, their heads pleasantly swimming, and there was a faint nutty smell in the air. Only after breakfast, as he got up and stretched and looked ahead at the horizon, did Anton realize where the smell came from. There, blue and hazy like a mountain ridge in the distance, was Borneo.

He turned round and said to Flabbinga, with a lump in his throat: "I think that's Borneo." Flabbinga nodded. Anton swallowed, and asked in a voice that was slightly cracked: "By the way, how does one hire coolies?"

"Need coolies?" Flabbinga asked, looking up.

Anton blinked. "Yes," he said.

"How many?"

"Sixteen."

"Okay," Flabbinga said, rising, "I'll hire sixteen coolies for you. Let's go to the bar."

They stayed in the bar until the ship moored. Flabbinga drank whisky, Anton drank beer. Finally Flabbinga went ashore and Anton followed. Flabbinga walked with dignity. He didn't go far, just to a little wooden shack fifty yards away that had a sign nailed on it, saying *Harbor Master's Office*. Before entering he turned around, said to Anton: "Wait here." Then he vanished.

Anton waited outside in the hot sunlight for half an hour, while inside the little wooden shack he could hear guffaws of laughter and the clinking of glasses. By the time Flabbinga came out, Anton's nightmares had begun again; he was seeing moaning shapes, covered with horrible plague sores, in every shadow. "What coaster are you on?" Flabbinga asked, smelling of beer.

"A ship called *Henny*," Anton answered.

Flabbinga frowned. "The *Henny?* In that case you'd better look out; the captain is a crook. Steals the knife and fork out of your hands while you're eating."

"What about my coolies?"

"Coolies? Oh yes, coolies. Let's have a drink first."

"No," said Anton.

Flabbinga shook his head as if to clear his vision. "What d'you mean, no? You asked me to do you a favor, and you're too stingy to stand me a drink."

"I'll stand you as many drinks as you like," Anton said tremulously, "but I want my coolies first."

Flabbinga shook his head again. "You're hard to get on with," he said. "You're a nice man, Doctor, but you're too domineering. Take my advice and don't be domineering here, not with the white man. I know you've got culture, for I've got culture myself, but believe me . . ."

"For heaven's sake," said Anton, "let's get those coolies. Please."

"All right," said Flabbinga, "I just said it for your own good." Then he stuck two fingers in his mouth and whistled shrilly. "Sado!" he called. There was a sound of hoofs slithering to a standstill and, as Anton turned round, he saw a miniature hansom as big as a goat cart pulled by a tiny pony, a naked native with an enormous straw hat inside. Flabbinga and he got in. The springs creaked, the pony was lifted off its feet as the cart tipped backward, then the native got out and started to lead them toward the future.

THE HIRING of the coolies was the most degrading spectacle Anton had ever witnessed. It took place in a small, strong-smelling courtyard, and, if the animals in the stables had been horses or stray dogs, he would have felt like reporting it to the Society for the Prevention of Cruelty to Animals. But they were human beings; there was no society to report to. Meanwhile Flabbinga looked over the ghastly creatures like a cattle buyer, pinching their arms and opening their mouths. Anton thought of Bert and how she would have looked if she had seen this. He saw her face clearly in the quivering heat of the courtyard, and he shut his eyes.

"Okay," he heard Flabbinga say, "these will do. They're not much good but it's all he's got left. This little runt is your mandur."

Anton looked down and saw a scurvy one-eyed dwarf grin at him with a gaping mouth from which two yellow teeth jutted. "He'll do the kicking," Flabbinga said. "Don't touch the animals yourself; let him get the lice."

Anton looked at them. Fifteen indifferent skeletons with pointed knees and big mouths red from chewing sirih. "Thank you," he said. "Tell them to get my stuff off the boat and take it to the *Henny.*" Flabbinga took a breath, as if to say something, then turned to the mandur and gave an order in Malay. "Ah-ee!" yelled the dwarf, and started kicking. The fifteen skeletons began to move. Anton wanted to shut his eyes, but he resisted. He couldn't spend three weeks with his eyes shut; the sooner he got used to it the better. When finally they had climbed back into the sado and started downhill, Flabbinga said: "Don't be soft with those coolies. They don't understand anything but kicks."

"All right," said Anton.

"You should have given that order yourself," Flabbinga went on. "Don't let that little runt get the idea that you're a totok. Behave as if you had planted every single tree in the jungle yourself."

"All right," said Anton.

"And don't be impressed by it," said Flabbinga. "It's just like the zoo, only bigger."

For an instant, Anton knew that this was the moment to ask something basic and important, one big question that would cover everything: the fear, the loneliness, the horror of those coolies, the nightmare of the onion peeled in the hands of God. But he couldn't put it into words. They sat silently side by side while the goat cart, bucking and swaying, rushed downhill, toward a bar.

III

THE COASTER *Henny* was a shabby ship with two thin funnels side by side, leaning backward like the ears of an angry mare. The captain proved to be a black-haired wrestler in a dirty tropical suit. The ship smelled of pepper and cheese; its deck was a tangle of crates, ropes, goats and screaming pigs. Captain Krasser, so Flabbinga had told him, kept two Siamese women in his quarters; he must have been right, for as Anton glanced into the chartroom he saw a lipstick on the chart. The crew seemed to consist mainly of Chinese, and the cook who peeped at him out of his galley had the vacant grin of an idiot.

There was no cabin for him; he was supposed to sleep on a couch in the captain's cabin with a missionary on another one opposite, and the captain in the bunk. The cabin was a dark hole in which green flies flitted like sparks through the beams of sunlight from the portholes. He decided to go ashore before the ship sailed and went toward the gangway. "Where are you off to?" Captain Krasser asked.

"Ashore for a minute."

"Be back within the hour!" the captain shouted after him. "I'm not waiting for you! This is a ship, not a bus! Bos'n! Get a move on with that yellow rabble!"

Coward, weakling . . . It was no good scolding himself. He was on his way to the last man who might, please heaven, give him the password, the answer to his big question: van der Waard, the district medico. After he had left Flabbinga sprawled over a beer-splashed table in a bar, yet another layer had fallen off the onion. He knew nothing, nothing at all; he was about to be chased into the jungle like a shivering domestic animal, a Pekingese in the wilderness. He was alone now, alone with a pirate, sixteen skeletons and a missionary of whom the only thing he had seen so far was a pathetic cardboard suitcase with a bit of string around it.

An onion in God's hands; he felt more helpless and more naked all the time, and the worst thing was the knowledge somewhere in his mind that he would fail. He'd never make it, never; it was hopeless. Coward, coward! No good! He knew himself too well — always smaller and weaker than other people thought he was. So far he had gone through life without being unmasked. But now God had him on the palm of His hand, utterly alone, and God was asking: "Well?"

He walked along the low streets of Bandjermasin with the jungle at the far end of every one of them. He elbowed his way through a crowd of haggling Chinese, begging urchins, and native women with baskets of cackling hens on their heads; but he didn't see them. He saw again that somber planter on the ship, gazing at the coast of Africa. "Those who say in the jungle He does not exist," the planter had said, "He takes on His pitchfork and makes them squirm."

Over the crowd a banner swayed, stretched between two poles. *Tonight at 8:30 in the Salvation Army Hall Captain Koebeest will speak about "The Mouse and the Trap" with lantern slides. Come to Jesus! Admission — 1 cent.* It was written in Dutch, Malay and Chinese, with a picture of a mouse and a big trap with cheese in it. An arrow pointed to the cheese, and on the cheese was written: *Sin*.

No, God would not give him the chance to hide. God had given him brains and scientific knowledge; now he stood alone and would have to fight it out on a river somewhere in the wilderness. God, he thought, give me one minute of true faith, and I would go for that jungle like St. George for the dragon.

Professor G. J. van der Waard, M.D., the name plate said, on the gate of the drive. He hesitated at the gate; then he went in.

He did not quite know what to expect. He had hoped for somebody fatherly, soothing, sensible. A pale scarecrow peered through the crack of the door.

"Professor van der Waard?"

"Yes."

"My name is Zorgdrager. I'm new in the Service, on my way to the interior, and I . . . I just called to say hello, on behalf of Dr. Sardjono, in Batavia."

"Fancy," said the scarecrow, suddenly hostile. "Thank you very much indeed."

"My boat leaves in half an hour, and I would love to . . ."

"In that case, you'd better hurry," said the scarecrow. "Good-by." And he shut the door.

Anton stood in front of the door for a minute, wanting to kick it; then he turned round and went back down the path, cursing. Halfway to the harbor, he was suddenly overcome by a suspicion: he didn't dare! He didn't dare to talk to me; he is the district doctor, he knows what is going on, and that I haven't the ghost of a chance of coming back alive. Yes, van der Waard had given him the password after all: death patrol. They had sent him, the totok, the tenderfoot, on a death patrol.

The thought was ridiculous. He made his own diagnosis: hysterical cowardice. But it didn't make any difference: a death patrol, that's what it was. He didn't even feel ashamed of the word that came straight out of the penny dreadfuls. During all his years of training, he had never received an image of the jungle strong enough to chase away the visions from his boyhood reading: witch doctors, head-hunters, crocodiles, death patrols. A death patrol, Dr. Zorgdrager; they have sent you on a death patrol.

When he arrived back at the *Henny,* he had already died and rotted, his flesh had been eaten by snakes and lizards, his skeleton had been found by an expedition three years later, and Els had married a dentist. A little boy with trachoma accosted him at the gangway, asking for alms in a high shrill voice: "Money, tuan?" As he climbed the gangway he heard the childish voice again, behind his back: "Money, madam?" He turned round and saw a priest in a cassock following him on board.

HE WOULD not forget the first meal on board the *Henny* as long as he lived. For half an hour he forgot all his problems, as he sat between Captain Krasser and Father Ambrosius underneath the swinging paraffin lamp, and watched a duel between a Christian and a loud-mouthed oaf, fought out with knife and fork.

Outside, on the foredeck, the Chinese crew were miaowing at the moon to a flute and a lute, a monotonous tune that spiraled around one note, as if it accompanied the circling of the moths around the paraffin lamp. The lamp shed a harsh, yellow light that flashed on the teeth of Captain Krasser, and glistened in the sweat on the waxy forehead of Father Ambrosius.

"Missionaries!" said Captain Krasser, tearing the meat off a chicken leg with his teeth. "Hypocrites, the lot of them! You can't go anywhere, you can't even enter a pub — there they are, sneaking about in their long skirts, sweeping the floor with their broom of sin and making you cough your heart up. Sin! What the devil is sin? An invention of those hypocrites, that's all. I'm not worrying about sin — no!" — and he gnawed the bone, crushing it. "Fu Ling!"

The Chinese steward materialized like an apparition. "Yes, Mistel Captain Sir?"

"Three coffees with a sting."

"Yes, Mistel Captain Sir."

Anton looked back at the priest — a fat little man with a face that did not seem to match his body. He had been sitting there for over half an hour now, unmoved under the onslaught. The captain's reserve of curses had taken Anton's breath away; he hadn't let up for more than a few seconds, and yet never repeated himself. He had challenged and mocked God in several languages, he had cursed and slavered until his moron's face glistened with sweat and grease, but not with a single frown had the father betrayed that he was disturbed or even listening.

It had started when the priest had made the sign of the Cross before the meal. It had raged like a tempest during the meal, and it finished after the meal with a thunder-and-lightning finale that made Anton's mouth sag in horrified admiration. At the beginning of the captain's monologue he had wondered whether it wasn't his duty as a gentleman to come to the aid of the poor defenseless priest, but at his first word, "Captain . . ." the father had looked up, his eyes so impressive with controlled strength that it had not been necessary for the captain to shout, "Shut up!"

Fu Ling brought in the coffee and three glasses of brandy: the priest drank only the coffee. The captain had either eaten too much or was too exhausted to say more; and after the coffee, he went to the bridge to take over the watch. Anton tried to start a conversation with the priest; the little man smiled, said, "I don't want to seem impolite, sir, but I'm rather tired," and lay down on his couch after praying on his knees, a spectacle at which Anton, embarrassed, tried not to look. He knew of nothing better to do than to lie down himself, and he lay listening to the caterwauling Chinese until he fell asleep.

The next day, he didn't talk to the captain or the priest until the evening meal. The captain was on the bridge or in his locked cabin; the priest sat reading his breviary under the awning on the aft deck. The ship was filled to the brim with natives and Chinese; whole families were camping on the deck, cooking their meals on little fires inside perforated petrol tins, making a smoke cloud that sailed with the ship along the blue-green coast of Borneo.

Flabbinga had said that Anton needn't bother about his coolies until they arrived in Rokul, at the mouth of the Kali-Woga River; that the mandur would take care of their rations and the more he left them alone the better it was. Yet he couldn't resist the temptation to look for them in the crowd, squatting without any protection on the scorched deck. They were sitting, all sixteen in a heap, absorbed in some sort of dice game. Nobody looked up at his arrival except the mandur, who grinned and said: "Tuan." He stood looking for a while at their mysterious game, listening to their guttural noises. It was swelteringly hot, not a breath stirred the stench and heat that hung overhead. He went back to the cabin and lay down, panting, his arms spread, his head back.

After the short blood-red dusk, when night fell like a net of stars and the paraffin lamp in the cabin was lit again, the singing of the Chinese on the foredeck brought a strange suspense, like the overture to an opera. The priest had hardly sat down at the table when the captain appeared and, even before sitting down, he attacked the priest with a breath-taking ferocity. The night before, he had reviled the saints; this night he opened the floodgates of his scabrous mind. But the obscenities that he strung together produced no change in the imperturbable chastity of the priest's face.

When the captain at last gave up, hoarse and panting, Anton began to understand that this was more than just a one-man brawl. The miaowing of the orchestra behind the dead eyes of the portholes gave it the background of a fable. That night he looked with jealousy at the praying priest, draining cosmic strength out of the universe into himself by merely folding his hands, while he, the unbeliever, could only sit and watch.

The next day, he once more tried to talk to the priest, who was leaving the ship the following day; this meant that the last act of the drama would take place that evening, and sin would either triumph or break its neck. The priest was very kind but not talkative. He said that he was going back to his mission school in the jungle after his yearly leave and that he knew the captain quite well. He had sailed with him before, a curious man.

During the hours of waiting for the evening to fall, Anton sat in a patch of shadow, watching the smooth sea and the unchanging coast of Borneo. It seemed to be cooler, yet he could not lift his thoughts out of their lethargy. When evening fell, he did not wait for the sunset and was sitting at the table when Fu Ling came to light the lamp and lay the plates for the meal.

The priest was the first to join Anton; the meal had already been served when at last the captain appeared. He was quieter than on the previous night and for a short while Anton thought nothing would happen. The scoundrel seemed to have had enough and drank his soup noisily, with his mind on it. But then, after the soup plates had been taken away, Fu Ling brought in glasses and a decanter containing green liquid, and the captain said: "Father, I don't want to put you back into the forest without a little celebration. Here's looking at you."

He filled the glasses; the priest shook his head with a smile and went on eating bits of bread with a steady hand. The captain said: "Come on, Father, you can't refuse that! Would you like me to call in a couple of guests to give you a heart?" When the priest did not answer, only stopped breaking bread, the captain clapped his hands and two Siamese girls came in, giggling, in white sarongs. He greeted them with a hungry grunt, pulled them down on his knees and fed them the green liquor.

They were frightened black-eyed girls with heavy coils of oily hair and the ingratiating coyness of pet animals. The captain slapped their bare shoulders, pointed at the priest and said: "Well, there he is! Come on, give a look at Uncle Holypuss!" They looked and giggled; after the captain had thrown back three glasses of the green drink, he described, in mounting richness of detail, what he liked about his living toys. Then he pushed one of the girls toward the priest and shouted, "Here, Father!"

Anton thought: now I ought to get up, now I ought to get up and knock the swine's teeth in. But he did nothing; he remained seated, toying with his fork, and noticed suddenly that there was no music tonight, only the throbbing of the engine below and, somewhere above, a soft hissing of steam underneath the stars.

Meanwhile the priest ignored the girls, looking up only to thank Fu Ling when he brought in the coffee.

Finally Captain Krasser got to his feet, kicked the girls into the night and strode out. The priest looked up, and his eyes met Anton's. There was nothing to be seen in them; they were calm and kind, almost childish; then a drop of perspiration ran slowly down his forehead and along the bridge of his nose.

The next morning, the priest went ashore. The ship lay with its engines stopped at the mouth of a river that was no more than a rabbit hole in the wall of the jungle. A prahu had come out of it with two natives inside, and it took the priest away. As he stood at the rail, his cassock lifted to step onto the rope ladder, the captain said: "Hey! What about thanking me for your board and keep?"

"God bless you, my son," said the priest; then he went down the ladder.

The prahu sailed away and was soon lost in the blue and the green of the sea and the jungle. Then the white speck of the cassock vanished as the wilderness closed over it.

THAT NIGHT during supper the captain said nothing. The next night he didn't say anything either, and the morning before they were to arrive at Rokul he still hadn't said a word. He sat naked in his bunk, beset by flies, and watched Anton packing his box.

"What are you going to do in the jungle?" he asked finally.

"Deliver medicine," Anton answered, without looking up.

"High up the river?"

"Three weeks."

"Have you got a guide?"

"No."

"Prahus?"

"No."

"Well," he said, getting out of his bunk. "Surely you've got a gun?"

"No," said Anton.

He shook his head. "Some people," he said, "ought to be shot." Then he got up, dressed, and went to the bridge.

While the ship was approaching another rabbit hole in the wall of the jungle, Anton wondered who the captain considered ought to be shot. He himself? The Government Health Service? As the anchor chain rattled out he longed for a drink, but he did not want to ask the captain. Though he had not been able to intervene while the captain tortured the priest, he felt that the least he could do now was to ignore him.

As soon as the anchor was down, the captain, unasked, lined up Anton's coolies and, ignoring his protest, examined them in such a thorough fashion that Flabbinga's inspection seemed gentle in comparison. After this, he discarded three of them and shanghaied three others among the deck passengers, despite their shrill protests and the miserable wailing of their families. Then he went into his cabin, came out with a double-barreled gun, held it out to Anton and said: "Here you are."

"But — but in Batavia I was told I wouldn't need any arms."

"That may be so for a man who knows where he's going, but you had better take it. Those coolies smell a totok ten miles off." He hung the gun round Anton's neck. "Bos'n! Lower the long-boat!"

"But, Captain," Anton remonstrated, "it's very kind of you, but I wouldn't even know how to work the thing."

The captain shrugged. "That's all right. It's for show only, and if the show isn't enough, the bang will do."

The longboat was lowered. The coolies, screamed at by the

horrible little mandur, lowered his chest and his tins into it and then filed down the rope ladder themselves. He followed them. So did the captain, and the boat rowed to Rokul, a miserable hamlet of huts on mossy poles, standing spiderlike in the mud flats. In Rokul the captain commandeered four prahus by taking them away from four huts, after shouting a few coarse words up at the dark holes in the floors of the huts, out of which small brown children's faces peered like baby swallows out of a nest. Then they went to a fifth hut, into which he climbed. After he had vanished inside there were sounds of altercation, terminated by a smack. He came back with a trembling old man. "The best guide there is," he said to Anton. He grabbed the old man by the scruff of his neck, shook him, pointed at Anton and made a little speech that sounded bloodcurdling even though Anton didn't understand a word of it. "All right," he concluded. "I've told him that if he tries to run away you will shoot him through his stomach. It'll take him three days to die and he'll regret every minute of it."

After that, he divided the coolies into four crews, four men to each prahu, the guide in the first one, Anton and his mandur in the last. "Be careful you stay in the rear," he said. "Once they pass you downstream, you'll never catch them again. Now those tins. They all contain the same?"

"No," said Anton. "Four of them are special."

"All right," he said, and divided them over the four boats, putting one P.G. in each. Anton wanted to keep them all in his boat, but Krasser said, "Why do you think they told you to commandeer four prahus? Because if one of them capsizes, you only lose five tins. And if it's only one, you'll be lucky. Got your map and your compass?"

"Yes."

"Sit down in the stern and put the gun across your knees."

He obeyed; the captain held the edge of the prahu until he sat. It was a portentous moment, and yet somehow ridiculous, reminding him of the times when he had hired a rowboat in his student days.

"Don't drink from the river," the captain said. "Leave that to those apes. Here . . ." He handed over a small crate of beer that

Fu Ling had been carrying after him. "Don't drink more than two per day, otherwise they won't last out."

"But, Captain," Anton said. "I definitely don't want . . ."

"Shut up!" said the captain. "I've got enough beer for an orphanage. Ah-ee!" he shouted at the guide, and the first prahu cast off. When Anton's turn came the pirate said: "That business with the priest was personal. Forget it." He pushed the prahu off. "Good luck, and don't let the jungle get you down."

The prahu shot, turning, into the heart of the stream.

"If you come back with those tins," the pirate shouted, "I'll kick you to death. . . ."

He didn't hear any more. The coolies dipped their paddles into the water and swung them in a slow rhythmic movement to the tune of the mandur's plaintive chant: "Ah-ee . . . ! Ah-ee . . . !"

He waved at the pirate, small and white underneath the gigantic spider of a hut; then he looked ahead. The river looked like a creek that ended abruptly, so closely did the walls of the forest approach one another.

"Ah-ee . . . ! Ah-ee . . . !"

He was alone with the Far East.

IV

B Y DAY it was an adventure, by night a delirium.

By day he sailed up a fairy-tale river, with always and everywhere the eternal green, the sky a narrow blue gap high up between the crowns of the trees. Occasionally there was the sudden color of a cluster of flowers, or a floating island of snowed-down white blossoms, and always there was the smell of putrefaction. He let himself be rowed, reclining under his awning, listening dreamily to the chanting of the mandur and the twittering of thousands of birds, that ceased only in the hottest hour of the day, when all sound seemed to be scorched away by the murderous sun.

But by night, this dream world became a nightmare. First the twittering of birds turned into the whining of mosquitoes; then there were rustlings, splashes, shrieks and maniacal laughter. He lay, panting, under the pressure of this teeming darkness, with a feeling of terror he had never known before, separated only by the gauze of his mosquito netting from the delirium of the tropical night.

During the first days he was alert and full of curiosity. But the deeper they penetrated into the jungle, the slower his thoughts became. His mind seemed to get gluey, lethargic, until in the end he could hardly think at all. All he did was to turn over lazily in his mind some strings of words. "Death patrol." "Tomorrow may be too late." "Tiptoe through the tulips with me." He hummed it, out of tune with the chanting of the mandur, then the thought flashed through his stupor: "I'm letting myself go. I ought to do something, stay awake. . . ."

But the mandur sang him back to sleep, "Ah-ee . . . Ah-ee . . ."; the birds twittered, one endless tremolo of twittering; the drops of the paddles drew dotted lines on the river — the river, on which they had spent only three days of the three weeks. He wanted to rouse himself from this paralyzing lethargy, do something, but he sat motionless under his awning, making only a few movements a day: open a beer bottle, take a sip, eat a bite, wipe sweat. "Ah-ee . . . Ah-ee . . ."

Sometimes, in the short coolness before sunrise, as the birds awakened him from a heavy, exhausting sleep and he watched the pink clouds of morning mist roll slowly up the tree trunks, it occurred to him how disgusting it was to let himself be smothered by the jungle without so much as lifting a finger. As soon as there was no one left to show off to, no Els, no Bert, no Flabbinga, not even a Captain Krasser, his knees had given way and he had collapsed with a sigh. The paddlers paddled, the birds twittered, the river flowed, relentlessly; only he remained motionless, sitting underneath his little awning, and let himself be carried, asleep, a Boy Scout in the magic forest.

In the end he did nothing at all. He moved only in his thoughts. In his thoughts he took out the wallet with Els's photograph and looked at it, but it no longer meant anything to him, just a pale face from the past.

He searched for things to think about in order to remain awake.

He tried to remember his life from childhood onward; he tried
to think about nice things, things that would not change, even if
he never came back. Els's love. Bert's friendship. His first pipe.
Smoke. Crematorium. As a child he had imagined what his own
funeral would be like; how he would stand among the mourners
around the grave, and hear the sad songs sung. Now, suddenly, this
dream seemed to turn into reality. It seemed as if the real Anton
Zorgdrager had secretly sneaked out of his body and floated upward, up like a child's balloon, tied to the sleeper in the prahu by
a gossamer thread. He saw, more clearly than by opening his eyes
and looking, the small procession of four narrow prahus creeping
slowly through a crack in a continent of green. It drifted on, and
on — only by using all his strength could he haul back that thread,
slowly, until at last he was back in his hot body, and opened
his eyes, and awakened to the cradle song of the mandur and
the birds.

"Ah-ee . . . Ah-ee . . ."

As he groped for a beer bottle he started to hum: "Tiptoe, tiptoe
through the tulips . . ."

Hopeless. The jungle had obliterated him. Dr. Zorgdrager was
no more; he had returned to the womb of time, to the world as it
was before the advent of man.

"Ah-ee . . . Ah-ee . . ."

He fell asleep again.

BY THE TIME they reached the rapids, he had become a sleepwalker. He did what the mandur told him to do, without thinking.
He got out of the boat clumsily, watched with dull eyes the coolies
drag the prahus through the foaming turbulent water, stepped
from stone to stone with unconscious sureness: a sleepwalker.

The only straw to which his will to live still clung was: twenty
tins. Twenty tins, sixteen anti-plague and four P.G. The P.G. are
the most important; if anything should happen to the P.G. I'll have
to swim after them and drown. Each time the prahus were dragged
through rapids by the slithering, panting coolies, he counted them:
sixteen anti-plague, four P.G. Inside himself nothing was left, not
a hope, not a memory, not a feeling of shame; but if anything

should happen to those twenty tins, his life would be in danger, he would be dead. Those tins were the last positive element; everything else had become pointless in the unchanging jungle, where every day was exactly the same as the one before; where the riverbanks never varied, as if during the night they had floated back to the point from which they had set out the previous day, like damned souls who had to make the same voyage over and over again, for all eternity, without ever arriving anywhere.

One afternoon, after he had thrown a beer bottle overboard and followed it with his eyes as it was swiftly carried away, the hallucination that had recurred every day suddenly turned round. The real Anton Zorgdrager no longer floated over the jungle, connected with the body under the awning by the gossamer thread; suddenly the real Anton Zorgdrager was sitting in the prahu, and the sleeping body was drifting away with the beer bottle, home.

Home! It was like a blow on a gong, a sudden, violent awakening. He was lost! He would vanish in that jungle like a ghost! He had only one chance left to save his life: go home!

The beer bottle vanished from sight, but it took the thread with it, pulling him back to the world, to life, home. The wish to turn back was stronger than sleep; that night he lay awake staring into the darkness with throbbing temples, listening to the insane cacophony of the jungle. He saw feverish visions, and the last certainty left him. If he did not flee, climbing plants would sneak up his body, creep around his neck, weave a paralyzing net around him. Somewhere at the edge of his consciousness, he knew his own symptoms, knew it was the madness of the jungle, the lone man's last enemy; but knowing it did not help. He was powerless in the grip of the wilderness. Even though he knew what he was dying of, he was dying all the same.

The next day the mandur began to sing, "Ah-ee . . . Ah-ee . . ." once more. Anton folded his hands around the cap of a beer bottle, closed his eyes and prayed, "God, dear God, save me, give me a sign . . ." Then he threw up the cap, and thought, "If it falls the right way up, it means: go home; the wrong way up: carry on." He opened his eyes. It was lying the right way up. Go home, God said. He threw once more — carry on. Once again — go home.

Then he threw the cap overboard, feeling lost. He had spoiled the significance of the sign because he had had no faith. Now it no longer meant anything.

The thread stretched longer and longer. He lay under his awning and let himself be carried as if on a stretcher: too cowardly, too weak to escape.

"Ah-ee . . . Ah-ee . . ."

He tiptoed through the tulips toward death.

THE THREAD that connected the phantom with the body could hardly be felt any more, when the rapids that seemed to repeat themselves every day were suddenly different.

He was standing on a stone in white foaming water; the coolies were dragging the prahus across; the mandur shouted and the guide shouted; then, suddenly, the voices fell silent and the men stood motionless, looking at something that changed the world.

In the small stillness behind a rock lay a dead body, half under water. Two thin arms pointed at the sky, and the current made rings round two drawn-up knees. But it was not death that made them all stare at the body with horrified eyes; it was the boils on the arms, as big as fists, and black. It was the plague.

One of the prahus shot back, some coolies jumped inside, others were dragged off their feet clutching the gunwales; the current dragged the prahu downstream, home.

And then the thread snapped. He suddenly stood bolt upright, the water foaming round his legs, and cried: "Stop! Stop, damn you!" The other prahus started to rumble down the rocks of the rapids, all the coolies tried to flee in a panic of fear; he took down his gun, put it against his shoulder, and fired. The shot barked; the butt hit his shoulder; wood splintered off the stern of the second prahu; the coolies ducked. He fired again; then the mandur started to scream, to shake his fists at the coolies, to kick them; he drove them back, up the rapids. They strained, moaning, in the ropes and dragged the remaining prahus into the next stretch of the river. In the distance the fugitive vanished: one tin of P.G., four anti-plague, and the guide, the only man who knew the way to Rauwatta.

"Mandur!"

The mandur came splashing toward him, bowing. *"Saja, tuan besar . . ."*

"Pick up that chest; put it ashore."

The mandur obeyed, splashed to the bank, and put down the medicine chest respectfully. All of them watched as Tuan Doctor opened the chest, took out a box, a bottle, a pack of cotton wool. Then he fetched a tin out of the nearest prahu, cut it open and took out a stack of wooden boxes containing phials.

Intramuscular, four cc. He gave twelve injections to twelve trembling creatures, after having first given himself a shot in the arm to show them that he wasn't going to murder them. Then he put his instruments away and said to the mandur: "Now nobody need be afraid any more. None of you will get the plague. I am taking the first boat with the map; you take the last one. Anyone who makes a move that looks like running away will be shot. Translate that."

The mandur started to talk to the coolies. Anton did not stay to listen, but went back to his prahu. As he turned round he saw that they were looking at him with a respect that no one had ever shown him before. But it did not give him any satisfaction, or even surprise him; he registered it and thought: "Good. We have twelve days to go, those injections will take effect ten days from now, so when we arrive they'll be immune."

He didn't give a thought to the miracle that had happened. A new man had been born in the jungle: Dr. Zorgdrager of the Government Health Service. The boy, the coward, the traveler without destination had vanished. "Ah-ee!" he cried.

The coolies jumped into the boats, pushed off and chanted after him. His prahu shot ahead, leading the convoy. He spread out the map in front of him and put the compass on top of it. We may get lost a hundred times, but don't worry, Dr. Brits-Jansen, I'll find you even if it takes a year.

"Ah-ee . . ." the mandur chanted. "Ah-ee . . ."

That awning above his head was wrong. They should see him in the bright sunlight, attentive from morning till evening, looking round with his gun ready. He took it down.

"Ah-ee . . . Ah-ee . . ."

The birds twittered; the water of the rapids foamed around the small stillness where the body lay, its arms stretched toward the sun. The prahus sailed away and were soon lost in the green and the blue of the jungle and the sky. Then the white speck of Anton's topee vanished, as the wilderness closed over it.

V

THE FIRST white man to sail up the Kali-Woga as far as Rauwatta had been Dr. Brits-Jansen, the Wise Old Man of the Government Health Service.

Thirty years ago, a telegram had ordered him to proceed at once to Tarakan, to the palace of the Governor of Borneo. Sultan Rahula Rattan Rauwari of Rauwatta, the Governor told him, was dying. And the Sultan was an enlightened ruler, a stanch ally of the government, the only Dyak chief who had been to Holland and even spoke Dutch — this man should be kept alive at all costs.

A very important mission, the Governor had said, a great chance for the new Government Health Service to prove its mettle. Brits-Jansen, deeply impressed, had left at once, traveled three weeks up the river, dragging a medicine chest, to arrive, after a nightmarish trek, in Rauwatta: desolate breeding ground of plague and malaria on the mudbanks of the Kali-Woga.

He was led by the village elders to the Sultan's palace, where, in the red dusk of torches, the first thing he discerned was a billiard table, its legs standing in coconut shells filled with water to keep the ants at bay. On the walls hung the dried heads of the Sultan's late enemies, and in their midst a gilt-framed photograph showed a sly little native in frock coat and top hat beaming with pride on a swivel chair in the main cigar store in Amsterdam. That native was Sultan Rahula Rattan Rauwari, enlightened ruler of a territory three times the size of Holland, with a population of three thousand.

Malodorous girls lifted a curtain behind the billiard table; there, in a dark smelly room, he found an ornate Victorian bed: on that bed, the royal patient lay in a coma, thin, tiny and impressive in his motionless suffering. The girls cautiously lowered the curtain again behind the giant doctor with the terrible beard; Brits-Jansen sat down on the edge of the bed, that sagged with a twang of springs, and from the startled glance the patient shot him he concluded that the coma was not a deep one. The Sultan moaned, and he swallowed with a choking sound, but the man who could fool Brits-Jansen with a faked illness had still to be born. While examining the childish body he asked himself what purpose an Enlightened Ruler could have in pretending to be ill. When he completed his examination he still did not know the answer.

"Tell what matter Sultan . . ." the patient whispered. "Tell what illness Sultan suffers. . . ."

Brits-Jansen slapped the little man's buttocks, answered, "Nothing," and got to his feet. "You'd better get up, sire," he concluded. "You're as healthy as a pig."

For one speechless second, the Sultan gaped at him, flabbergasted by such disrespect. Then his sly little eyes filled with fury and he whispered: "Doctor worst doctor Sultan ever seen. Doctor eye and mind of *sappo-lidi*."

"Possibly," Brits-Jansen answered. "I may have the eye and mind of a fly swatter, but I'm the best billiard player in the Far East."

That was too much. Sultan Rahula Rattan Rauwari rose in his bed like a cobra, with the murder of twenty head-hunting generations blazing from his black eyes, and hissed: "Sappo-lidi! We shall play! Sultan shall play Sappo-lidi till he is slain!"

"All right," Brits-Jansen answered. "But on one condition: if I win, Sultan is cured forever."

"And if Sappo-lidi loses?" the Sultan asked, slyly.

"Then I'll retire from the Service," Brits-Jansen said, "and nurse Sultan until my death, as his private doctor."

The Sultan got out of bed without a word. He lifted the curtain and went toward the billiard table. The malodorous girls, frightened out of their wits, took flight. After the Sultan had chalked his cue, made his first shot, and scored twenty, eyes were peering through all the cracks in the bamboo walls and a silence reigned in the jungle as if an act of God were taking place.

They played on until the red sun rose out of the morning mist and the birds started twittering in the trees; the Sultan played like a demon, but Brits-Jansen played as only one man could play east of Singapore: Dr. Brits-Jansen of the G.H.S. That morning, after he had won with an astronomical score and made the Sultan weep with rage, he went out and made a tour of the village, while the inhabitants fled from him in panic. He walked past age-old, rotting huts, and he saw why the Sultan had been ill. The miserable dwellings surrounding the gaudy palace were memorials to exploitation and slavery; the sly little despot obviously fooled his victims with frequent sickbeds so as to give them hope that he would soon die anyhow. The billiard table alone was a monument to a demigod: it must have cost scores of lives to drag the unwieldy thing upriver across all those rapids.

The government might consider this slave trader to be an enlightened ruler; Brits-Jansen thought differently, and decided to teach him a lesson. He knew that the magic power of the demigod would be finished as soon as his subjects were shown a real god compared to whom their Sultan was a midget. Brits-Jansen decided that an official dinner should take place in his honor, when he would show Sultan Rahula Rattan Rauwari a miracle that would make him gape with astonishment.

The Sultan haughtily agreed to his proposal, and ordered that a feast to celebrate his recovery should be served that night in the village square. During the whole day the village was full of the smells of cooking. When darkness fell, a table stood in the flickering torchlight, laden with enough food for a dozen people: piles of fruit, fish, chicken, eels, and a whole billy goat, filled with eggs. Brits-Jansen's contribution was a pint of gin, his month's ration.

Hours beforehand, the square was packed with silent, staring villagers. When the Sultan finally appeared, he was in full court dress; and when their eyes met, Brits-Jansen saw the Sultan realized that they were about to fight another duel, this time for something more important than a lifelong deathbed.

Brits-Jansen gave the Sultan a perfunctory bow, rubbed his hands, and sat down opposite him, facing the crowd. Then he poured out a full beaker of gin for the Sultan and half a beaker for himself, said, "Sire, here's mud in your eye," threw back the drink, slammed down the beaker and started eating. He ate as only one man could eat east of Singapore: Dr. Brits-Jansen, G.H.S. The Sultan, after his first sip of gin, shot his opponent a glance of pure hatred, but he took up the challenge, and drained the beaker in one gulp, choking.

The banquet lasted until the small hours. During all that time, not a word was said and not a finger moved in the crowd squatting in the square. It was much more of a battle than Brits-Jansen had expected; he had to gorge to keep ahead of the Sultan, and the world had been slowly distorted into a whirlpool of darkness when, at last, Rahula Rattan Rauwari turned turtle. After three beakers of gin, four fish, eighteen eggs, a leg of billy goat and two chickens, he slowly sagged sideways and slumped to the ground without uttering a sound, majestically silent to the end.

When the demigod fell off his throne, the crowd in the square retired in horror to the very edge of the torchlight; but when the god went on eating as if nothing had happened, they stealthily crept nearer again, helpless in the grip of curiosity. Never in his life had Brits-Jansen eaten such a disgusting amount of food, never had he felt so close to a stroke. Yet he went on eating — fish, eggs, goat — until he knew: one more bite and I'll burst.

Then, as he sat swaying on his stool, gasping for breath, shaken by hiccups, he performed the final miracle — the Horrible Deed, that would be whispered down from generation to generation in the Borneo jungle until Judgment Day. He wiped his mouth, shoved his topee on the back of his head, looked, for the first time, at the mesmerized crowd; then he took his upper jaw out of his mouth and smacked it on the table. One second later, the square was empty of villagers; they were swept into the jungle as by the blast from a bomb.

How he managed to get to his feet he could never remember; he woke up in the Sultan's bed, crawling with fleas. He reeled with nausea, yet he managed to make a tour through the village, ignoring the panic he provoked. When he returned to the palace, followed by hundreds of eyes, he knew that his work was done. That night the Sultan accompanied him to his prahu. As they bowed to one another in dignified farewell, Brits-Jansen was certain that the Sultan would remain healthy and enlightened until his death, for fear that Sappo-lidi might come back; but he knew also that His Highness would spend the rest of his life brooding on a means to get even with him.

Thirty years passed before Dr. Brits-Jansen sailed up the Kali-Woga again toward Rauwatta. Between the two expeditions lay a life that had become a legend in the Far East. The fat, impertinent young man had become the foremost leprosy specialist in the world; the stunt with the dentures had become one of the classic stories of the East Indies; and the jungle, that had once seemed so menacing, had become as familiar to him as the Royal Gardens to the head keeper.

The second expedition was really a holiday trip. When he had heard that Dr. Brinkman had fallen ill in a plague outbreak in Rauwatta, he had volunteered to go, but not for the sake of Brinkman. It was a pilgrimage to the Sultan and to his youth. He was inoculated with anti-plague vaccine and left rather hastily, with only six native male nurses, plenty of vaccine, but only a quarter of a tin of P.G. He cursed his carelessness when he discovered this, and he thought of turning round, but decided they would probably send a second expedition after him which was sure to have plenty of P.G. Then he settled down to three weeks of rest, shooting crocodiles and eating bananas, to be followed by a game of billiards with the Sultan when he reached Rauwatta. He hardly thought of Brinkman, dying in the wilderness, and not at all of the plague, which he had managed to tame to such an extent during these thirty years that it virtually bolted the moment it saw his beard.

As his small convoy crawled up the river and he sat lolling under his awning, he tried to recall his first expedition. The first thing he remembered was the fear; he remembered it so vividly that it almost became real once more. Then he started to recognize the bends in the river, the twittering birds and the chattering monkeys. Nothing seemed to have changed in those thirty years, not a tree, not a leaf: everything had remained unchanged for tens of thousands of years. The thirty years of Dr. Brits-Jansen, the leprosy specialist, were reduced to nothing; he had never been away from this forest, he had only dozed for a minute on the river. The hallucination was strong, but no stronger than was to be expected. The jungle went after souls, not lives — for thirty years he had taught this to his assistants, when they were new to the East.

He knew the jungle well enough to know exactly how far he could go in giving way to this feeling. In the jungle, the one thing that counted was vitality, the superiority of the lion tamer. One had to remain utterly sure of oneself; whatever threatened that self-confidence, whether it was a bad conscience or simply fatigue, had to be crushed with merciless animal force. He won the battle against his hallucination by cursing the coolies with a thundering voice, and shooting at the crocodiles with a barrage of badly aimed shots. But it cost him his holiday. He had to fight as doggedly as any totok to arrive in Rauwatta with his sanity intact. The giant who finally set foot ashore in the plague-stricken village felt like a dwarf compared to the trees: he knew that he had not defeated the wilderness yet.

Rauwatta looked entirely unchanged; the mud flats, the huts, the village elders who met him on the riverbank, all seemed exactly the same as they had thirty years ago. But after his first step ashore, things turned out to be very different indeed. It was almost dark, and the first difference he noticed was the smell of the plague. The village was surrounded by a ring of little flames: the witch doctors' torches, magic circle against the black death. Within this circle, hundreds of natives lay dying. Moaning and wailing troubled the silence, together with the buzzing of clouds of mosquitoes. The village was a chaos of dying, dead and lunatics; heaps of corpses were stacked between the huts, and in the village square the witch doctors danced with their bewildered patients around a huge fire made of animal sacrifices.

The spectacle struck even Brits-Jansen with momentary horror; but it liberated him from the spell of the jungle. He made the village elders announce his arrival to the Sultan, and ask for an audience at ten o'clock. That gave him three hours to clean this pigsty and tidy up the witch's caldron in the village square.

To begin with, he chased the quacks from the square with bellowed commands and a shot in the air; then he ordered the boats to be burnt. As the panicking villagers tried to flee to their prahus, they found the riverbank cordoned off by six armed male nurses, and they saw all their boats, even the ones in which the giant had arrived, dragged ashore and thrown into the fire of the sacrifices. After communication with the outer world had thus been cut off, the invaders, in white coats, wearing high rubber boots and long gloves as a protection against the fleas, started to rake the corpses together and throw them into the fire too. The natives, completely dazed by these magical actions, resumed their interrupted tribal dance, this time around the fire in which their prahus were being consumed and their dead reduced to ashes.

In the meantime, Brits-Jansen had cleared the ground for the first stage of the battle. He had ascertained that poor old Brinkman, the other doctor, was dead and buried; he had localized the epidemic by burning the boats; he had burnt the corpses. The next step would be to split up the village into sectors for the healthy, the ill and the dying; to rope off a doctors' camp; to build a hospital and laboratory; and to dig an anti-flea moat around it. It was a bad epidemic, but no worse than ones he had coped with elsewhere, and the position of the village was ideal for isolation.

The Sultan had sent word that he would be unable to receive Tuan Doctor until eleven fifteen the next morning. It was a deliberate insult, but understandable. If Brits-Jansen had observed court ritual himself, he would not have started cleaning up the place before getting permission from the old man. His omission had a purpose, however: to make it clear right from the beginning who was in command.

Everything seemed innocent and normal. He could find no reason at all for the alarming fact that, while watching the fire in the village square, he suddenly found himself humming "Auld Lang Syne."

He had as much musical sense as a monkey, and the only music his head had ever harbored was "Auld Lang Syne." He had hummed it for the first time, all alone, one New Year's morning in New York, thirty-two years ago. The night before, he had celebrated the New Year with the crowd in Times Square, in the company of a girl with a halo of gay innocence with whom he had fallen in love at sight, and she had been lured away from him by a greasy fellow with a little mustache. The rest of the night he had wandered about the streets, making plans.

On New Year's morning, as he stood shaving in his hotel room, he had heard himself hum "Auld Lang Syne," the tune he had been taught by the crowd the night before, and he had suddenly realized, thinking of the man with the mustache, that he was capable of murder. He had stood quite still for a minute, the razor between him and his reflection; then he had wiped the razor clean and started shaving the other cheek, humming: *"We'll take a cup o' kindness yet For auld lang syne."*

That moment of self-revelation made him decide to leave New York at once. Three days later he was on his way to Batavia, one of the first officers in the foreign legion of the Government Health Service: a fat, impertinent young man with one pair of socks, a pocket comb and a topee from a pawnshop, who possessed only one talent: a gift for diagnosis that was almost genius, and only one merit: that he had not murdered a man with a mustache, thanks to a Scottish New Year song.

During the thirty-two years that had passed since that morning he had occasionally found himself humming the tune, and it had always been just in time to prevent himself from committing an irrevocable mistake. It was uncanny — as if a guardian angel warned him at the last moment by humming that tune into his ear.

The last time it had happened he was in the room of a woman stricken with leprosy, with his syringe ready, about to murder someone after all, though this time it would have been for love. The moment came back to him with uncanny clarity, as he stood in the village square of Rauwatta: the little white room, the bed in its tent of mosquito netting, the mutilated body that was Betsy. He had just finished examining her, as he had examined her hundreds of times, but instead of straightening up with a sigh he had edged away from her with a sudden secretiveness. He had gone to the washbasin and cautiously filled the syringe, holding the needle to the light, humming *"Should auld acquaintance be forgot, And never brought to min'? . . ."*

Then he had fallen silent. His eyes, squinting at the needle, had slowly focused beyond it, on the cross on the white wall, the only decoration in the room. For the first time he had realized that the cross was not a decoration, but the symbol of the life he was about to extinguish. It was the credo of the mutilated body on the bed, to whom nothing now remained of the days when she had been a beautiful woman, except her faith, which was more than he had ever possessed himself.

He had stood there a long while, staring at the cross; then he had emptied the syringe in the basin, and he had gone back into the night without saying good-by, shutting the door softly behind him. The white buildings of the leper colony had shimmered like ivory in the moonlight as he crossed the courtyard to his laboratory. In his laboratory he had not put on the light; he had slumped down at his workbench, head in hands, and wept among the bottles and the test tubes.

Why had he hummed that tune now, tonight, while looking at the funeral pyre in Rauwatta? He tried doggedly to hunt down the reason, but in vain.

His mandur had put up a temporary shelter of palm leaves on the edge of the village, after having burnt down a square of grass and dug a flea moat around it. He undressed, lay down on his camp bed and tried to sleep, but the stench of Lysol and burning kept him awake. Also, his thoughts would not rest; they kept going back to "Auld Lang Syne" and Betsy, the woman he had almost murdered. He wondered how she was, and how Willem was, nursing her with his unfailing love and devotion. As he went on tossing on his bed, there came a moment when he cursed the day he had met those two; but instantly he mumbled, "Nonsense, of course I don't mean that. Nonsense!" as if he were addressing God, who had listened, frowning, to his thoughts.

And God was right — if he hadn't met Betsy and Willem Waterreus he would most certainly have gone to hell. Well, let's say, a different kind of hell. For now that he was back in his thoughts at Betsy, the dominating element of his life, he was not so sure it would not have been better to have gone to that other hell, the one of the godless, the drunks, the killers. He had been unhappy before he met her, he had known moments of black despair in those first years in the jungle, but gin had always helped and so had the company of his fellow doomed.

What rabble they had been, those first doctors of the G.H.S.; what a soulless scoundrel he had been himself. During those first years, the Service had consisted almost entirely of the medical outlaws of the world: adventurers, illegal practitioners, bigamists: a pack of wolves. He tried to remember their faces, but it was difficult. They were all dead now; Habermann of cholera in Celebes, years ago; Mercure knifed by a Balinese who was running amok; van Dam of delirium tremens in Batavia. He tried to remember his own face as it had been then, but all he could remember was that his beard had been fair then, instead of gray; and he remembered his eyes as he had seen them in mirrors, sometimes with a feeling of alarm and despair. They were the eyes of a sadist who treated all natives as if they were monkeys in a laboratory, and who had used his gift of diagnosis only to impress his superiors or to gratify himself. Suppose he had gone on like that? Suppose he had never met Betsy and Willem? Suppose he had never happened on them, that night in Java, when he had got lost?

As he had broken through the undergrowth on that long-ago night, he had seen an open space in the jungle, a fire in the center. Dark shapes crawled around, moaning, and, even before he came near enough to distinguish them, he recognized the sickly sweet smell of leprosy. He spurred his horse to cross the clearing; a chorus of wailings answered the hoofbeats, and mutilated arms stretched out to him. He cursed, forcing forward; then he stopped. A woman in white had suddenly risen behind the flames. A white woman. Next to her was a man in white, kneeling by the side of a monster. The woman was very beautiful, her eyes looked at him kindly. "What are you doing here?" he asked, roughly, to defend himself against those eyes.

"Helping," the woman answered. She had a hoarse, low voice. Her companion stood up too, a man with a tired face, holding a mass of dirty bandages.

"Are you out of your minds?" Brits-Jansen cried. "Do you know what you are doing?"

"Of course," the woman said, and the man smiled. The hor-

neighed, and from all sides ravaged bodies came crawling near in the flickering firelight.

"Who has given you permission?" he shouted. "Don't you know leprosy is infectious? What precautions have you taken?"

"None," the woman said. "God protects us."

"Is that so?" he asked mockingly, suddenly sure of himself, for he had seen her hands. "Then let me tell you that your God has made a mug of you. You have it, my dear." He said it with a wide, fatherly smile. But as he stared intently into her eyes, waiting for the fear that never failed to reveal itself, his smile slowly disappeared, and he was overcome by amazement, incredulity, then emptiness. For she went on looking at him calmly, and the kindness in her eyes deepened to pity. Never before had anyone looked at him like that, with such compassion; yet he was convinced she could not have known the truth before, so slight were the signs of the white death.

"Yes . . ." he said, a last defense against the void growing inside him, "you have leprosy!" He pointed at the lepers. "You'll be like them! God knows how long it will take before He puts an end to you: maybe thirty years!"

When she still gave no sign of terror, still looked at him with that terrible, tender strength, he dismounted, turned her toward the fire, took her hands, opened them, closed them, looked up, and asked, "Who are you?"

The man answered, "Salvationists," and his voice broke on the word.

A hand pulled at his trouser leg; he saw the stump of an arm; without a word he turned away to remount and flee. But the feeling of emptiness made him feel so lost that he turned round again, and went back to the woman, who had bent down once more over the most horrible suffering in the world. He stood watching her for a long time, but she did not look up. Then he took a bandage out of a basket standing by the fire, and started a new, bewildering life, bandaging a fingerless hand.

So it was that he had met Betsy and Willem. And often during the years that followed, he asked himself: what exactly happened that night? Something had happened, because he had been unable to take up his old life again. He gave up drinking and playing poker; he went through a change of morals that made his fellow doctors bellow with laughter; they called it a grotesque conversion. He alone knew that it was not a conversion at all, but something else, something to do with her, not with God or his soul. Something drew him back to her that was stronger than his sense of shame, his urge for freedom and self-preservation. He worked, pleaded, intrigued, fought for them with much more doggedness than he had ever fought for his own sake. He pestered the government relentlessly, trying to get a sanatorium for their patients. At last, after more than a year, the harassed authorities granted them an old military hospital somewhere in the mountains in Java, a scandalous place, two centuries old, that had been a fortress, a prison and an army hospital, but abandoned by the army because the prisoners went mad and the patients died of a mysterious fever.

He feared the worst, but Betsy and Willem were delighted. He helped them to fit out their hospital, he saw to it that they got instruments, drugs, beds, kitchen utensils, and took off his topee at their first holiness meeting in the new hospital. As he hummed tunelessly with their odd, happy Salvation Army songs, he suddenly stopped because of a calm question in his thoughts: what the devil am I doing here? Then he shrugged his shoulders and hummed on.

The impossible succeeded. The fortress that for two hundred years had been a monument to cruelty became the first leper colony in the islands, a model of its kind. Once they could do without him a feeling of resentment had grown inside him: they ought to be more grateful for everything he had done for them, and, quite frankly, he was getting a bit sick of their religion and their irritating cheerfulness. Then he learned that they had a child of sixteen months, that it had been three months old when they were forced to send it away, after he had told her she had leprosy. She mentioned it casually, while the leper orchestra played for a funeral. It was a girl, she said, Bertha; she was now in a Salvation Army home in Holland, and they would probably never see her again. Then the trumpets blared the triumphantly unharmonious final chord of "When the Roll Is Called Up Yonder," and the trum peters, pressing the stops with sticks because their fingers had become too short, had tears in their eyes at their own beautiful sound.

He did not breathe a word about it, but that day he started his battle with God. God, who had promised to protect His servants, and who had smitten with leprosy the most wonderful woman in the world. Specializing in leprosy with a vindictiveness that gave him, within a year, a reputation all through the East Indies, he hunted lepers everywhere, traveled for weeks to look at a special case; he fitted out a laboratory at the leper colony, and every hour he could spare from his heavy duties he worked there, mumbling, sweating, a staggering giant in the harsh glare of hissing primus lamps, until he fell asleep at the breakfast table and snored during grace. Every leave he got, sometimes just a single night as he passed through, he wrestled there with God like Jacob in the desert. But at the end of each year he had to look back on a series of lost battles, and add another defeat to Betsy's case history. He sometimes asked himself whether it was love that had made him attack leprosy with such ferocity; whether he had challenged God only out of frustrated desire. But if this was love, it was different from what he had always known it to be, for the thought of holding her in his arms made him hide his face in his hands with shame.

Dr. Brits-Jansen, the foremost leprosy specialist — it was nobody's business that he was battling with God for a mutilated woman somewhere on a mountain on an island called Java. The Head of the Service, who had once been his assistant, sometimes asked him why he refused promotion, why he insisted on volunteering for jungle expeditions where a young nonentity might have done just as well. Then he would shrug his shoulders, hiding his embarrassment behind his beard. For who would understand that he was on a lifelong pilgrimage in search of someone he knew he would never find, and yet went on expecting with foolish hope? Someone — saint, hermit or lunatic — who would know the answer to this question: How was it that in a room on a mountain in Java, a blind, mutilated woman could lie dying in a blaze of glory, while he, the giant, slowly sank into a morass of despair?

VI

THE FIRST morning in Rauwatta, Brits-Jansen was up at sunrise. His plan of campaign was simple and he was certain of the outcome; the only depressing element in the situation was the lack of P.G. He would have to get this campaign over very quickly indeed.

The splitting up of the village into sectors of dying, ill and healthy was basically a simple operation; a trained dog could have done it. But as always the emotional element was his main obstacle; the natives stuck together in family groups. To split them up was unnerving, for the dying wept or laughed madly in their fever, the ill tried to flee on all fours, and the healthy shrieked, beat their chests and pulled their hair out; to a native the family is the last straw to cling to in a catastrophe.

He had never got used to those heart-rending scenes. There was only one solution to make it easier for everybody; Habermann had discovered it twenty-eight years ago, in Celebes. Give the lot of them two shots of P.G. and they let themselves be separated like lambs. But he had no P.G.; all he had left was about 400 cc. of it, and that dose he intended to eke out for his own use. So the separations had to be carried out without the aid of science, and it was a nasty job. He was glad when, after three hours of screams, he could leave the rest to his male nurses; for it was nearly eleven o'clock, and he had a date with the Sultan.

He went to his tent to change his clothes in the Sultan's honor. But after he had started to take off his flea boots and rubber gloves, a thought struck him. He remembered waking up the morning after the banquet, thirty years ago, in the Sultan's bed; the most memorable thing about the Sultan's bed was that it had been alive with fleas. Many more generations of fleas than of men must have bred and lived in the palace. Fleas meant rats. It would not surprise him if the whole building was just a roof on a vast, intricate fortress of zigzagging rat runs. Plague had come to Rauwatta before; it might well be that the explanation was an enormous colony of rats, living underneath the palace. In that case he would have to go very easy this morning, placating the Sultan, for, if his conclusion about the rats was right, there was only one way to finish off the plague in Rauwatta once and for all: he would have to burn down the village and blow up the palace.

So he did not change after all. He only put on a clean white coat. When he presented himself at the palace gate he was struck by an eerie atmosphere. He waited a long time before anyone answered his calls. In the end, tired shuffling steps dragged across the courtyard and the gate was creakingly opened, after some clumsy fumbling, by an invisible hand. As he entered the courtyard, he saw still bodies lying everywhere in sleeping positions. No wonder he had felt uneasy; everybody he passed on his way to the Sultan was dead. Even the man who had opened the gate was tottering and giggling like a drunk; once he lay down, he would never get up again. Something had to be done about this palace, and quickly.

He followed the stumbling native along a pitch-dark corridor. In the dark billiard room, he found the Sultan playing billiards, an old dwarf with a cue. Time had certainly taken its toll; his face looked like an old apple, mummified. Either Rahula Rattan Rauwari had shrunk with the passing of the years, or he himself had grown, which seemed unlikely. He had grown only in circumference, whereas the Sultan had diminished in stature, for he could barely peep over the billiard table any more.

"I see you, sire," Brits-Jansen said, bowing with a plopping sound as he bent his hip boots.

The Sultan did not look up. He peered along his cue, remained frozen for nearly a minute, then the cue flashed like the tongue of a snake, a white ball with a blue spot whirled across the table, hit first the red and then the other white one. Both vanished into the bags at the corners, then the spotted ball rolled slowly back to the Sultan. Brits-Jansen raised his eyebrows. "Hot shot, sire," he said with admiration. "Let's have a game tonight."

Only then the Sultan looked up. His black eyes looked his visitor over, slowly, from the boots upward, until their eyes met. Brits-Jansen's smile vanished. He didn't like the look the Sultan gave him; it set an alarm bell ringing somewhere.

"I see you, Sappo-lidi," the Sultan said, softly.

Brits-Jansen did not lose any time. "Sire," he said, "if you want to stay alive, you're in for a move. I won't trouble you with details, but the black sickness is carried by fleas, and fleas are carried by rats. If you want me to kill the black sickness, I'll have to kill the rats first, then the fleas. You've got a lot of both."

The Sultan lowered his eyelids, a demonstration of modesty. "Sultan has lot of everything," he said.

"Except subjects," Brits-Jansen added, "and at this rate Sultan won't have any left at all a moon from now. What would Sultan be without subjects?"

Rahula Rattan Rauwari raised his eyelids again, looked at his guest with an absent-minded gaze, and answered: "Sultan would be happy. Sultan not like subjects; Sultan like billiards and Her Majesty Queen."

"That, I am sure, is mutual," Brits-Jansen said, as a brilliant idea crossed his mind. "I am sure that Her Majesty the Queen in Holland would be delighted to meet Sultan again and talk about old times. Would Sultan be agreeable to that?"

Rahula Rattan Rauwari stood thinking for a long time, holding his cue, an old dwarf with a lance; then he answered: "No."

"Come, come," said Brits-Jansen, "you don't mean that. Think of all the wonderful things you could do in Holland. Have yourself photographed again, go up and down in an elevator all day long, as you did last time. And Her Majesty the Queen is an old woman now, like the Sultan. You would have lots ..."

"Sultan not old woman!" the little man hissed, with unexpected fury. "Sultan stay here! Sultan only likes billiards."

Brits-Jansen sighed and shoved back his topee. "All right," he said, "if that's the way you want it, sire, you leave me no choice. I've come to tell you that you'll have to be out of this palace by tomorrow night."

"Why?" asked the Sultan, quietly.

"Because I'm going to blow it up," Brits-Jansen said.

"Aah ... ?" said the Sultan, a long, melodious sound of mock wonder. "Perhaps Sappo-lidi also going to catch moon? Pick stars from river and feed them to big god-crocodile, yes?"

"No good baby-talking, sire," Brits-Jansen said, exasperated. "I hate to remind you, but I represent your government. Your government tells you with my voice that you'll have to be out of your palace by tomorrow night, or I'll have to blow it up with you inside. Is that clear?"

Then the Sultan smiled. It was a disturbing smile, for he had no teeth left and his pink tongue lived inside the cave of his mouth like a shellfish. "Quite clear," he said coyly. "Sappo-lidi: cuckoo!" At this, he made a little gesture with his hand by the side of his temple; then he added, soothingly, as to a child, "Let's play little game. Yes?"

Brits-Jansen did some rapid thinking. The old man was too cunning by half. Of course, he couldn't blow up the palace without the Sultan's permission, and the Sultan knew it. If Sultan Rahula Rattan Rauwari should ever get back to civilization and whisper into the Governor's ear that his palace had been blown up by Dr. Brits-Jansen against his will, there would be trouble. To a colonial official's mind, it was quite acceptable that a Sultan should perish with his entire population in an outbreak of the plague; that his life could be saved by blowing up his palace was beyond their comprehension.

What now? Somehow he would have to trick the old man into giving his permission. He needed time for thought, so he said: "Tonight, sire, I'll be delighted to give you a game; now I have other things to do. Would you allow my men to come into your palace and take out the corpses, please?"

"No," said the Sultan. "Sultan wants to keep corpses and weep over old friends."

You old hyena, Brits-Jansen thought, but he smiled the smile of the humble civil servant and said: "Just as you wish, sire. I only wanted to protect you against the black sickness." A splendid solution struck him. With all those corpses lying about, the Sultan would probably soon be a corpse himself.

As if the old man had read his thoughts, he smiled in return. "Sultan not afraid of black sickness," he said, "Sultan immature."

"Is that so?" Brits-Jansen said, baffled. "In that case: so long, sire. See you tonight." He turned round and strode out authoritatively.

Then he paused. Looking back, he said to the Sultan, "The word is 'immune,' " and walked on out.

The sunlight hit him like the flash of an explosion. He had to stand still for a while, to get accustomed to the glare. As he stood there, the smell of the corpses sickened him. He wondered how the Sultan could stand it. He opened the gate and stepped into the village square, fighting a short battle with his civil servant's conscience. He ought to give Sultan Rahula Rattan Rauwari an anti-plague injection: during the first ten days it gave a greater susceptibility. No civil servant on God's earth could blame him for giving the Sultan an anti-plague injection; it was the responsible thing to do. He could even give him an intravenous anti-plague injection, the surest way of killing anybody. Suddenly he was struck by the violence of the solutions he was considering. It was like killing a sparrow with a blunderbuss. Never before had he thought so emotionally about the passive resistance of a native ruler. In any other circumstance, he would have simply sent in his male nurses to carry the Sultan out, and signed the man's certificate of insanity in the presence of two witnesses. So he came to the surprising conclusion that he must be fond of the old man.

As he sat down to the frugal lunch his mandur had prepared, he took his three cc. of P.G. absent-mindedly. He thought about friendship and what it meant to old people; he concluded that it was a matter of time, the result of a process of elimination. The Sultan and he were the only ones still alive from those old, wild days; they had been enemies for so long that now they had become fond of one another. To old people, it was the relationship itself that mattered, not its nature. When his coffee was served, he drank it noisily, deep in nostalgic thoughts. He had found the solution to the palace problem. He would play billiards with Rahula Rattan Rauwari with the palace as a stake, win, clean out the plague, and take the old man home.

After he had lain down for his nap, his thoughts became vague and silly. He would take the Sultan with him on his expeditions, like a pet monkey. They would take a small-size billiard table with them, with folding legs, like a camp table. Or an even smaller one, as big as a tray, with ping-pong balls. Then he pictured to himself the smallest billiard table in the world: as big as a match-box, with rabbit shot for balls and toothpicks for cues. While they played, kneeling with their heads close together like two children peering at a miniature tortoise, he fell asleep.

HE ARRIVED back at the palace that night well rested, dressed in crackling white and feeling on top of the world. That afternoon, his men had finished dividing up the natives and he had injected anti-plague into the healthy ones. Now his coolies were building a laboratory, a bit of nonsense really, but it was always better to have a close look at the nature of a local plague germ. That was how discoveries were made. He had sent his mandur into the sector of the dying to collect some nice fat fleas and tomorrow he would start studying them. Two of his male nurses were Javanese medical students: it was mainly for their benefit that he had ordered the laboratory built. He liked Javanese students; they were calm, intelligent and discreet. He hated the pale, emotional boys sent over from Europe to pester him with lectures expanding the theories of his worst enemies, and with lengthy confessions about their love life. They all ended by growing out of their suits and getting transferred to hospital service in Java or Sumatra. The fact that he was thinking about his pet aversion, totoks, on his way to the Sultan was a sure sign that he was in good form. He was looking forward to the game of billiards.

"I see you, sire," he said jauntily as he found the Sultan waiting by the billiard table amid smoking torches.

"I see you, Sappo-lidi," the Sultan said.

"Yes," said Brits-Jansen, hanging up his topee on one of the dried heads on the wall. "Let's face it. We see one another through and through." He rubbed his gloved hands; he wasn't going to take those gloves off, even if it cost him a few points. Then he put his proposition to the Sultan.

He had been prepared for a struggle, but the old man simply said, "I agree. If Sappo-lidi wins, palace: bang. Affoo." And with that word, which thirty years ago he had defined as *"A vous,"* the game started.

After his first shot, which scored nothing, he realized that the gloves made delicate playing impossible. The cue squeaked between his rubber fingers and the ball darted off at an unexpected angle. While the Sultan was quietly piling up points with a series of master strokes, he fought an inward battle and then took off the gloves. It was essential that he win this game. The fate of Rauwatta depended on it.

During the first hour of the match, he still thought piously of Rauwatta. After that he thought only of winning. For that little runt, that old monkey from the jungle, went quietly on performing miracles on the green baize, while he himself played like a drunken farmer. Lord knew what was the matter with those balls; they seemed to have stopped obeying the laws of physics and darted about as if under the spell of black magic. It was infuriating, it was more than that, it was a tragedy. Never in his life had he played so badly, and never had he played against an opponent of such dazzling skill.

He called to aid all his ruses and tricks. He sweated, panted, and cursed in his beard, leaned backward over the table, the cue behind him, leaned over the edge with one leg stuck out, his beard touching the baize. He lost the buttons of his coat; his rubber boots filled with perspiration. He ripped open his collar, growled, took aim, stabbed; the ball swirled halfway across the table, made a little jump, and missed once more. He shook his cue at the ceiling, then put it down with a crash. The old dwarf, saintly and unruffled, stood chalking his cue with a soft, squeaking sound. Only then, glaring at his tiny opponent, did Brits-Jansen realize that this was the revenge. For thirty years the Sultan had practiced billiards every day, waiting for Sappo-lidi to come back in order to get even with him: this was the return match for the slap Brits-Jansen had given him when he feigned illness, for the young man's arrogance, for the banquet.

They played on until dawn. By then, Brits-Jansen had not a single button left, one boot had sagged down to his calf, and his eyes were bloodshot with rage. When at last the match ended, after the Sultan had won his thirty-eighth game, Sappo-lidi roared, broke his cue across his knee and threw it at the wall.

"Tea?" the Sultan asked, his head on one side.

Brits-Jansen glowered; his hands opened and shut; then he said: "The devil knows I'm a man of my word, but today, at noon sharp, I'm going to blow up this palace and this table with it."

"Why table?" the Sultan asked, politely amazed.

"Because it's full of rats!" Brits-Jansen shouted. Then, overcome by shame, he wiped his brow and said, "All right, tea."

The Sultan clapped his hands, then started putting cues and balls away while he waited for the slave to appear. He put everything away neatly, but still no slave came. It gave Brits-Jansen a small satisfaction. He said, pleased: "All right, no tea."

The Sultan said nothing.

"Well now," Brits-Jansen went on, "you have had your little moment, now let's talk like adults. If I tell you that we must set fire to the palace to defeat the black sickness, do you believe me?"

"Oh yes," said the Sultan.

"All right, then. When?"

The Sultan smiled. "Never," he said. "Black sickness here many times. It will pass."

Brits-Jansen said: "Listen, sire, I don't care whether you die of plague, old age or murder. If you make it impossible for me to do my job, I'll call it a day and go home."

"In what?" the Sultan asked, smiling.

"Well, in my bo . . ." His mouth remained open. It dawned on him, at last, why he had hummed "Auld Lang Syne" as he stood looking at the funeral pyre in Rauwatta. The Javanese students, whom he had ordered to burn the boats, had burnt all of them.

Sultan Rahula Rattan Rauwari smiled, triumphantly. "Sappolidi no go home," he said. "Sultan lonely; Sultan play billiards with Sappo-lidi forever, all day, until last darkness."

"Oh no you won't," Brits-Jansen exploded, with an oath; but he felt suddenly tired, an old man.

It was three o'clock in the morning, but the lamp in the doctors' tent was still burning. At his camp table, Dr. Brits-Jansen, G.H.S., sat writing; an empty tin of P.G. lay on the floor. He wrote: *Recent experience has suggested to me a necessary addition to Chapter 11, paragraph 1, in Eykman's* Vade Mecum. *The paragraph in* question runs: *"As a first measure to localize an epidemic, all communications should be cut off. In the case of communication by water, all prahus and rafts should be destroyed by fire."* I suggest the addition of the words: *"except one."*

Then he picked up the tin of P.G. and shook it above his beaker; as nothing came out, he cursed and threw it with a clatter underneath the bunk. Then he wrote, on a page torn out of his journal: *My dear van der Waard: Owing to an accident, I have lost my own prahu after having burnt the others to localize the outbreak. As I expect to finish in about two weeks' time, you would oblige me if you could send some boats to fetch me, or I'll sit here twiddling my toes for months, waiting for that donkey in Batavia to wake up to the fact that I am missing. If you could send some P.G. with the convoy, this would be greatly appreciated. How are the butterflies? Yours ever, Jansen.*

He called, "Mandur!" folded the letter and wrote the address on it in three languages, with the addition *Urgent and Secret.* The mandur appeared. "Pick your best man and have him carry this through the forest to Rokul," Brits-Jansen said. *"Saja tuan besar,"* said the mandur. Then, at last, the lamp in the doctors' tent went out.

The first thing the doctor saw the next morning was the mandur's best man, trussed like a pig, hanging from a stake, carried by two of the Sultan's warriors.

So that was that.

VII

LATER Anton would write to Els: *... and then, after twenty-three days, we arrived in Rauwatta. The riverbank was black with shouting Dyaks and a white giant came to the forefront and shouted, "Shoot at them! They are* mataglap! — mad!" *Of course I did not land.*

He had not known that natives, when beckoning someone, make the gesture used by the white man to chase someone away. Now hundreds of natives stood dancing up and down on the river's edge, shouting, shaking their fists, jumping with excitement. He lay, undecided, in midstream with his small fleet, surrounded by a mass of floating tree trunks.

During the twelve days that had passed since the discovery of the corpse in the rapids, he had never lost his self-confidence. He had led his expedition through the jungle with steel-jawed grimness, his gun at the ready, his topee on the back of his head. He had shouted commands, shared out rations, driven his coolies without ever wondering that Anton Zorgdrager, who had prayed for a sign over a beer-bottle cap, should be doing all this without a moment of hesitation. He had not worried about the future, for the future was fixed in his mind. He had seen his arrival a hundred times in his imagination. An open space in the jungle, a riverbank strewn with corpses. He would stand up in his prahu and be paddled ashore. Village dogs would bark, monkeys would scream, but there would be no one else to welcome him. He would step ashore with his gun under his arm and, without so much as a glance at the corpses, he would enter the deserted village. In front of the doctors' camp, a dead male nurse would lie, a syringe fallen from his hand. Out of a tent a white-haired, emaciated creature would stagger, tears streaming down his hollow cheeks. Then he would salute, hold out his hand and ask, calmly: "Dr. Brits-Jansen, I presume?"

Now the great moment had come, the reward for his superhuman performance, and not only were there no corpses on the riverbank, not only was the Dr. Livingstone of his daydreams a healthy-looking, shouting fat man, but, to crown it all, he made a fool of himself by giving a girlish scream as the tree trunk he pushed with his gun jumped with a splash, and snapped at him with huge jaws full of teeth. "Shoot!" the fat man shouted angrily. "Shoot, curse you, or they'll pinch your boats!" He took hold of himself, though he was badly rattled; he aimed over the heads of the crowd, and pulled the trigger. There was only a click. He had forgotten to reload this morning, after shooting like a bored boy at two monkeys in a tree. He reloaded with trembling fingers, cursing under his breath; then he fired a shot standing up in the unstable prahu, which heeled at the kick and almost toppled him backward among the crocodiles. The crowd fled, and at last he could go ashore.

The effect of his shot on the natives gave him back some of his self-confidence. He shoved the topee onto the back of his head, waved at the fat man, a wave of equality; the prow of his boat ran aground and he stepped off it. The fat man shouted, "Careful!" but it was too late; he had already made the step and sank up to his waist in the mud.

He laughed it off, hysterical with shock, while the fat man, cursing, pulled him ashore with his gun. As he finally stood on dry land, the lower half of his body pitch black and dripping, he saluted and said, "Dr. Brits-Jansen, I — I suppose?"

"Who did you expect?" the fat man asked. "The Queen of Sheba? Have you got P.G. with you?"

"Yes," said Anton. "My name is Zorgdrager and I . . ."

"Fine!" the fat man cried, and slapped him on the shoulder with a force that made him drop his gun. "Where is it?"

He picked up his gun mechanically, turned round and called: "Mandur! A tin of P.G.!"

The mandur picked up one of the precious tins for which Anton had risked his life at every rapids, and as the native hesitated, afraid of the mud, Anton called, "Throw me a rope!" wanting to pull the boat ashore. But the fat man shouted: "Throw the tin!"

The mandur threw the tin. Anton's heart missed a beat as he saw it sail, glinting, through the sunlight. The fat man caught it nimbly, broke the seal, screwed off the cap and filled it to the brim with a colorless liquid. He threw the cap back in his beard, smacked his lips, sighed, and poured out another cap. Then he noticed Anton, staring at him, and said: "Want one?"

"What — er — what kind of medicine is it?" Anton asked, casually.

The fat man frowned and answered: "Medicine? What do you mean? This is gin."

Anton repeated, mechanically: "Gin."

"P.G.!" the fat man said. "Pure gin. Here," and he held out the cap toward him.

Then it happened: the catastrophe, which he would try to live

down for the rest of his life. It would come back in his memory as
a sign on the wall in moments of self-assurance, it would unnerve
him whenever he saw someone else making a fool of himself.

Dr. Zorgdrager, G.H.S., burst into tears.

FOR ONE alarming second, Brits-Jansen thought that the jungle
had got the better of him after all and that he was delirious. For
there stood, between a *kampong* full of plague and a river full of
crocodiles, a young man, black with mud to his waist, the price
ticket still on the collar of his tropical shirt, bawling his head off.

But then he realized, with a feeling of relief, that it must be a
totok who had just gone through his baptism of fire, and whose
knees had given way when he heard that some of his precious tins
were filled with gin. He stood a moment embarrassed, scratching
his head, then he patted the boy's shoulder awkwardly, ordered
his mandur to unload the tins, set one of the students to guard the
prahus, and took the sniffling boy with him to his tent. There he
set him on a stool, put the kettle on, got out mugs, filled his pipe
and sat down on his camp bed, to have a look at the child.

For a child it was. They seemed to get younger all the time. Of
course that cruel-eyed little Kramer in the Head Office had kicked
him straight into the jungle, without any transition. It was one of
his idiosyncrasies that served no purpose but to turn the doctor
at the receiving end into a wet nurse. Kramer had sent him a totok
before, in New Guinea. What was his name? Fat, red hair, freckles,
and the photograph of an even fatter girl in his wallet which he
had shown him the very first night saying, "But for her . . ."

Yes, sure enough, this one too was wearing an engagement ring.
He was in for another set of evenings of interminable stories about
Kitty, or Mary; snapshots of Mary on a horse, Mary on the beach,
Mary as a smudge because the camera had moved. "Ah, but for
her . . ." When you met them two years later, they had forgotten
all about her. Curse Kramer! Now someone would again keep the
lamp burning for hours because he sat writing to "My sweet only
darling," or "My baby, baby, honey lamb." And then, after a fort-
night's clumsiness and snoring and mistakes in the laboratory, the
question: "Doctor, are you asleep?" He would grunt, "Yes," but

the voice would continue: "May I ask you a question?" He would answer, "No," but he might just as well have said "Birmingham" or "Cuckoo," for all the difference it made. The voice would inexorably ask: "Do you think I'm suited to this work?" He always answered that question with the "No" it deserved.

The kettle started to boil and the boy, who sat staring gloomily at his feet, his head in his hands, looked up at the sound. He must have been a long way away — three guesses where. It was a mean trick on Brits-Jansen's part, but he could not resist saying, "Bet you a tin of P.G. that I know whom you are thinking of," with a honeyed voice, a fatherly smile.

"Pardon?" the boy asked.

"Show her to me," he said, and the boy's mouth fell open. He sat gaping for a moment, then he put a muddy hand in his hip pocket, took out a wallet and pulled a photograph out of it.

He took it, looked with feigned interest at the child with the tooth-paste smile, grunted his approval, and asked, "How old is she?" the standard question. After the boy had answered, "Twenty-three," he hesitated whether he would try for another tin of P.G., but decided to be sensible and not stake his prize. A few seconds later, he regretted it bitterly, for, after he had mumbled, "Quite a girl," and handed the photograph back, the boy sighed and said, "Yes . . . but for her . . ."

The water boiled; Brits-Jansen muttered, "Blast," and made the tea.

ANTON, after his arrival, behaved with great dignity but took care not to talk to anybody unless it was unavoidable.

He put on this act mainly for the benefit of the two Javanese students among Brits-Jansen's male nurses. They called him respectfully "Doctor" but he was conscious of the faint amusement in their eyes. They had seen him sink in the mud, drop his gun and burst into tears. If they were at all as he had been himself in his student days, they were now calling him by some unflattering nickname.

The Javanese students might be taken in by his stern behavior, eventually; Dr. Brits-Jansen was not susceptible to it. He treated him as one would treat a neighbor's dog: kindly, but only for the neighbor's sake. The depressing thing about Dr. Brits-Jansen was that one could not imagine, even in one's wildest dreams, ever becoming like him. He was not only of a different generation, he seemed to belong to a different race of men. He must be over sixty, but he had the vitality of a bull, the stamina of a camel, and a personality so grotesque, and yet so uncomplicated, that he would have made Freud and his pupils tear up their notes and send him to a zoo.

Dr. Brits-Jansen had told him that the epidemic was over; the drawback was, so he said, that the plague was sure to come back unless the rats were exterminated. Dr. Brits-Jansen had waited for nearly a month now because he did not want to act hastily. After all, a jungle doctor was a bit of a missionary. But now, he said, he had made up his mind: the rats would have to be exterminated, which meant burning the village and blowing up the palace. All this Dr. Brits-Jansen told while sipping his tea, as if he were discussing the potato crop. So far, so good. Dr. Brits-Jansen's missionary considerations had seemed real and impressively human. Then they went to the palace with electric torches, clad in rubber boots, white coats and arm-long gloves, to look for rats.

To look for rats in itself was alarming enough; to look for rats in an Eastern palace made one feel even more apprehensive; to look for rats in an Eastern palace ravaged by plague made one gargle behind the tent, drink four caps of P.G. and check up on one's rubber armor twice during the short, hot walk to the palace gates.

Anton had a mental picture of the inside of an Oriental palace; it came from a silent German film called *The Indian Tomb* which he had seen in Amsterdam when he was fifteen. The accompanying music had been played by a woman at a piano and a violinist who also struck cymbals during battle scenes. Now, as they stood waiting in front of the palace gates, Anton remembered the violin's tremolo and the nervous tinkling of the piano which had expressed suspense. Then, in his memory, the cymbals clashed and the gate was opened, on creaking wooden hinges.

He saw a deserted courtyard, surrounded by a sagging veranda with deck chairs, the seats of most of which were torn. There was not a single statue or mythical animal in sight. The gate was opened by a dirty old native who said: "I see you, Sappo-lidi." Brits-Jansen answered, "I see you, sire," and this was the only indication Anton got that the dirty old man must be the Sultan himself, unless Brits-Jansen was jocular with the servants. Brits-Jansen did not take the trouble to introduce him, nor did the dirty old native express any interest in him. He might not have been there at all; it gave him the feeling of a child taken into a dark museum: too afraid of losing his elders to look at the pictures.

They entered a pitch-dark corridor, which smelled so strong that he was nearly sick; then they arrived in a dark room, lit by torches, the walls of which were decorated with clay heads. In the center of the room stood a billiard table. "Okay," said Brits-Jansen. "Let's get cracking," and he switched on his electric torch. Anton switched on his electric torch also. It shone on the wall and he nearly dropped it, for the head grinning at him with glass eyes was not made of clay. He stared at it, while behind him Dr. Brits-Jansen was saying: "We just want to have a look under your floors, sire. Don't you worry, it's only a matter of . . ."

The voice suddenly stopped and, for some reason, the silence that followed was so alarming that Anton looked round. He saw Brits-Jansen standing at the billiard table, his electric torch shining down on the baize. He was inspecting the baize, rubbing it with his fingers. Then he fumbled in a pocket, took out a pair of steel-rimmed glasses, put them on with an angry gesture, and said: "You blasted, double-crossing runt! You cheating old crocodile! You — " He went on for most of a minute, slowly crowding in on the dirty old native, who backed around the billiard table. Then, suddenly, Anton was dragged into the bewildering scene by the doctor, who cried, "Totok, come here! Tell me, what do you see here?" pointing at the billiard table with an accusing finger. Anton swallowed, and said, at a loss, "Well — er — a billiard table, sir."

Dr. Brits-Jansen slapped his forehead and cried: "Ass! Look at the baize!" Anton stepped forward, looked, and blinked away sweat. Then he said, "Moth holes, sir."

Dr. Brits-Jansen let out a huge, greedy roar. "Aha!" he roared. "Moth holes! Do you hear, sire? Moth holes! You knew it; you played around them!" By then, the dirty old native was flattened, his back against the billiard table, by Dr. Brits-Jansen. "All right. This settles it. This afternoon, after my nap, I'll finish with the black sickness, sire. And if you want to do me a favor, stay here!"

They went out again into the hot sunlight, leaving the old native standing at the billiard table, rubbing his back. From that moment onward, the missionary element in Dr. Brits-Jansen's character waned. All the way back to the camp he muttered under his breath; Anton understood only a word here and there, but it was obvious that the doctor was not aglow with Christian spirit. Back in the tent, while taking off their anti-flea armor, the doctor said: "Lesson Number One — never trust a native! Lesson Number Two — never trust yourself! To think — " Then he suddenly noticed Anton, and shouted: "What are you doing in here?! Go and change outside! When I get back to Batavia, I'll have a word with that megalomaniac; I'm sick of him sending me pip-squeaks to clutter up the place!" The latter part of his monologue Anton heard outside, and the worst part of it was that the two Javanese students heard it too.

"May I inquire what you gentlemen are doing here?" Anton asked, his brave, African explorer's voice trembling with suppressed rage. "If I'm not mistaken, you were supposed to be classifying specimens in the laboratory?"

One of them answered, respectfully: "We have finished, Doctor."

Anton said, "Oh," and took off his boots.

THAT AFTERNOON, after a thorough preparation, Dr. Brits-Jansen burned down the village of Rauwatta. His thorough preparation was to say to his assistant, "Chase every living soul out of the village," and to go to bed.

Anton, after a moment's hesitation, decided to follow suit. He called the two Javanese students, said, "Chase every living soul out of the village," and went to bed as well.

As he lifted the tent flap, Dr. Brits-Jansen was already lying on his camp bed, his huge hands folded on his stomach, his beard sticking up. Anton tiptoed to his own bed and lay down, producing a series of creaks. The imperial corpse on the other side of the table asked, without opening its eyes, "What are you doing here?"

Anton answered, lightly, "I'm having my siesta."

The table seemed to shake at the blast, as Dr. Brits-Jansen bellowed, "You are *what?!*"

With a feeling as if he were applying the muzzle of a gun to his temple, Anton answered, calmly: "My siesta."

Now either the world would come to an end, or he would have won a battle. There was a moment of suspense, then a heavy creaking as Dr. Brits-Jansen rose on his elbows on his bed. "Are you trying to tell me," he asked, almost sweetly, "that you are evading an order?"

Anton did not move. He looked at the tent ceiling and heard himself say, in a calm voice: "I decided, sir, that as I have never before emptied a village of its inhabitants, it would be wiser to leave the job to those who have that experience. I have received a training as a doctor, not as an invading Hun."

He did not look aside, but he interpreted the ensuing silence as bafflement. Then he heard a deep sigh, a heavy creaking and the word "Poof." He lay waiting for more and was not disappointed.

"I suggest," said Dr. Brits-Jansen, in a very calm voice, "that you get up now, put on your little hat, and go carry out my order. You may delegate it to anyone you like, as long as you realize that it is you who are responsible. I suppose I can't keep you from being lazy, but I can keep you from being lazy lying down. Will you now get up, please?"

Anton knew it was a mistake, but some force stronger than his will made him lie silent. Then the tent seemed to blow up, beds, table, clothing and all, as Dr. Brits-Jansen bellowed: *"Get out!"*

As Anton stood in the blazing sunlight, literally with his pants down, he looked around for the Javanese students. Owing to some miracle, they were not there; the only one there was his mandur, who grinned and said, "Tuan." Anton acknowledged his greeting with a nod, buckled his belt and said, "Follow me."

As he left the doctors' camp he heard disturbing sounds coming from the village: screaming voices, dogs barking and, somewhere, a cock madly crowing. He discovered the cock on the roof of the first hut, being pursued by an old woman who must have been told to remove her belongings and livestock. Then he saw in the distance a crowd of people brandishing sticks; he hesitated, remembered his prestige and said to the mandur, "Get my gun."

The mandur hurried back to the camp. Anton stood watching the distant brawl, trying to roll a cigarette, a trick which only occasionally succeeded. It did not succeed this time. When the mandur came back with his gun he stuck between his lips a little paper trumpet which, as he lit it, went up in a sheet of flame. At that moment, the older one of the Javanese students ran past. He called, "You there!"

The Javanese stopped and said, politely, "Yes, sir?"

"How far have you got with the evacuation?"

"We're just starting, sir."

"Just starting?" he asked, raising his eyebrows. "What have you been doing all this time?"

"Talking to the villagers, sir," the Javanese answered, with the ghost of a smile.

Anton said, "I see," with the sudden suspicion that, after the way his cigarette had behaved, he might not have any eyebrows left to raise. He added, lamely, "Okay, but get a move on."

The Javanese said, "Yes, sir," and hurried away.

As Anton penetrated deeper into the village, he found complete confusion. Bands of shouting, stumbling natives ran in and out of the jungle, carrying armfuls of dead branches; weeping women trooped out, driving pathetic little herds of goats and squealing pigs; children carried flapping chickens by their legs. Inside the miserable huts, frantic people tried to stand their ground, barricading their doorways, brandishing sticks, and, as the search party of male nurses went from hut to hut, the screams, wailings, cackles, bleatings and barks multiplied until the whole thing became one vast madhouse.

If he had been facing this alone, Anton would not have known where to begin; but after an hour or so, he began to discover system in the chaos. The village was slowly but surely evacuated, and around it, on the jungle's edge, a huge barricade of dead wood was being stacked by the coolies, soon joined by villagers. When he arrived at the palace, fighting his way through a herd of goats, he saw that the dry wood went right round the palace and down to the river. He stood looking at the palace, wondering where the Sultan was, when he heard running steps behind him. It was the Javanese student, who said: "All set, Doctor."

"Nobody left in the huts?" he asked.

"I don't think so."

"You don't think so? What if there is?"

"I don't think we need worry," said the Javanese. "When they see us set fire to the village, they'll soon move out."

Anton searched for something else to ask, then the Javanese said, "I've lined up the rat beaters, Doctor."

Anton said, "Good. I'll call Dr. Jansen." He went back to camp, wondering what rat beaters were.

As he entered the tent Dr. Brits-Jansen was lying exactly as before. Anton asked: "Sir?"

The sleeper let out a sigh. "What is it?"

"We're ready, sir."

"All right." The body remained motionless. "Light the fire."

"Yes, sir. Only . . . I don't think the Sultan is out yet, sir."

There was a silence, then the voice asked: "What are you standing there for?"

"Nothing, sir," Anton said. "Er — I just wanted to tell you that the rat beaters are standing by."

"Is that so?" the voice said. Then, after another silence, "What are rat beaters?"

In a flash, Anton saw it all. Those blasted Javanese students had got him at last. Controlling his fury, he decided he had better own up. "Frankly, sir," he answered, "I don't know."

"All right," said the voice. "I suppose I'd better come along."

The bed creaked. Anton, remembering the remark about pip-squeaks, went outside to wait. Dr. Brits-Jansen appeared after a lot of throat clearing, muttering, and an occasional curse. As he ducked out of the tent, he lost his topee and Anton knew that he would be held responsible for it.

"What in blazes are you loitering here for?" the doctor asked, picking up his topee.

"You told me to wait, sir."

"I did nothing of the kind! I said I was coming. I'll warn you when I'm getting amnesia. Run along and join the rat beaters."

Anton went back to the village. As he approached the barricade of wood, he saw a row of men lined up along it, armed with sticks. By the time he had found the Javanese students, he had seen about two hundred men with sticks, and he was no longer sure who had taken him for a ride: the students or the doctor. So, instead of the tirade he had been preparing, he said to them: "All right, light it."

The elder Javanese said, "Yes, Doctor," cupped his hands round his mouth and gave a sort of hunting call. The answer was a huge wave of cheering, the coolies threw burning clumps of grass into

the barricade, and a crackling of fire grew rapidly as red flames licked up the wood. Then, with a suddenness that took Anton aback, the whole barricade burst into flames.

The huts nearest the barricade caught fire first; then flames jumped from roof to roof with incredible speed. The sound and the heat were tremendous; the men with the sticks had to retire step by step. When the doors of the huts began to burn, the rats appeared. They ran across the open spaces, first in pairs, then in hordes, making for the barricade. The men raised their sticks and shouted and began to beat the ground, an unnerving drumming, which Anton felt creep up his legs from the soles of his feet. The rats swung round and ran back into the village; a few seconds later a great shouting and drumming sounded in the distance. Anton heard a voice say: "Well, that ought to do it." He looked round and saw Dr. Brits-Jansen standing behind him, weirdly lit by the flames.

"Yes, sir," he said.

"Seen the Sultan anywhere?" Brits-Jansen asked, casually.

"No, sir," Anton answered.

Brits-Jansen shrugged his shoulders and wandered off, a shambling white shape in the firelight.

VIII

WHEN DARKNESS fell, Rauwatta had turned into a black open space in the forest, in which, here and there, a dark red glow still brooded. The small fires that were left threw an eerie light, in which the stooping silhouettes of natives could be seen, rummaging among the charred remains of their huts. Where the palace had stood, a lone, fat silhouette was wandering about, poking in the ashes with a stick.

Anton stood watching it for a while, with satisfaction, and then strolled back to camp, feeling fine. Rat beaters did exist; Brits-Jansen was looking for the Sultan; all was well. Approaching the camp, he saw from afar that the lamp in the tent was lit. He wondered who had lit it, as everyone was busy sorting out and feeding the shelterless population.

As he entered the tent, he saw, sitting stiffly on the stool at the other side of the table, a creature so incongruous that it took him some time to believe his eyes: a very old native in a top hat, a frock coat shiny with age and covered with medals, striped trousers and white spats. The apparition said, sepulchrally: "I see you, tuan totok." Only then did Anton recognize him. He cleared his throat and said: "I see you — er — sir."

He wanted to go and tell Brits-Jansen, but then he thought it would do him no harm to poke about in the ashes a little longer. "Can I make you some tea, sir?" he asked.

The Sultan said, "Yes."

Anton filled the kettle, lit the primus stove, got the mugs ready and sat down. Then the Sultan's hand, resting on the table, caught his eye. He frowned sharply and looked up at the Sultan's eyes. They were hardly eyes, just two slits in a head of cracked clay. He didn't quite know what gave him the idea, but he suddenly saw, clearly in his mind's eye, the colored illustration of a leprous hand in a medical book. Then he shrugged his shoulders and thought: if so, Brits-Jansen of all people will have noticed it. Considering this, he gave the Sultan Brits-Jansen's mug.

After trying to start a teatime conversation several times without success, he felt that he really ought to go and tell his chief. He excused himself, and walked back to the village, whistling. As he stepped over the remains of the palace walls, he felt the heat increase underneath his feet until he could hardly stand it. Brits-Jansen had certainly been punished for his sins. He stood, sweating and disheveled, in the ruins with his stick. Before he could come out with one of his niceties, Anton said: "Sorry to trouble you, sir, but I thought I had better tell you that the Sultan is waiting."

"Waiting — where?" Brits-Jansen asked, with almost religious awe.

"In the tent, sir," Anton answered.

Brits-Jansen took it like a man. He must have swallowed several times before he said: "I see." Then he walked slowly toward the former village square. "How did you find him?" he asked.

"He was sitting there when I got back," Anton answered, "so I thought I'd better make him some tea."

Brits-Jansen stood still with his stick. Then he said, once more: "I see."

"I wouldn't have, of course," Anton went on, "if I had known he was a leper. I noticed only after I had given him your mug."

He waited for the squall of wrath to hit him. But Dr. Brits-Jansen merely said: "I see."

Anton did not know whether he was relieved or disappointed when the squall burst after all. "*What* did you say?" Brits-Jansen bellowed.

"Your . . . your mug. . . ."

"By all the bloody, burning saints!" the giant shouted. "This is

the limit!" Then he threw his stick away, brought his nose very
close to Anton's and said: "Look, boy, dear boy: I have let you get
away with everything. I've let you sob on my shoulder, drink my
P.G., pester me with honey lamb — but one thing I will not let you
do: diagnose leprosy! You may diagnose fallen arches, dandruff,
schizophrenia, anything you like *except leprosy*. Is that clear?"

Anton answered calmly, "Yes, sir." As Brits-Jansen waddled
away he stared after him, loathing his guts. So far he had been
impressed by the man, and his anger at his insults had been softened by admiration. Now the old man had gone too far, and he
would be damned if he would stand for it. He knew he was still
a totok, making a fool of himself at every opportunity, but, after
all, he was no longer a student.

In the knowledge that his relationship with Brits-Jansen had
entered a new stage, he sauntered back to the camp in silence.

As Brits-Jansen made his way, spluttering, to the tent where
Sultan Rahula Rattan Rauwari had sprung yet another surprise on
him, he was consumed by rage. He was at war with everything,
everybody — the jungle, the plague, the Sultan — but most of all
with the Government Health Service, that incredible organization
of fools, bureaucrats and nincompoops, which had grown like
poison ivy over the graves of the heroes who founded it. He could
have strangled that boy. A leper, indeed! The remark showed a
lack of the most elementary respect. He had never taken any
particular pride in it, but the fact remained that he was the foremost leprosy specialist in the world. No one of his own generation
would ever have dreamt of diagnosing tuberculosis in the presence
of Pasteur, or syphilis under the nose of Ehrlich. But these clumsy
louts who were piped into the jungle from some monstrous factory
in the Motherland made him feel sick at heart. He was too old now
to blame God, or Life; he blamed that little megalomaniac, Dr.
Piet Kramer. When he entered the camp, he had made up his mind.
He would go back to Batavia and shoot him.

As he lifted the flap of the tent, he was bristling with guns like
a battleship, ready to smite the Sultan with a broadside of curses.
The Sultan sat waiting for him, dressed like an undertaker, and

on the table were a teapot and a mug: his mug. He thought of picking up the boy's bed and flinging it out, then he decided to be dignified and have the totok told by his mandur that Dr. Brits-Jansen preferred him to sleep in a hammock outside, in the trees with the monkeys, where he belonged. He sat down and said: "I see you, sire."

The Sultan opened his mouth in a grin. "I see you, Sappo-lidi," he said. "Nice tea."

Then, suddenly, he saw the old leathery hand lying on the table. An awful precipice of emptiness opened at his feet. He shook his head; then he stared, took out his spectacles and put them on. He took the hand in his, and looked at the nails. Then he felt like getting up quietly, taking his gun, going outside into the darkness and shooting himself instead of Piet Kramer. The boy had been right. The Sultan was a leper.

But all he did was to take off his spectacles, breathe on them, wipe them with his beard and put them away. The precipice slowly became a morass, the morass of the future. He was an old man now, dragging a senile body toward the end of the road. He looked at his old friend and said: "Well, here we are. We're old now."

"Yes," said the Sultan, gaily.

"How old are you, sire?" he asked.

The Sultan straightened, proudly, and answered: "Three hundred and sixty-five."

Brits-Jansen stared at him, feeling lonely. "Is that so?" he said. "Want some more tea?"

The Sultan said: "Yes."

Yet, as he put a fresh kettle on the primus, the sun seemed to rise hesitantly once more over the future. Suddenly there seemed to be hope. In the back of his mind there had been a deep, hidden worry: what to do with the old Sultan once his palace had been turned to ashes. It was the Governor's headache really, but despite all the old boy's pranks he still kept thinking of Rahula Rattan Rauwari as a friend. Now, a wonderful solution presented itself: he would take him to Man-Pu-Ko-Chu, Willem's leper colony in Java. There he would get a little pavilion all to himself and be taught how to sing, to play the trombone or beat a kettledrum in honor of the Lord. He would be allowed to play billiards as much as he liked. In the evenings he would sit on the cool veranda and look at the sunset and play halma with the King of Rakka, who had been in there for twenty years now. He would be allowed to play pranks on everybody and cheat at bridge, for everything would be forgiven during evening prayers. Lord, what a wonderful solution! And what a satisfying prospect, to be able to play a return game so soon, on a billiard table without moth holes in the baize!

As he poured the boiling water into the teapot, the future was bathed in sunlight. Looking at the old head with the top hat across the table, he realized that his ghost would have haunted him for the rest of his life, if this solution had not presented itself. For outside of the colony, whether or not he made a trip to Holland, Sultan Rahula Rattan Rauwari would have become a sad monkey in an old people's zoo, a Dyak without his jungle.

Then Brits-Jansen thought about the boy. The boy had seen that the Sultan had leprosy, in the way he himself had seen it twenty-six years ago on Betsy's hands. It was no mean feat of diagnosis, even granting that he himself was myopic now and had until now only seen the Sultan's hands by torchlight. The boy, who had no practical experience of leprosy, must have an incredibly good eye.

Yet, as he sat sipping his hot tea, staring at the lamp, he couldn't bring himself to do the decent thing. If he were a man worthy of his age, he would call the boy in now, say, "Sorry I let myself go. You were right," and hold out his hand. But he knew that he would not let go of the hand, and would start kicking. Why? Why this violent reaction? The boy must be a symbol to him of his own lost youth, his lost eyesight, his once-resilient arteries, the daybreak of his genius, now fading into dusk. He knew it, but he could not help himself. He understood now why native tyrants in the hour of their death had their wives and children slaughtered and their palaces set on fire. The thought of leaving the world he had built in the hands of another was unbearable.

Yet, if he was quite honest, the thought of a successor had occasionally crossed his mind. Maybe this was the moment at last. Maybe he had to hand over his sword now, and resign himself to the short dusk of dotage.

No! He was not going to be sentimental over this! He would keep an eye on that boy, submit him to tests of fire and water, chase him up the trees, drag him through the mire, give him the worst life any totok ever lived in the wilderness, and only if he came out of that with all his wits about him would he slam the crown on his head and say: "Right! Now take over."

As he sat sipping his tea noisily, he forgot about the Sultan, and started to plan the Crown Prince's purgatory.

W HEN THE expedition left Rauwatta, a problem of space arose, for, as Dr. Brits-Jansen had burnt his boats, Anton's prahus had to carry the members and the luggage of the previous expedition as well. This would have been easier if the Sultan had not insisted on a prahu to himself. He sat bolt upright in it, without an awning, his top hat on his head, and he did not move a finger. The others, packed tightly together in their boats, felt as if they were taking back with them a grisly doll. The Sultan's black clothes absorbed the heat of the sun until his top hat set the air spiraling around it, like a stove; when his prahu came alongside before passing some rapids, Anton could literally feel the heat he was radiating. The Sultan was the only one who remained in his boat while it was being dragged through the rapids by the panting coolies; and by so doing he made their job ten times more difficult. But the coolies seemed to accept his attitude as normal. They slithered, lost their balance, fell in the water, grazed their shins, but scrambled back to their feet with great devotion, nursing the royal yacht across the rocks as if it were a giant egg.

Meanwhile, during the first days, Brits-Jansen claimed a good deal of attention for himself. He bathed at least twice a day, throwing himself in the water with a hearty splash; then, perpendicular like a floating bottle, he swam ten strokes, trumpeting so loudly that the birds swarmed out of the trees. After that he climbed back into the prahu, a hairy toad, and those inside the boat were forced to do some nervous balancing to prevent it turning turtle. During

this performance, the prahus formed a triangle around him and those who carried guns kept them pointed at the water, watching out for crocodiles. During the siesta he snored with such commanding resonance that his mandur hardly dared to raise his voice to chant the rhythm, and Anton caught himself lying motionless in the most uncomfortable position, too intimidated by the authoritative sawing to make a move.

It was Brits-Jansen himself who upset the balance of power in regard to the Sultan. When, on the third day, the royal prahu got stuck halfway down some rapids, Brits-Jansen came to the aid of the coolies. Singlehanded he dragged the boat across the rocks with such impetuosity that the Sultan's top hat and frock coat were sprinkled with flashing drops. This did much harm to Brits-

Jansen's prestige. The mandur no longer chanted in a muted voice when he lay sleeping, but began to follow the snores with his chant, to the delight of the coolies; and during the daily swimming session the natives formed the triangle of boats with obvious impatience.

Anton noticed all this with interest, but the giant himself seemed to notice nothing. He was as happy as a child, bellowed old-fashioned music-hall songs, laughed uproariously at his own jokes, and he committed the same mistake at every rapids. At the third rapids on the sixth day, when the Sultan's prahu got stuck again in the foaming water, Brits-Jansen again waded enthusiastically to its aid across the slippery rocks. He put the rope around his left arm, shouted, *"One — two — heave!"* and fell headlong into the water as the rope broke. He caused some dismay, for the current dragged him off at great speed; Anton kicked his coolies, and his prahu shot after the bobbing head. Dr. Brits-Jansen was dragged on board, and he nearly drowned them all because he insisted on grabbing his topee as it came swirling past with the speed of a train.

The only ones who remained unruffled were the Sultan and Brits-Jansen himself. The Sultan, after half an hour of abject self-sacrifice on the part of his coolies, was dragged through the rapids without moving a finger; the doctor undressed for the third time that day until he sat huge and steaming underneath the awning. He wrung out his clothes with a squelching sound and hung them out to dry. Then he fished a wallet out of a breast pocket of his shirt, emptied the water out of it and spread out its contents on the floor of the prahu: letters, a piece of comb, a nail file, a small key and a snapshot. When the letters were nearly dry, he put on his spectacles and started to read them. Then he shrugged his shoulders, tore them up and threw them overboard. He picked up the little key, looked at it with a frown, shrugged his shoulders and threw it overboard. He was in doubt about the nail file; but after a moment he started to clean his nails with it. When he had finished he shrugged his shoulders and threw the nail file overboard too. He put the piece of comb back in the wallet without looking at it. The only thing remaining was the snapshot.

It had been lying face downward and he turned it over, shaking his head as he looked at it with a sentimental expression. He looked at it over his spectacles, through his spectacles, ...n he took his spectacles off, and put the snapshot on his knees. Anton, who was sitting opposite him, could not help glancing at it. He saw the much-thumbed picture of a girl with two braids of hair, a high forehead and serious eyes. It instantly struck him as familiar, yet it took some time before he replaced the braids with a mannish haircut and cried: "That's Bert!" He stretched out his hand toward the picture, but Brits-Jansen snatched it away. When he looked up, he was startled by the expression on the man's face. It was as though he had caught him in a shameful act.

Minutes later, breaking the embarrassing silence, Brits-Jansen asked, in an artificial voice, "Remind you of someone?" and Anton answered, with equal casualness, "Yes, a girl friend of mine."

"Girl friend?" Brits-Jansen exclaimed, indignantly. "This child is as pure as — as I! I mean: the driven snow."

"I'm sorry," said Anton, feeling the blood rush to his cheeks. "I meant — a fellow medical student. She was my best friend, I — I never thought of her as anything else."

"Is that so?" Brits-Jansen said. "Fancy." He took down his shirt and trousers, dry by now, rolled them into a pillow and lay down. Then he folded his hands behind his head, scratched his right shin with his left foot, sighed and appeared to fall asleep. After a long silence, during which his belly swayed with the rolling of the prahu, he asked, without looking up: "What's the name of your friend?"

"Bert," answered Anton. "Bert Waterreus."

Brits-Jansen said nothing, and seemed to fall asleep again. But he did not snore, and Anton sat listening to the chanting of the mandur, while the small fleet drifted swiftly down the river, toward the sea.

THE PRAHUS had been dragged halfway up the shore, side by side. The crocodile fires on the riverbank made a small red twilight over the far ends of the boats. In the prahus, like dead in their coffins, lay the Sultan, the boy, and he, Dr. Brits-Jansen, the big bad wolf of the jungle.

Now he had told that boy everything — everything; and it seemed as if the night were hollow with loneliness, a boundless world full of hard, cold stars, in which he had lost something very dear, forever. Everything — even the thoughts that were so deeply hidden inside him that he had hardly been conscious of their existence. Like a simpleton he had lain there mumbling at the sky, revealing the pathetic secret of his life.

It had started with a hollow feeling in his stomach. He could not sleep and he knew the boy was awake too. As long as it had been daylight he had managed to behave casually. After feigning sleep for an hour that afternoon, he had sat up with a realistic yawn, stretched, blinked and asked: "Where are we?" It had all been natural and convincing. But then that wallet lay there, and he had been forced to put it back in his pocket. Although he had done so unobtrusively, he had seen the boy watching him, and he had realized that he would have to talk about it, sooner or later.

He had spent the rest of the day trying to decide how he would go about it. In the end, the desire to talk became so strong that he had gone to bed early, in order to compel the boy to lie down early too. He could not wait to start talking; after lighting a cigar he lay gazing at the stars in excited anticipation. He wanted to know everything: how the boy had come to know her, what she looked like now, if she was a good doctor, if she was healthy, and then, casually, toward the end: whether she had ever talked about him.

But he got off on the wrong foot. As he lay smoking in his boat it occurred to him that his going to bed so early must give the impression that he wanted to avoid conversation. The silence became so oppressive that he asked: "Zorgdrager, are you asleep?"

"No, sir," the voice from the other prahu answered, so patiently that he cursed under his breath. Under normal circumstances, the boy should have put that question to him, to be followed by, "May I ask you a question?" and "Do you think I'm suited to this work?"

Brits-Jansen lay silent for a while, feeling more and more unsure of himself, knowing that he would have to say something in order to justify his question. Then he asked: "How old is she now?"

The voice in the darkness answered, politely, "Twenty-six, sir."

It was preposterous, his lying there whispering in the darkness, with palpitations about the snapshot of a child whom he had never set eyes on in his life, but whom he had come to consider as his own. In the most stark and dangerous moments in the jungle, he had escaped from reality by daydreaming about her. How he would return to Holland after being pensioned off; how he would have gout and take the waters in some spa in Germany; how she would push him in a Bath chair underneath the linden trees, chatting about the weather and the hotel and the wicked prices.

On many occasions he had conjured up those daydreams; he remembered the occasions clearly. During the big cholera epidemic in Java twenty-three years ago, when the child had only been three. During an outbreak of lung plague in the Atjeh Mountains, when whole villages had been wiped out, and two coolies had stood on the bumper of his car with pitchforks to clear the corpses from his way. Sentimental bachelor's daydreams — she would have a little basket with a thermos flask, and when it became chilly in the evening she would pour out hot grog for him. Then she would ask, "Comfy?" and he would answer, "Lovely," and she would say, "Honestly?" with a tender smile, and tuck in his gouty foot with the rug. So they would sit for a while under the fragrance of the linden blossoms; and he would feel guilty for the way he had chained her to him, this lovely gay young creature. In the hotel, as she unwrapped his rug, he would say: "I feel guilty. I, a sick old man, you . . ." She would retort with a smile: "Uncle, if you start fishing again, I'll put you to bed."

Ass! Senile idiot! He had never seen the child; yet while she was still toothless, standing in her playpen, he had already conscripted her to drive him around in his old age. He had gloated over her letters, which the two innocent parents, Betsy and Willem in their leprosy hell, had given him to read. He had read them, lying on his bed, grinning like a cradle snatcher.

God bless Dady and Mummy love from Bertie — two lines of childish scrawl and a row of X's for kisses.

Dear Parents, Please find enclosed my report that I hope will please you; the mark in History is not quite my fault — three pages out of an exercise book, and a P.S. about pocket money.

My dear people, I have hesitated for a long time before writing this letter, but I feel that I cannot keep it to myself any longer. To take the bull by the horns — five pages of blue paper, at the end of which she finally took the bull by the horns by saying that everyone was the master of his own destiny.

That was the letter he had wanted to copy: that wonderful, revolutionary, merciless letter from a child who now wrote to those two innocent Christians that she did not want to join the Salvation Army; she wanted to be a doctor. But they had not given him the chance to copy it; they only wanted him to advise them, for, in the course of the years, he had become a second father to that ghost child whom none of them knew. And now she wanted to be a doctor! A doctor! While he had pretended to be considering earnestly what advice to give the parents, he had learned the letter by heart; then he had said: "Well — I think that everyone *is* the master of his own destiny. It is her life, not ours."

Those two noble souls had mastered their disappointment

bravely. "But . . . but what are we to do about the money?" Willem had asked. And then he had said: "Oh, don't worry about that. I haven't a soul in the world of my own, and I'm earning more than I need. I'll be happy to . . ." It was the only occasion on which they had nearly quarreled. No! They would not accept that! He had already done too much for them! Never, never . . .

Toward daybreak they had written, with his assistance, the reply that was copied five times before at last it was ready: Uncle Brits, the colony's doctor, had offered to pay for her studies on one condition: that she would pay back every cent as soon as she had a practice of her own. It had been their condition. He had taken the letter with him to post; once out of their sight, he had scribbled on the back: *In this letter you'll read about some money that you are supposed to pay back. I don't want it myself; if ever you should earn enough to repay it and can't think of anything better to do, give it to the Salvation Army. But you will send your uncle a photograph of yourself, won't you?*

He did not receive the snapshot until six months later. It had followed him via many outposts, to catch up with him at last in a lunatic asylum in the upper Digul where smallpox had broken out. He had opened the envelope at night, alone by the night nurse's table, and he had stared, as at a hallucination, at the face on the snapshot — the face of Betsy, her mother, the woman who had changed his life more than twenty years before. Those were the eyes he had always remembered, even though now they were sightless, and there was the same, unforgettable smile, which he had believed gone from the earth forever.

During the years that followed, he had slowly infiltrated the unsuspecting parents' correspondence, dictating questions about her studies without letting them tell her who had formulated them. In her answers, she replied in such esoteric medical terms that Willem had said: "I think you had better read this to Betsy, brother. I can't pronounce it." He inspired her father to put some questions on social and religious matters. At first, she had replied curtly and shyly, but gradually more frankly, until in the end the parents had wept with happiness because, although she never mentioned God, it was quite clear that she adhered to all the principles of the Salvation Army. She wrote about clinics and schools, about equality for all men.

So for years he had talked to that daughter, whispered with her, argued with her, laughed with her; she had become as familiar to him as the wart on his hand — but never, in all those years, had he mentioned her to anyone else. Nobody had known of his dream about the Bath chair, the paths underneath the linden trees, like a still life of happiness. But without that dream he would never have survived the jungle loneliness, the pointlessness, the doubt.

And now, in one silly monologue underneath the stars, he had given away his secret; she would never be entirely his own again. He had wanted to stop, dismayed, but then a cautious question would come at him from out of the starry night, and like a patient on a psychoanalyst's couch he chattered, miserable, delighted, about that clever, sweet, tender, wonderful angel — Bertha.

THE BLUE MIST was turning pink and the birds began to rummage in the trees when Anton heard the voice ask: "And — er — did she ever talk about me?"

Anton knew then that the climax had come of this strange night, during which he had heard a childlike poet dream aloud about a girl who had absolutely nothing in common with the hard, unsentimental Bert he knew as well as a sister.

When this odd conversation started, he had tried to stop Brits-Jansen talking, for it had been horribly embarrassing. Then the gruff voice had started to conjure up a creature that became more and more fantastic, and he had become interested as a doctor. This was very strange indeed; how on earth was it possible that a man of sixty, whom he had come to know as a tyrant on the one hand and a brilliant physician on the other, could harbor such childish fantasies? Then it had slowly dawned on him that he was listening to the daydream of a gigantic adolescent, a boy whose soul had remained untouched and undeveloped since the moment the wilderness had closed over him.

The night was hot and oppressive. The noises from the jungle and the river sounded romantic now they had lost the terror with which they had inspired him when making this voyage alone. Like a prince in a fairy tale, he had discovered a sleeping giant in the magic forest, touched him, and caused him to wake up in a world that was a generation older than when he had fallen asleep.

But gradually his amazement and fascination changed into uneasiness. What was he to do? Any moment the voice might ask, "Tell me: what's she like?" and he would have to choose. Must he leave this big child his illusion, or open his eyes to the truth?

Now Brits-Jansen asked whether she had ever talked about him. No, never. "An uncle in the Far East sent me money to pay for my studies," she had once said, as if with a shrug of her shoulders.

It crossed Anton's mind: tomorrow we'll be sorry for this uncomfortable intimacy, tomorrow we'll hate one another for this. It was this thought that made him decide, and answer: "Oh yes. She talked about you quite often."

"Is that so?" Brits-Jansen said. "Well, I'm — I'm not surprised." He hardly dared to go on yet he asked, his heart audible in his breath: "And — er — what does she call me?"

"Uncle," the boy answered, after a silence.

"Is that so? . . . Uncle who?"

There was another silence, in which Brits-Jansen held his breath; then Anton said: "Uncle Leprosy."

The stars, at which Brits-Jansen had been gazing fixedly all this time, started to flash with tears. He had imagined many names by which she would call him, in that dream of the Bath chair, but never one so moving, fitting in so well with his picture of them underneath the linden trees in that happy land of dreams.

XI

THEY CAME out of the jungle in the afternoon of the sixteenth day after their departure from Rauwatta. As the small fleet sailed triumphantly into the vast glinting expanse of ocean, even the coolies cheered; and every man felt that he was lucky to come back alive. Every man except the Sultan, that is, who remained motionless and indifferent until the moment he had to get up to climb the rope ladder onto the deck of the *Henny*.

The *Henny* was anchored in the muddy delta of the Kali-Woga and, seeing the rusty ship with its angry mare's-ear funnels, Brits-Jansen jumped up. Good old Krasser! That was a stroke of luck! They had been prepared to wait for the ship for days, perhaps weeks, in the fish stench of Rokul. Now they could go straight home. Brits-Jansen stood upright, waving his topee, the back of his shirt bellying in the wind. As they approached, he yodeled: "*Henny,* ahoy! Come on out, you old pirate!" A voice through a megaphone answered, "I see you, Fatso! Why didn't you get the plague?" Then, as they came alongside and Brits-Jansen clawed his way up the rope ladder, the voice through the megaphone called down, alarmingly close: "Hullo, Wet Pants!"

It took Anton a moment before he realized that he was being addressed. Offended, he returned the greeting, mumbling: "*Bonjour,* Captain." Only later, after the luggage had been stowed on board, did the real portent of that greeting penetrate to him. He had stamped out an epidemic that was menacing the whole of Borneo; Captain Krasser himself might have died but for him, and the term with which he was rewarded was "Wet Pants"!

Vanity, vanity, all is vanity. What the devil was he doing here? He knew he was being childish, and reacting to the excessive strain he had undergone, yet he was unable to forget the name Captain Krasser had given him. From that moment on board the *Henny* everything that happened seemed to be aimed at waking him up from a romantic dream. Everything that had seemed impressive, frightening or mysterious during the past weeks had been so only in his own totok imagination.

To start with: Captain Krasser. In his memory a black pirate, a grandiose agnostic. But as Brits-Jansen explained him, Krasser was a pathetic, sin-haunted half-wit, tortured by the notion that he would go to hell at his death, unless he could prove that God did not exist and that hell was an invention of the priests.

Then: Professor van der Waard, the district doctor in Bandjermasin. In Anton's memory, a sinister scarecrow who had not dared talk to him because he had known the trip to Rauwatta was a death patrol. When Brits-Jansen suggested having a drink with good old van der Waard, he refused, and when Brits-Jansen asked,

amazed, "Why?" he told him what had happened when he had
introduced himself and delivered greetings from Dr. Sardjono.
Brits-Jansen laughed until the tears ran into his beard; that Sardjono! Then he told a story about the fifth of December, some years
ago, when old van der Waard was in Batavia to address the Medical
Service at its annual meeting, in a long rambling speech trying to
prove that dysentery was carried by butterflies. As it was Santa
Claus Eve, the night on which the Dutch give presents and play
practical jokes, Sardjono had suggested they play a prank on Dr.
Kramer. He persuaded old van der Waard to let himself be shut
in a trunk filled with feathers and confetti, with a hook on the
inside so that he could open it. The others were to carry it into the
dining room in Dr. Kramer's residence. Van der Waard would
wait until dinner was under way, then jump out of the trunk
crying, "Santa Claus!" snowing the room under with feathers and
confetti. They closed the trunk, but secretly carried it instead into
the Governor General's palace, where they put it down in the
dining room as a gift from the Government Health Service, and
hastily made their escape. That night the Governor was to give an
official dinner for the Ambassador of Annam. They never heard
the end of the story; only one thing was certain: van der Waard,
who was the gentlest soul alive, said he would murder Sardjono
with his bare hands the next time he set eyes on him.

Anton went to have a drink with van der Waard after all, and
found him to be a shy, absent-minded old scientist who played
ping-pong with the wall for a partner and who had a bookcase
which held such books as *Gone With the Wind, One Thousand
Tips for the Home Handyman,* a bound collection of *The Lancet*
and copies of the French *Illustration.* If only he had seen this
bookcase before sailing up the river, Anton reflected, what a
difference it would have made.

The last illusion left to him concerned his return to Batavia. In
Batavia he would certainly receive some recognition for the work
he had done. Surely he would be invited to dine with the Head
of the Service, and at the least he would receive some admiring
words of praise. But when they stood at last in front of the desk
covered with telephones in the room with the map on the wall,

Dr. Kramer looked only at Brits-Jansen and said, "Oh, there you are. Splendid. I didn't think you'd make that coaster, but now you're here, that's fine. You can have that ambulance you requested to take the Sultan up to the leper colony tomorrow, and you can go with him if you want. But you'll have to come back here straight off. Your boat leaves in three days' time."

"Is that so?" Brits-Jansen said. "What is it this time?"

"Cholera in Celebes," said Dr. Kramer. "Martens has all the details. Have a good trip." To Anton he said: "You'll report tomorrow morning at the Central Hospital, to start your training."

Brits-Jansen, already at the door and with his hand on the knob, turned round and said: "He'll do nothing of the kind. I'm taking him with me, and I'll make you pay me for training him."

"I'm afraid there is no question of that," Dr. Kramer said calmly. "He has to go through his hospital training here first. Those are the regulations."

"Is that so?" Brits-Jansen answered. "Allow me to remind you, Piet Kramer, that *I* was the one who built your hospitals and that it was my friend van Dam, old enough to be your father, who wrote those regulations before he died of delirium tremens. This boy is coming with me because I'm not going to Celebes without an assistant, I don't want any other assistant but him, and if you carry on in that tone I'm afraid I'll have to speak my mind to you."

"Before we start losing our tempers," Dr. Kramer said patiently, "I'd like to have a word with you in private."

"If you want privacy," Brits-Jansen said, "take me into the Gobi Desert. If you think I'll lower my voice to please an upstart who climbed into his seat by stepping on my toes, whom I suckled as he lay writhing with fever in the jungle . . ."

"Succored," the other corrected him, unruffled, and to Anton he said, "Would you mind?"

"Succored?" Brits-Jansen said. "You pompous megalomaniac! If ever there was a sucker, it is me! I . . ."

Anton went out and slammed the door. In the cool corridor he shut his eyes and thought, *Vanity of vanities, all is vanity,* while behind the closed door Dr. Brits-Jansen bellowed his mind. He thought of walking out of the building to the nearest travel agency, and calmly ordering a passage to Amsterdam, single, third-class. They would declare him bankrupt, try him for breach of contract and put him in prison, but he didn't care. It was a matter of saving his soul. Who the devil did they think they were, haggling about him as if he were up for sale in a slave market? Oh, for an evening with Bert, sitting on the floor and smoking cigarettes! Only Bert could help him to sort out the tangle of his thoughts, his wishes. Something was wrong, terribly wrong, but he was too emotionally affected, too disillusioned and upset to work it out himself. Behind the door a furious row was raging that seemed to be working its way up to physical violence. Then, suddenly, the door opened and Brits-Jansen came out, beaming, a big cigar in his mouth. "Okay," he said. "You're coming with me. Now we're going to have curried chicken in the Hotel des Indes."

"No, we're not," said Anton.

"Huh? Why not?"

"I don't care for curried chicken, and I don't care for the Government Health Service either, and I'm not sure that I care to come to Celebes with you."

Brits-Jansen raised a huge forefinger to his lips, said, "Ssh!" and thumbed at the door. Then he whispered, audibly enough to be heard in the office: "If he hears that, I'll have to start all over again. Come on! Come on!" He grabbed Anton by a sleeve, and pulled him out of the building.

Outside Anton angrily jerked himself free and said, "I'm afraid I must have given you the wrong impression, Dr. Jansen. I prefer to do my hospital service first. As a matter of fact, after the way you treated me in the jungle, I — I have no respect for you."

It was out before he could stop it; such a childish thing to say that he felt like running away like a schoolboy who has thrown a stone at a window. But Brits-Jansen said, quietly, "Of course you haven't," and then, with his big nose and beery breath nauseatingly near, he added, "That, sir, was my intention."

Anton turned round and walked away. He walked into the town, impressed by his own composure. As he sauntered in the hot shadows of the royal palms that lined the central square, he repeated: "Vanity, vanity, all is vanity." Everything: his job, his ambitions, his philosophy, his life. The whole Anton Zorgdrager was vanity — not a talented, sensitive boy, who could be courageous when his fear left him no other way out. Oh, no. A living instrument that the state had bought on the installment plan. Take the late Dr. Brinkman. "Broken? Pity, get another one." And the other one had been delivered promptly: Zorgdrager, A., untested. Now he had been tested. All in one piece? Fine: Celebes, cholera. Have a good trip!

What was the point of ideals, illusions, dreams of the future? All it led up to was *One Thousand Tips for the Home Handyman,* or a molehill underneath a coconut tree with a wooden cross on it, or — a dazzling exception that happened once in fifty years — a bloated belly and a beard and daydreams about a nauseating marshmallow sweetheart, but then everybody raved about your genius. What a character was Brits-Jansen! Foremost leprosy specialist in the world! And there he went, with his sagging trousers and his snapshot, on his way to curried chicken in the Hotel des Indes like a child on its way to an ice cream, clutching a penny. And that after stamping out a plague outbreak that would have filled the newspapers in Europe for weeks.

Was that a life worth living? Was that a goal to strive for?

The answer evaded him. He walked, and his thoughts became more and more confused and entangled. Six days west of Rokul, on the River Kali-Woga, the old Anton Zorgdrager had died. But he still had no conception of who or what was the new Anton Zorgdrager. The jungle. Back to the jungle? Back to the teakettle, the stench of Lysol, the helpless patients?

He remembered a motto in a YMCA hostel: "Tomorrow may be too late." Was that what was wrong? Had he thought too much in terms of tomorrow instead of today? He felt a sudden nostalgia for Rauwatta, and realized how much he had missed by thinking all the time on that river, "Next week, day after tomorrow, we'll be in Rokul, then Batavia . . ." Well, here was Batavia, and what a triumph! Praise? The only thing lacking was that the bureaucrat behind the desk should have forgotten his name.

A girl went by him on a bicycle, and all at once he remembered Els. . . . Letters! The old porter at the Head Office had handed him some letters, which he had forgotten in the excitement. He took them out of his breast pocket. *Dr. A. Zorgdrager, c/o Head Office, Government Health Service, Batavia, Netherlands East Indies.* Nice, rounded handwriting. Els's father had paid a lot of money for that handwriting, and for English, French, Latin, Elocution and Ballet. Fat lot of good these would do her in Bandjermasin....

My darling Anton, he read, *my dearest dearest sweetheart, I have just received your letter from Sabang. Wonderful! I couldn't help reading passages from it to Professor van Goor, who happened to be here having tea with Daddy....*

He sat down then on a bench beside an elderly gentleman with a straw hat, and while the old gentleman doodled in the sand with a parasol, he read Els's letters, all five of them. He read them with an increasing feeling of discomfort, almost pity, as if they were letters addressed to a colleague who had been killed in action. Those letters had been written to a fiancé who had died on the River Kali-Woga. When finally he leaned back and stuffed them again into his breast pocket, he felt afraid. The devil, he wanted to say. The devil with your silly letters!

The jungle; back to the jungle. He was sure that, back there, everything would make sense again; perhaps it was not such a bad idea after all to go to Celebes with Brits-Jansen. A lifetime separated him from the boy who had fallen asleep that first night in Batavia, in the YMCA hostel, full of apprehension. Now he was no longer apprehensive; nothing could be worse than Rauwatta.

He got up and wandered down the avenue. A few minutes later he stopped a passerby and asked the way to the Hotel des Indes. He began to walk quickly and purposefully. After all, he was Doctor Zorgdrager, home from the plague, on his way to the cholera. Tomorrow might be too late.

BRITS-JANSEN had settled down at the hotel in a mood of high spirits. He ordered dinner, but told the waiter not to bring it yet. Propping a newspaper in front of him on the marble table, he began drinking beer. There was no doubt in his mind but that Anton would go with him to Celebes; the boy would come round; in the meantime he had a few things to think over.

He had almost surprised himself with his own vehemence in arguing with that pip-squeak Kramer in the Head Office. But he knew he had been right. A feeling had come over him increasingly since that moment in Rauwatta when Anton had diagnosed the Sultan's leprosy; he had fought against the feeling, kicked and struggled, but he knew that he had to face reality. He needed a successor for his work on leprosy. For more than twenty years he had been compiling material for a standard work, *Elephantiasis Graecorum,* but no one except himself would ever be able to sort out that material and organize it into a book. And now he doubted whether, at his age, he himself could still do it. His squirrel's hoard of notes had become so vast by now that only a young mind could blow away the cobwebs, separate the good from the bad. He had to face it: he needed a successor, and he had been jealous of, nay, hated the successor for years, before he ever knew the identity of the adolescent lout who would come along someday and receive the fruits of his life for nothing. Why should it have to be Anton, that moonsick cretin who had run off from him just now outside

the Head Office, with his jaw set and his letters from honey lamb
in his pocket? But there was reality again, staring him in the face:
Anton had just one twist in his personality that made him prefer-
able to all the other totoks he had encountered in thirty years —
the boy was a born doctor.

Brits-Jansen slapped his unread newspaper aside and ordered
another beer. As he sat drinking it, noisily and enthusiastically, he
saw Anton threading his way toward him around the marble
tables. "Ha!" he said, standing up with a large alcoholic gesture.
"There you are! I've ordered for you." His eyes gleamed. "Let me
look at you, dear boy."

Anton stood there, startled. Brits-Jansen took him by the chin,
turned his face toward the light and gazed at him with disturbing
intensity.

"What — what is the matter?" Anton asked.

Brits-Jansen laughed. "Nothing," he said, carnivorously. "Nothing at all, boy," and then, suddenly, he gave him a playful stab
in the stomach. Anton uttered a feminine squeak that was thoroughly humiliating, and was about to punch his nose, when all at
once the headwaiter came up.

"You wish to begin now, sir?" the waiter said. "Or are you waiting for the other gentlemen?"

Other gentlemen? Anton's illusion flickered for the last time.
The Head of the Service was joining them! . . .

"No, that's all right," Brits-Jansen said. "One portion is for this
gentleman; I'm the other three. Sit down, dear boy. I have a lot of
grim things to tell you concerning conditions in Celebes. . . ."

In spite of himself, the Crown Prince settled down to listen.

Jan de Hartog

AT THE AGE of ten Dutch-born Jan de Hartog ran away to sea and sailed with a fishing smack on the Zuider Zee. Later he became a cabin boy on a two-masted schooner, and worked on ocean-going tugboats, writing his first stories during night watches. After Holland fell to the Nazis in 1940, he escaped from his occupied homeland and served in England.

Mr. de Hartog is well known in this country and abroad for such distinguished novels as *The Lost Sea, The Distant Shore* and *The Little Ark*. Two of his plays, *Skipper Next to God* and *The Four Poster*, have been Broadway successes. He combines his love of writing with his love for the sea: he lives and works on a seagoing houseboat named the *Rival*.